TEACHER'S GUIDE

S0-BJO-360

CONNECTED MATHEMATICS® 3

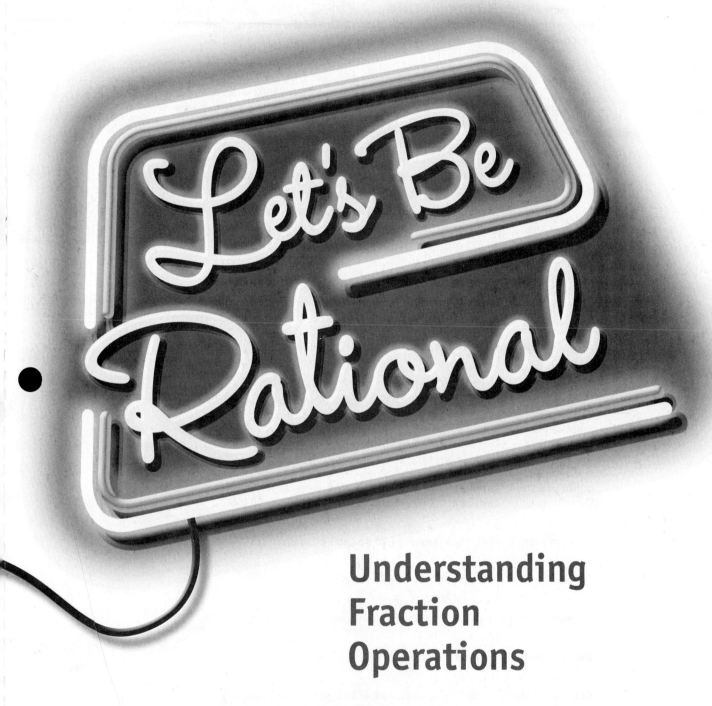

Understanding Fraction Operations

Glenda Lappan, Elizabeth Difanis Phillips,
James T. Fey, Susan N. Friel

PEARSON

Boston, Massachusetts • Chandler, Arizona • Glenview, Illinois • Upper Saddle River, New Jersey

Connected Mathematics™ was developed at Michigan State University with financial support from the Michigan State University Office of the Provost, Computing and Technology, and the College of Natural Science.

 This material is based upon work supported by the National Science Foundation under Grant No. MDR 9150217 and Grant No. ESI 9986372. Opinions expressed are those of the authors and not necessarily those of the Foundation.

As with prior editions of this work, the authors and administration of Michigan State University preserve a tradition of devoting royalties from this publication to support activities sponsored by the MSU Mathematics Education Enrichment Fund.

Acknowledgments appear on page 228, which constitutes an extension of this copyright page.

PEARSON

13-digit ISBN 978-0-13-327673-2
10-digit ISBN 0-13-327673-2
2 3 4 5 6 7 8 9 10 V063 17 16 15 14 13

Authors

A Team of Experts

Glenda Lappan is a University Distinguished Professor in the Program in Mathematics Education (PRIME) and the Department of Mathematics at Michigan State University. Her research and development interests are in the connected areas of students' learning of mathematics and mathematics teachers' professional growth and change related to the development and enactment of K–12 curriculum materials.

Elizabeth Difanis Phillips is a Senior Academic Specialist in the Program in Mathematics Education (PRIME) and the Department of Mathematics at Michigan State University. She is interested in teaching and learning mathematics for both teachers and students. These interests have led to curriculum and professional development projects at the middle school and high school levels, as well as projects related to the teaching and learning of algebra across the grades.

James T. Fey is a Professor Emeritus at the University of Maryland. His consistent professional interest has been development and research focused on curriculum materials that engage middle and high school students in problem-based collaborative investigations of mathematical ideas and their applications.

Susan N. Friel is a Professor of Mathematics Education in the School of Education at the University of North Carolina at Chapel Hill. Her research interests focus on statistics education for middle-grade students and, more broadly, on teachers' professional development and growth in teaching mathematics K–8.

With... Yvonne Grant and Jacqueline Stewart

Yvonne Grant teaches mathematics at Portland Middle School in Portland, Michigan. Jacqueline Stewart is a recently retired high school teacher of mathematics at Okemos High School in Okemos, Michigan. Both Yvonne and Jacqueline have worked on all aspects of the development, implementation, and professional development of the CMP curriculum from its beginnings in 1991.

Development Team

CMP3 Authors

Glenda Lappan, University Distinguished Professor, Michigan State University

Elizabeth Difanis Phillips, Senior Academic Specialist, Michigan State University

James T. Fey, Professor Emeritus, University of Maryland

Susan N. Friel, Professor, University of North Carolina – Chapel Hill

With...

Yvonne Grant, Portland Middle School, Michigan

Jacqueline Stewart, Mathematics Consultant, Mason, Michigan

In Memory of... William M. Fitzgerald, Professor (Deceased), Michigan State University, who made substantial contributions to conceptualizing and creating CMP1.

Administrative Assistant

Michigan State University
Judith Martus Miller

Support Staff

Michigan State University
Undergraduate Assistants:
Bradley Robert Corlett, Carly Fleming,
Erin Lucian, Scooter Nowak

Development Assistants

Michigan State University
Graduate Research Assistants:
Richard "Abe" Edwards, Nic Gilbertson,
Funda Gonulates, Aladar Horvath,
Eun Mi Kim, Kevin Lawrence, Jennifer Nimtz,
Joanne Philhower, Sasha Wang

Assessment Team

Maine
Falmouth Public Schools
Falmouth Middle School: Shawn Towle

Michigan
Ann Arbor Public Schools
Tappan Middle School:
Anne Marie Nicoll-Turner

Portland Public Schools
Portland Middle School:
Holly DeRosia, Yvonne Grant

Traverse City Area Public Schools
Traverse City East Middle School:
Jane Porath, Mary Beth Schmitt

Traverse City West Middle School:
Jennifer Rundio, Karrie Tufts

Ohio
Clark-Shawnee Local Schools
Rockway Middle School: Jim Mamer

Content Consultants

Michigan State University
Peter Lappan, Professor Emeritus,
Department of Mathematics

Normandale Community College
Christopher Danielson, Instructor,
Department of Mathematics & Statistics

University of North Carolina – Wilmington
Dargan Frierson, Jr., Professor,
Department of Mathematics & Statistics

Student Activities
Michigan State University
Brin Keller, Associate Professor,
Department of Mathematics

Consultants

Indiana
Purdue University
Mary Bouck, Mathematics Consultant

Michigan
Oakland Schools
Valerie Mills, Mathematics Education Supervisor

Mathematics Education Consultants:
Geraldine Devine, Dana Gosen

Ellen Bacon, Independent Mathematics Consultant

New York
University of Rochester
Jeffrey Choppin, Associate Professor

Ohio
University of Toledo
Debra Johanning, Associate Professor

Pennsylvania
University of Pittsburgh
Margaret Smith, Professor

Texas
University of Texas at Austin
Emma Trevino, Supervisor of
Mathematics Programs, The Dana Center

Mathematics for All Consulting
Carmen Whitman, Mathematics Consultant

Reviewers

Michigan
Ionia Public Schools
Kathy Dole, Director of Curriculum
and Instruction

Grand Valley State University
Lisa Kasmer, Assistant Professor

Portland Public Schools
Teri Keusch, Classroom Teacher

Minnesota
Hopkins School District 270
Michele Luke, Mathematics Coordinator

Field Test Sites for CMP3

Michigan
Ann Arbor Public Schools
Tappan Middle School: Anne Marie Nicoll-Turner*

Portland Public Schools
Portland Middle School: Mark Braun,
Angela Buckland, Holly DeRosia, Holly Feldpausch,
Angela Foote, Yvonne Grant*, Kristin Roberts,
Angie Stump, Tammi Wardwell

Traverse City Area Public Schools
Traverse City East Middle School
Ivanka Baic Berkshire, Brenda Dunscombe,
Tracie Herzberg, Deb Larimer, Jan Palkowski,
Rebecca Perreault, Jane Porath*, Robert Sagan,
Mary Beth Schmitt*

Traverse City West Middle School
Pamela Alfieri, Jennifer Rundio,
Maria Taplin, Karrie Tufts*

Maine
Falmouth Public Schools
Falmouth Middle School: Sally Bennett,
Chris Driscoll, Sara Jones, Shawn Towle*

Minnesota
Minneapolis Public Schools
Jefferson Community School:
Leif Carlson*,
Katrina Hayek Munsisoumang*

Ohio
Clark-Shawnee Local Schools
Reid School: Joanne Gilley
Rockway Middle School: Jim Mamer*
Possum School: Tami Thomas

*Indicates a Field Test Site Coordinator

Contents

Let's Be Rational
Understanding Fraction Operations

▼ Unit Overview

Unit Description

The goal of *Let's Be Rational* is to develop meaning for and skill with computations involving fractions. Students will have had some experiences during upper elementary grades with developing fraction operations. Typically, however, students will not have developed a sense of which operation to use in a particular problem situation.

Students can learn to carry out an algorithm as a procedure, but the real power of this *Connected Mathematics* Unit lies in the experiences that foster students' abilities to examine a problem situation and determine which operation or operations are needed to solve that problem. In middle school, our goal is to help students develop the deep understanding of rational numbers that comes from experiencing operations when solving a variety of problems, including those that require more than one operation.

When students finish this Unit, your students should know, understand, and fluently use algorithms for computing fractions with all four operations. This Unit does not explicitly teach a specific or preferred algorithm for working with rational numbers. Instead, it helps the teacher create a classroom environment in which students work on problems and generate strategies that make sense to them. At a point in the development of each operation, students are asked to pull together their strategies into an algorithm that works for all situations involving that operation on fractions. As they work individually, in groups, and as a whole class on the problems, students practice the algorithms to develop skill and fluency in carrying them out. This development process allows students to recognize special cases that can be easily handled and also provides students with an efficient general algorithm that works for all cases within an operation.

Investigation 1 is important because it serves as a formative assessment. Investigation 1 also provides a foundation for experiences with multiplication and division of fractions by connecting these operations to students' understanding of addition and subtraction. This is necessary because multiplication is conceptually related to the idea of repeated addition, and division is conceptually related to repeated subtraction. Also, division is the inverse operation of multiplication.

In this Unit, students solidify their earlier work with fraction operations by using diagrams, number lines, and symbolic representations. This focus provides a mathematical context for the algorithms of multiplication and division of fractions. At the end of this Unit, students will learn the valuable life skill of differentiating which of the four operations can be applied in various contextual situations.

We expect that when students finish this Unit, they will understand the meanings of computations with fractions. Students will be able to decide which operation is appropriate in a given situation. In addition, students will be able to use number sense, benchmarks, and operation sense to estimate solutions to situations as well as using estimation to decide if exact answers are reasonable.

▶ UNIT
OVERVIEW

GOALS AND
STANDARDS

MATHEMATICS
BACKGROUND

UNIT
INTRODUCTION

Summary of Investigations

Investigation 1: Extending Addition and Subtraction of Fractions

Investigation 1 focuses on estimating sums of fractions and decimals and then moves to finding algorithms for precise computations. It builds on *Comparing Bits and Pieces* by extending skills with benchmarks, equivalent fractions, and the relationship between decimals and fractions.

Students play a game in which they estimate the size of sums. Students also explore estimation as a strategy to reason about contextual situations. They identify whether their estimate is an underestimate or an overestimate.

This Investigation also focuses on developing computational understanding and skill in adding and subtracting fractions. Students are not given algorithms for computation. Instead, students figure out how to add and subtract fractions by being flexible in finding equivalent fractions. This Investigation serves as an important formative assessment of students' understanding of fractions.

In the course of solving the problems, students develop strategies for adding and subtracting fractions and mixed numbers. Through class discussion, these strategies are made more explicit and efficient.

Investigation 2: Building on Multiplication With Fractions

Investigation 2 focuses on developing computational skill with and understanding of fraction multiplication. Various contexts and models are introduced to help students make sense of when multiplication is appropriate.

In Problem 2.1, students develop an understanding of multiplication with simple fractions. Problems 2.2 and 2.3 focus on multiplication with fraction, mixed-number, and whole-number combinations.

Estimation is used across the Problems so that students can determine the reasonableness of their answers. Also, students develop the idea that multiplication does not always lead to a larger product. Within these Problems, students form a general algorithm for fraction multiplication.

Investigation 3: Dividing With Fractions

Investigation 3 explores the operation of division. Problem 3.1 emphasizes estimation. The context involves measurements that provide a familiar setting for the first interpretation of division. Students are asked to consider *How much of this is in that?* using fractional dividends and divisors. Everyday situations are used to help students make sense of when division is an appropriate operation. The first two Problems in the Investigation involve the measuring interpretation of division, and the third involves the sharing interpretation. The last Problem uses presorted division problems to develop a general algorithm for fraction division.

Investigation 4: Wrapping up the Operations

Investigation 4 concludes *Let's Be Rational*'s exploration of the four arithmetic operations with fractions, first by considering more abstract relationships among the four operations, and second by considering what kinds of contexts lead to each of the operations in order to highlight their structure. Problems 4.1 and 4.2 have students use fact families to express additive and multiplicative relationships among fractional quantities. In doing so, students also work on the ideas of inverse and decomposition, each of which is an important numerical precursor to algebra work. Problem 4.3 presents students with a variety of contextual problems. Students have to sort out for themselves which operations apply in each situation. Being able to recognize which operation is called for in a problem situation strengthens students' understanding of the meaning of each operation.

Unit Vocabulary

- algorithm
- benchmark
- fact family
- number sentence
- overestimate
- reciprocal
- underestimate

▶ UNIT
OVERVIEW

GOALS AND
STANDARDS

MATHEMATICS
BACKGROUND

UNIT
INTRODUCTION

Planning Charts

Investigations & Assessments	Pacing	Materials	Resources
1 Extending Addition and Subtraction of Fractions	4½ days	**Labsheet 1.1A** Getting Close Fraction Game Cards **Labsheet 1.1B** Getting Close Decimal Game Cards **Labsheet 1.1C** Getting Close Number Squares **Labsheet 1ACE:** Exercise 22 (accessibility) **Labsheet 1.3** Land Sections **Labsheet 1ACE:** Exercise 27 (accessibility) **Labsheet 1.4:** Recipe Cards (accessibility) **Labsheet 1ACE:** Exercises 31, 32, 37, 38 (accessibility) fraction strips, calculators, colored pencils or markers, containers of spices of different weights	**Teaching Aid 1.1A** Estimating Sums of Fractions **Teaching Aid 1.1B** Student Strategies for Estimation **Teaching Aid 1.1C** Benchmarks of Sums–Classroom Dialogue Model **Teaching Aid 1.3A** Land Divided Into 64ths **Teaching Aid 1.3B** Question C— Classroom Dialogue Model **Teaching Aid 1.4A** Student Strategies **Teaching Aid 1.4B** Student Algorithms • Fraction Game
Mathematical Reflections	½ day		
Assessment: Check Up 1	½ day	• Check Up 1	• Spanish Check Up 1
2 Building on Multiplication With Fractions	3 days	**Labsheet 2.1A:** Brownie Pans (accessibility) **Labsheet 2.1B** Extra Brownie Pan Problems **Labsheet 2ACE:** Exercise 33 (accessibility) colored pencils	**Teaching Aid 2.1** $\frac{1}{2}$ of $\frac{2}{3}$ **Teaching Aid 2.3A** Takoda's and Yuri's Strategies **Teaching Aid 2.3B** Student Model of Problem 2.3 **Teaching Aid 2.3C** Diagrams for Question B, part (3)
Mathematical Reflections	½ day		
Assessment: Partner Quiz	1 day	• Partner Quiz	• Special Needs Partner Quiz • Spanish Partner Quiz

continued on next page

Planning Charts *continued*

Investigations & Assessments	Pacing	Materials	Resources
3 Dividing With Fractions	4 days	**Labsheet 3ACE:** Exercise 6 (accessibility) **Labsheet 3.4:** Algorithms for Dividing Fractions (accessibility) poster paper	**Teaching Aid 3.1A** Dividing With Fractions **Teaching Aid 3.1B** Student Strategies
Mathematical Reflections	½ day		
Assessment: Check Up 2	½ day	• Check Up 2	• Spanish Check Up 2
4 Wrapping Up the Operations	3 days		**Teaching Aid 4.1** Fact Families for Addition and Subtraction **Teaching Aid 4.2A** Fact Families for Multiplication and Division 1 **Teaching Aid 4.2B** Fact Families for Multiplication and Division 2
Mathematical Reflections	½ day		
Looking Back	½ day		
Assessment: Self-Assessment	Take Home	• Self-Assessment	• Spanish Self-Assessment
Assessment: Unit Test	1 day	• Unit Test	• Spanish Unit Test
Total	20 days	**Materials for All Investigations:** calculators; student notebooks; colored pens, pencils, or markers	

Block Pacing (Scheduling for 90-minute class periods)

Investigation	Block Pacing
1 Extending Addition and Subtraction of Fractions	3 days
Problem 1.1	½ day
Problem 1.2	½ day
Problem 1.3	½ day
Problem 1.4	1 day
Mathematical Reflections	½ day
2 Building on Multiplication With Fractions	2 days
Problem 2.1	½ day
Problem 2.2	½ day
Problem 2.3	½ day
Mathematical Reflections	½ day

Investigation	Block Pacing
3 Dividing With Fractions	2½ days
Problem 3.1	½ day
Problem 3.2	½ day
Problem 3.3	½ day
Problem 3.4	½ day
Mathematical Reflections	½ day
4 Wrapping Up the Operations	2 days
Problem 4.1	½ day
Problem 4.2	½ day
Problem 4.3	½ day
Mathematical Reflections	½ day

Parent Letter

• Parent Letter (English)
• Parent Letter (Spanish)

▼ Goals and Standards

Goals

Numeric Estimation Understand that estimation is a tool used in a variety of situations including checking answers and making decisions, and develop strategies for estimating results of arithmetic operations

- Use benchmarks and other strategies to estimate results of operations with fractions

- Use estimates to check the reasonableness of exact computations

- Give various reasons to estimate and identify when a situation calls for an overestimate or an underestimate

- Use estimates and exact solutions to make decisions

Fraction Operations Revisit and continue to develop meanings for the four arithmetic operations and skill at using algorithms for each

- Determine when addition, subtraction, multiplication, or division is the appropriate operation to solve a problem

- Develop ways to model sums, differences, products, and quotients with areas, fraction strips, and number lines

- Use knowledge of fractions and equivalence of fractions to develop algorithms for adding, subtracting, multiplying, and dividing fractions

- Write fact families with fractions to show the inverse relationship between addition and subtraction, and between multiplication and division

- Compare and contrast dividing a whole number by a fraction to dividing a fraction by a whole number

- Recognize that when you multiply or divide a fraction, your answer might be less than or more than the numbers you started with

- Solve real-world problems using arithmetic operations on fractions

Variables and Equations Use variables to represent unknown values and equations to represent relationships

- Represent unknown real-world and abstract values with variables

- Write equations (or number sentences) to represent relationships among real-world and abstract values

- Use fact families to solve for unknown values

Standards

Common Core Content Standards

6.NS.A.1 Interpret and compute quotients of fractions, and solve word problems involving division of fractions by fractions, e.g., by using visual fraction models and equations to represent the problem. *Investigations 2 and 3*

6.NS.B.3 Fluently add, subtract, multiply, and divide multi-digit decimals using the standard algorithm for each operation. *Investigation 1*

6.NS.B.4 Find the greatest common factor of two whole numbers less than or equal to 100 and the least common multiple of two whole numbers less than or equal to 12. Use the distributive property to express a sum of two whole numbers 1–100 with a common factor as a multiple of a sum of two whole numbers with no common factor. *Investigation 1*

6.EE.A.2 Write, read, and evaluate expressions in which letters stand for numbers. *Investigations 1 and 4*

6.EE.A.2a Write expressions that record operations with numbers and with letters standing for numbers. *Investigation 4*

6.EE.A.2b Identify parts of an expression using mathematical terms (sum, term, product, factor, quotient, coefficient); view one or more parts of an expression as a single entity. *Investigations 1, 3, and 4*

6.EE.A.2c Evaluate expressions at specific values of their variables. Include expressions that arise from formulas used in real-world problems. Perform arithmetic operations, including those involving whole-number exponents, in the conventional order when there are no parentheses to specify a particular order (Order of Operations). *Investigation 4*

6.EE.A.3 Apply the properties of operations to generate equivalent expressions. *Investigation 2*

Essential for 6.EE.A.4 Identify when two expressions are equivalent (i.e., when the two expressions name the same number regardless of which value is substituted into them). *Investigation 1*

Essential for 6.EE.B.5 Understand solving an equation or inequality as a process of answering a question: which values from a specified set, if any, make the equation or inequality true? Use substitution to determine whether a given number in a specified set makes an equation or inequality true. *Investigation 1*

6.EE.B.6 Use variables to represent numbers and write expressions when solving a real-world or mathematical problem; understand that a variable can represent an unknown number, or, depending on the purpose at hand, any number in a specified set. *Investigations 1 and 4*

6.EE.B.7 Solve real-world and mathematical problems by writing and solving equations of the form $x + p = q$ and $px = q$ for cases in which p, q and x are all nonnegative rational numbers. *Investigations 1 and 4*

Facilitating the Mathematical Practices

Students in *Connected Mathematics* classrooms display evidence of multiple Standards for Mathematical Practice every day. Here are just a few examples where you might observe students demonstrating the Standards for Mathematical Practice during this Unit.

Practice 1: **Make sense of problems and persevere in solving them.**

Students are engaged every day in solving problems and, over time, learn to persevere in solving them. To be effective, the problems embody critical concepts and skills and have the potential to engage students in making sense of mathematics. Students build understanding by reflecting, connecting, and communicating. These student-centered problem situations engage students in articulating the "knowns" in a problem situation and determining a logical solution pathway. The student-student and student-teacher dialogues help students to not just make sense of the problems, but also to persevere in finding appropriate strategies to solve them. The suggested questions in the Teacher Guides provide the metacognitive scaffolding to help students monitor and refine their problem-solving strategies.

Practice 2: **Reason abstractly and quantitatively.**

Students transition from contextual problems to abstract and quantitative reasoning in Problem 1.4 by describing real-world situations that match equations. Additionally, students represent pizzas and blocks of cheese with appropriate quantities (whole numbers and fractions) and then reason through Problem 3.2 abstractly. In Problem 4.3, students use quantitative reasoning in deciding which mathematical operation to use in a given situation. Throughout the Unit, students describe algorithms for finding sums, differences, products, and quotients of fractions.

Practice 3: **Construct viable arguments and critique the reasoning of others.**

Students analyze different strategies in Problem 2.3. They examine sample strategies for multiplication, which include using the Distributive Property and converting mixed numbers into improper fractions. Students critique sample work and use the strategies they analyzed.

Practice 4: **Model with mathematics.**

Students use brownie-pan models and other drawings to support their thinking in Problems 2.1, 2.2, and 2.3. They use these drawings to visualize fraction multiplication as well as to prove their answers.

Practice 5: **Use appropriate tools strategically.**

Students use calculators to check the accuracy of their estimates in Problem 1.1. They also use the Fraction Game digital tool as a supplement to Problem 1.3. In Investigation 2, students may use colored pencils to represent the factors of rational products.

Practice 6: **Attend to precision.**

Students work to make estimates increasingly exact in Problem 1.1. Students also decide whether estimates are overestimates or underestimates during Problem 1.2. They explore whether estimates are sufficient or if exact answers are necessary throughout Investigation 1.

UNIT
OVERVIEW

▶ GOALS AND
STANDARDS

MATHEMATICS
BACKGROUND

UNIT
INTRODUCTION

Practice 7: **Look for and make use of structure.**

Students find patterns when multiplying fractions in Problem 2.1. They notice relationships between the numerators and the denominators of factors and products. By doing this, students are able to develop an algorithm for multiplying proper fractions.

Practice 8: **Look for and express regularity in repeated reasoning.**

In Problem 3.4, students use repeating patterns they had found in division problems to devise two algorithms for dividing fractions. Students also use fact families to rewrite equations and solve for variables. In Problem 4.1, they look at patterns of addition and subtraction to discover the relationships of numbers in addition and subtraction problems.

Students identify and record their personal applications of the Standards for Mathematical Practice during the Mathematical Reflections at the end of each Investigation.

▼ Mathematics Background

Building Proficiency Using Algorithms

Rational numbers are the heart of the middle-grade experiences with number concepts. Understanding and using fractions and operations on fractions can be challenging for students as they transition from elementary into the middle grades. Students will have had some experiences with addition, subtraction, and multiplication with rational numbers in earlier grades. They are unlikely, however, to be proficient with these operations, in particular in choosing and using the appropriate operation or sequence of operations to solve a problem.

Operations

Addition	$3 + 1 = 4$	Subtraction	$5 - 3 = 2$
Multiplication	$3 \times 2 = 6$	Division	$8 \div 4 = 2$

Students may become confused about rational numbers if they rush into symbol manipulation with fraction operations. They need to spend time making sense of the concepts and building experiences that show reasons for why the algorithms work. In addition, students need to understand the operations in ways that help them judge what operation or combination of operations is needed in a given situation.

Let's Be Rational is designed to provide experience in building algorithms for the four basic operations with fractions, as well as opportunities for students to consider when such operations are useful in solving problems. Building this kind of thinking and reasoning supports the development of skill and fluency with the algorithms. By the end of this Unit, expect students to understand and be able to use efficient algorithms for all four basic operations with fractions, including mixed numbers.

For all four operations we use the same type of development.

- The development of algorithms for each operation and the understanding of those algorithms involve experiences with contextual problems, models, strategies, and estimation. Problems in context help students make sense of an operation and how the operation can be computed.

- The contexts lead students to model situations and write number sentences that are representative of a particular situation, so they begin to understand when an operation is appropriate. By analyzing the diagrams and models they develop and their resulting number sentences, and relating this to their symbolic work, students develop algorithms for fraction operations.

- Important goals of all this work are for students to write and read mathematical language and to make decisions using what they know.

UNIT
OVERVIEW

GOALS AND
STANDARDS

▶ MATHEMATICS
BACKGROUND

UNIT
INTRODUCTION

This development of algorithms draws upon concepts and procedures developed in elementary grades and *Comparing Bits and Pieces*. In *Comparing Bits and Pieces*, students developed an understanding of basic interpretations, models, equivalence, and ordering of rational numbers. In *Let's Be Rational*, they draw upon this development and the models that were introduced—fraction strips or bars, number lines, grid area, and partition models—because these concepts connect directly to operations on rational numbers. (See Mathematics Background for *Comparing Bits and Pieces* for a full discussion of the concepts and models introduced here.)

Fraction strips

Partition model

Choosing Appropriate Operations

Estimation

The initial question CMP helps students ask is, "About how big will the answer be? What answer makes sense?" Having a ballpark estimate gives students a way to know if their computations are sensible, whether the calculation has been done by hand or with a calculator. At this point in the curriculum, students have had quite a bit of practice finding equivalent fractions and decimals and changing forms of fractions. They have developed some benchmark fractions that they can use to estimate relative size and to check their computations.

The strategies used to estimate can differ. In a situation in which the goal is to decide what whole number a sum of fractions is closest to, rounding each fraction to the nearest whole number or benchmark fraction, for instance a half, is a useful strategy. In some contexts, you may want to use an estimation strategy that leads to an estimate that you know is too large (overestimate) or too small (underestimate). As a general rule, to be sure you have enough, you overestimate what you need, and you underestimate what you have or what you can do. This can be applied to shopping and other contexts, such as ingredients for cooking and materials for home projects.

Overestimate what you need.	Underestimate what you can do.
You need to make a frame. $10\frac{3}{8}$ in. by $17\frac{7}{8}$ in. Use benchmarks to estimate. $10\frac{1}{2} + 10\frac{1}{2} + 18 + 18 = 57$ You need 57 inches of wood, and you can round up to 60 inches.	You hiked $12\frac{7}{8}$ mi in $4\frac{3}{4}$ h. Use benchmarks to estimate. $12\frac{1}{2} \div 5 = 2\frac{1}{2}$ You can hike at a speed of $2\frac{1}{2}$ miles per hour.

continued on next page

Building and Extending Addition and Subtraction Fluency

We build on and extend students' earlier experiences with addition and subtraction of fractions to connect with contexts, models, and diagrams. Addition and subtraction of fractions serve as a foundation for exploration of multiplication and division, both of which use similar models and diagrams. Strategies for operations with fractions can be developed with contexts that help students learn how to put fractions together and take them apart.

As students model and symbolize aspects of contextual situations, they develop meaning for and skill in using the operations of addition and subtraction. As well, students learn the value of equivalence when changing the representation of fractions to a form with a common denominator.

Example

Common Denominators

Addition

$$\frac{1}{2} + \frac{1}{3} = \frac{3}{6} + \frac{2}{6} = \frac{5}{6}$$

Subtraction

$$\frac{1}{2} - \frac{1}{3} = \frac{3}{6} - \frac{2}{6} = \frac{1}{6}$$

Students' previous work with equivalence and partitioning is critical to the development of strategies for adding and subtracting. The following area model provides a context in which both naming fractional parts of a whole and equivalence can emerge as students try to write number sentences to model combining square *A* with square *B*. Visit Teacher Place at mathdashboard.com/cmp3 to see the image gallery.

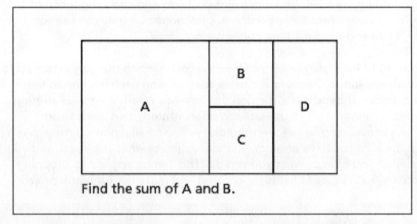

Find the sum of A and B.

In order to find the sum of $A + B$, or $\frac{1}{2} + \frac{1}{8}$ of the whole, students need to use equivalent fractions to rename $\frac{1}{2}$ as $\frac{4}{8}$. The area model helps students visualize *A*, which is $\frac{1}{2}$, as 4 eighth-size sections. By asking students to write number sentences, and to explain how the number sentence helped them arrive at the sum $\frac{5}{8}$, students begin to understand why it is necessary to rename fractions when adding and subtracting and the role that equivalence plays in doing so.

UNIT
OVERVIEW

GOALS AND
STANDARDS

▶ MATHEMATICS
BACKGROUND

UNIT
INTRODUCTION

There are other models that can be used to highlight the role of equivalence and support understanding of addition and subtraction. The fraction-strip model was used in conjunction with the number-line model in *Comparing Bits and Pieces* to develop meaning for fractions and equivalence. Here fraction strips are used to represent $\frac{1}{2} + \frac{1}{3} = \frac{5}{8}$.

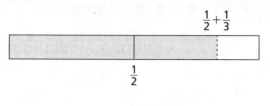

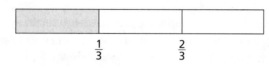

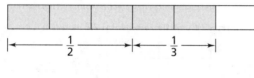

The number-line model helps make the connection to fractions as numbers or quantities. This is a number line for 0 to 2 marked to illustrate $1\frac{1}{3} - \frac{2}{3} = \frac{2}{3}$.

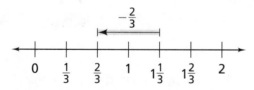

Multiplication of Rational Numbers

One of the first hurdles for students in understanding multiplication of fractions is realizing that multiplication does not always "make larger," as their experience with whole number multiplication has firmly established. In fact, with multiplication of a fraction by a whole number, the fraction can be interpreted as an operator that may stretch (make larger) or shrink (make smaller) depending on whether the fraction is greater or less than 1. This is an important aspect of multiplication of fractions.

Stretching

$9 \times \frac{4}{3} = 12$

Shrinking

$9 \times \frac{2}{3} = 6$

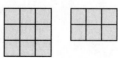

continued on next page

A second hurdle for students is understanding that when they encounter a situation where one needs to take a fraction of a quantity, *of* means multiplication. For example, to find $\frac{2}{3}$ of 9, you multiply $\frac{2}{3} \times 9$ to get 6. Avoid the temptation to start by telling students this rather than have them see it for themselves. In discovering what *of* means in this context, student learning is enhanced.

Words	Mathematics
two thirds *of* nine	$\frac{2}{3} \times 9$

Models for multiplication of fractions used in *Let's Be Rational* are both area models and partitioning. (Area models are also useful for representing multiplication of decimals and percents.) The area model below shows $\frac{4}{5}$ of $\frac{1}{3}$.

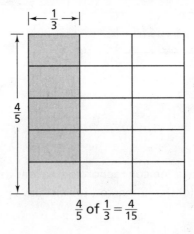

$$\frac{4}{5} \text{ of } \frac{1}{3} = \frac{4}{15}$$

Students also use a model of fraction situations that is based on partitioning a number line or strip. The number lines below show finding $\frac{4}{5}$ of $\frac{1}{3}$, or $\frac{4}{5} \times \frac{1}{3}$.

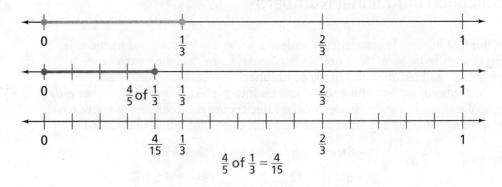

$$\frac{4}{5} \text{ of } \frac{1}{3} = \frac{4}{15}$$

UNIT
OVERVIEW

GOALS AND
STANDARDS

▶ MATHEMATICS
BACKGROUND

UNIT
INTRODUCTION

You may see students use discrete models to make sense of situations where the objects they are working on are separate objects. An example of a discrete situation is finding $\frac{3}{4}$ of 16 apples. Here each apple represents a separate entity.

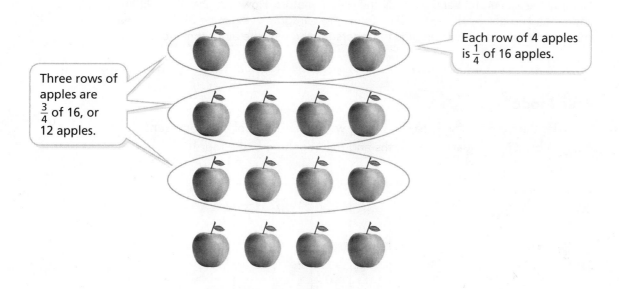

Each row of 4 apples is $\frac{1}{4}$ of 16 apples.

Three rows of apples are $\frac{3}{4}$ of 16, or 12 apples.

Discrete models can also represent mixed numbers. The animation below shows a discrete model for evaluating $2\frac{1}{2} \times 3\frac{1}{2}$. Visit Teacher Place at mathdashboard.com/cmp3 to see the complete animation.

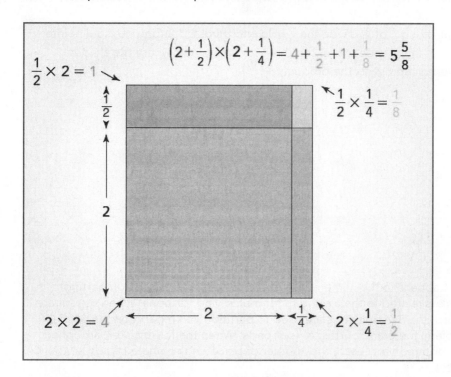

$$\left(2+\frac{1}{2}\right) \times \left(2+\frac{1}{4}\right) = 4 + \frac{1}{2} + 1 + \frac{1}{8} = 5\frac{5}{8}$$

$\frac{1}{2} \times 2 = 1$

$\frac{1}{2} \times \frac{1}{4} = \frac{1}{8}$

$2 \times 2 = 4$

$2 \times \frac{1}{4} = \frac{1}{2}$

Developing a Multiplication Algorithm

Students notice that multiplication is easy for proper fractions because they can just multiply the numerators and multiply the denominators. However, they have little understanding of why this works. The following paragraphs examine both the area and the number-line model as aids to understanding why the algorithm works.

Area Model

Consider the problem $\frac{2}{3} \times \frac{3}{4}$. To show $\frac{2}{3} \times \frac{3}{4}$ with an area model, first represent the $\frac{3}{4}$ by dividing a square into fourths and shading three of the fourths.

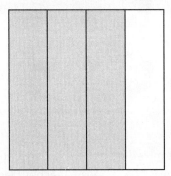

To represent taking $\frac{2}{3}$ of $\frac{3}{4}$, divide the whole into thirds by cutting the square into three rows and then shade two of the three rows. The part where the shaded sections overlap represents the product, $\frac{6}{12}$.

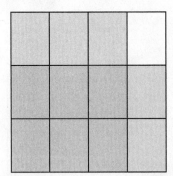

Note what happens to the numerator and the denominator when you partition and how this is related to the algorithm for multiplying fractions. When the square is partitioned, the denominators are used to partition and repartition the whole. In this problem, there are fourths, or four parts. When the fourths are partitioned into thirds, or three parts each, the number of pieces in the whole triples, so there are 12 pieces.

UNIT
OVERVIEW

GOALS AND
STANDARDS

▶ MATHEMATICS
BACKGROUND

UNIT
INTRODUCTION

In the algorithm, when you multiply the denominators (3 × 4), you are resizing the whole to have the correct number of parts. This means that the denominator in the product has the same role as the denominator in a single fraction. The role is to determine how many parts are in the whole.

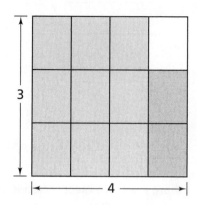

denominator $\frac{2}{3} \times \frac{3}{4} = \frac{2 \times 3}{3 \times 4} = \frac{6}{12}$

Likewise, the numerator is keeping track of how many of the one-twelfth parts are in the product. During the original partitioning, $\frac{3}{4}$, or 3 fourth-size parts, were shaded. In order to take $\frac{2}{3}$ of the 3 one-fourth size parts, you have to take 2 of the one-twelfth sections from each of the 3 one-fourth size parts. This can be represented by the product of the numerators, 2 × 3.

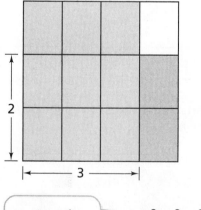

numerator $\frac{2}{3} \times \frac{3}{4} = \frac{2 \times 3}{3 \times 4} = \frac{6}{12}$

continued on next page

Note that dividing a square with both horizontal and vertical lines to represent the first fraction does not lead to the kind of partitioning that suggests multiplication of numerators and denominators. For example, represent $\frac{3}{4}$ this way.

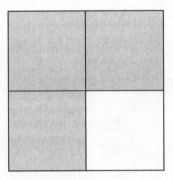

Then you may find $\frac{2}{3}$ of $\frac{3}{4}$ by noticing that there are three pieces shaded and you are concerned with 2 of them, so the answer is $\frac{2}{4}$. This strategy is perfectly reasonable for this problem. The question is whether this strategy will always work for all fractions. For $\frac{1}{5} \times \frac{2}{3}$, this strategy does not help us solve the problem.

Number-line Model

Next, take a look at how the number-line model is helpful for $\frac{1}{5} \times \frac{2}{3} = \frac{2}{15}$. You can also generalize the model, even if the process is tedious with large numerators or denominators.

Draw a number line and label 0 and 1. Partition the number line into thirds and mark $\frac{1}{3}$ and $\frac{2}{3}$.

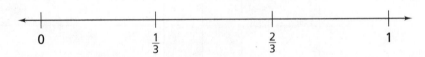

Now break each third into 5 equal parts to get a total of 15 equal parts.

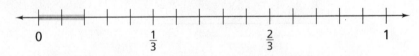

Each fifth of a third is $\frac{1}{15}$, so the two parts marked are $\frac{2}{15}$. Again, the product of the numerators gives the numerator of the product and the product of the denominators gives the denominator of the product.

UNIT
OVERVIEW

GOALS AND
STANDARDS

▶ MATHEMATICS
BACKGROUND

UNIT
INTRODUCTION

Using Distribution as a Strategy to Multiply Fractions and Mixed Numbers

The Distributive Property is a requirement of the Common Core State Standards for Mathematics. The Distributive Property can be useful when multiplying mixed numbers. However, students often use this strategy incorrectly. Therefore, Problem 3.4 provides an opportunity to use the Distributive Property. It is not the only approach to multiplying fractions, but it is one that is sensible in some situations.

The Distributive Property was introduced in the mathematical context of whole-number multiplication in *Prime Time* and then related to the process of the multiplication of mixed numbers. This approach can help students develop a better understanding of the property and its uses. Here is an algorithm for whole-number multiplication that uses this approach. Consider the expression 32×24. You can quickly evaluate it.

$$
\begin{array}{r}
32 \\
\times 24 \\
\hline
8 \\
120 \\
40 \\
600 \\
\hline
768
\end{array}
$$

The algorithm you are following is much like multiplying binomials in algebra. It involves breaking up both numbers into their tens and ones place values, as shown explicitly below.

Use distribution to find	32×24
Rewrite the expression.	$(30 + 2) \times (20 + 4)$
Multiply 30 times 20.	$30 \quad \times 20 \quad = 600$
Next, multiply 30 times 4.	$30 \quad \times \quad 4 = 120$
Then multiply 2 times 20.	$2 \quad \times 20 \quad = 40$
Multiply 2 times 4.	$2 \quad \times \quad 4 = 8$
Add the partial products.	$= 768$

continued on next page

With a problem such as $2\frac{1}{2} \times 2\frac{1}{4}$, students may break up each factor and try to work with $\left(2 + \frac{1}{2}\right) \times \left(2 + \frac{1}{4}\right)$. If they distribute correctly, they can reason through the solution as shown below.

Use distribution to find	$2\frac{1}{2} \times 2\frac{1}{4}$
Rewrite the expression.	$(2 + \frac{1}{2}) \times (2 + \frac{1}{4})$
Multiply 2 times 2.	$2 \quad \times \quad 2 \quad = 4$
Next, multiply 2 times $\frac{1}{4}$.	$2 \quad \times \quad \frac{1}{4} = \frac{1}{2}$
Then multiply $\frac{1}{2}$ times 2.	$\frac{1}{2} \times 2 \quad = 1$
Multiply $\frac{1}{2}$ times $\frac{1}{4}$.	$\frac{1}{2} \times \quad \frac{1}{4} = \frac{1}{8}$
Add the partial products.	$= 5\frac{5}{8}$

The animation here demonstrates an area model approach for multiplying mixed numbers. Visit Teacher Place at mathdashboard.com/cmp3 to see the complete animation.

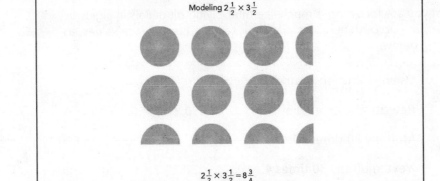

Modeling $2\frac{1}{2} \times 3\frac{1}{2}$

$2\frac{1}{2} \times 3\frac{1}{2} = 8\frac{3}{4}$

Another approach that makes sense with this problem is to work with $\left(2 + \frac{1}{2}\right) \times 2\frac{1}{4}$. If you only break up the first factor, the reasoning is as follows.

Use distribution to find	$2\frac{1}{2} \times 2\frac{1}{4}$	
Rewrite the expression.	$(2 + \frac{1}{2}) \times 2\frac{1}{4}$	
Multiply 2 times $2\frac{1}{4}$.	$2 \quad \times 2\frac{1}{4}$	$= 4\frac{1}{2}$
Next, multiply $\frac{1}{2}$ times $2\frac{1}{4}$.	$\frac{1}{2} \times 2\frac{1}{4}$	$= 1\frac{1}{8}$
Add the partial products.		$= 5\frac{5}{8}$

Division of Rational Numbers

Division presents a number of conceptual difficulties. A quotient involving fractions is not necessarily smaller than the dividend. Again, the size depends on the size of the fraction for both the dividend and the divisor. For example, $3 \div \frac{1}{3} = 9$ and $\frac{1}{4} \div \frac{1}{3} = \frac{3}{4}$ result in a quotient that is larger than the dividend or the divisor. In $\frac{1}{3} \div 9 = \frac{1}{27}$, however, the quotient is smaller than either the dividend or the divisor, and in $\frac{1}{4} \div \frac{3}{4} = \frac{1}{3}$, the quotient is greater than the dividend but less than the divisor.

quotient smaller than dividend

$$\frac{1}{3} \div 2 = \frac{1}{6}$$

quotient larger than dividend

$$2 \div \frac{1}{3} = 6$$

Examination of division of fractions in context can help students build an understanding of the operation as well as skill in predicting (or estimating) the kind of answer expected.

In order for students to make sense of any division algorithm, they need to think about what the problem is asking. Creating diagrams to model division problems is a key part of developing this understanding. There are cases where the use of pictorial reasoning is more efficient or just as efficient as an algorithm. Also, the development of an efficient algorithm is tied to the ability to understand pictorially and linguistically what the problem is asking.

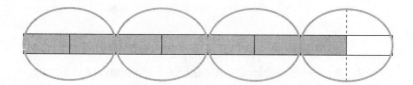

As students work toward developing and using algorithms, they may continue to draw pictures to help them think through the problem. However, they also need to learn to talk about what the problem is asking, what the answer means, what makes sense as a solution strategy, and how this language is related to the algorithm.

Our goal is to help students develop an efficient algorithm. Not all students may get to the "reciprocal" algorithm for division of fractions, but they should have efficient strategies that make sense to them to solve problems that call for division with fractions.

continued on next page

Understanding Division as an Operation

There are two situations associated with division, sharing and grouping situations. To provide support for solving problems, both teachers and students need to understand these two division situations.

Division as a Sharing Situation (partitive model for division)

You can focus on division as a sharing operation in problems such as this one.

> Ms. Li gave peanuts as a prize for a relay race. Suppose the members of the winning team share the peanuts equally among themselves. If four students share $\frac{1}{2}$ pound of peanuts, what fraction of a pound of peanuts does each student get?
>
> **3.3** Sharing a Prize: Dividing a Fraction by a Whole Number

The question is how much each of the four team members will get if the amount is shared equally. You can also think of this as a partitioning, sometimes called partitive, model.

Division as a Grouping Situation (measurement model for division)

Another kind of situation calling for division is a grouping situation. The example below is from Investigation 3.

> Naylah plans to make small cheese pizzas to sell at the school carnival. She has nine blocks of cheese. How many pizzas can she make if each pizza needs the given amount of cheese?
>
> **3.2** Into Pieces: Whole Numbers or Mixed Numbers Divided by Fractions

Here the question is how many groups of size $\frac{1}{3}$ can be made from nine blocks of cheese? Another way to ask this is "How many $\frac{1}{3}$'s are in 9?" This kind of problem has multiple names—measurement, subtractive, or quotitive model. Knowing all of these names is not important for your students, but it is important for teachers to understand them in order to provide experiences with situations representing these different models of division for students. Otherwise students will not have all the tools for deciding when division is the appropriate operation.

UNIT
OVERVIEW

GOALS AND
STANDARDS

▶ MATHEMATICS
BACKGROUND

UNIT
INTRODUCTION

As they master the meaning of operations, we ask students to write problems that fit a given computation expression. This will tell you whether students can interpret different kinds of division situations and whether they can make sense of what the answer to a division problem, including its fractional part, means in a given situation.

Developing a Division Algorithm

Let's Be Rational develops understanding of division of fractions by looking at three cases—division of a whole number by a fraction, division of a fraction by a whole number, and division of a fraction by a fraction. From these situations, several approaches to division are developed: multiplying by the denominator and dividing by the numerator, multiplying by the reciprocal, and the common-denominator approach.

Multiplying by the Denominator and Dividing by the Numerator

When you see a whole number divided by a fraction, such as $9 \div \frac{1}{3}$, it is easiest to interpret this as finding how many $\frac{1}{3}$'s are in 9. To evaluate the expression, students find how many $\frac{1}{3}$'s are in a whole and multiply by 9 to find the total number of $\frac{1}{3}$'s in 9. The reasoning is as follows.

> In $9 \div \frac{1}{3}$, I have to find the total number of $\frac{1}{3}$'s in 9.
>
> I know that there are three $\frac{1}{3}$'s in 1, so there are 9 x 3 or 27 of the $\frac{1}{3}$'s in 9.
>
> In summary, $9 \div \frac{1}{3} = 9 \times 3 = 27$.

The next problem is $9 \div \frac{2}{3}$. A key to understanding division of fractions is the relationship between the two problems $9 \div \frac{1}{3}$ and $9 \div \frac{2}{3}$. The question is how are the answers related? The answer to the first problem is 27 and the answer to the second is $13\frac{1}{2}$. Why does it make sense for the answer to the second to be half that of the first? One student provided the following reasoning.

> You can interpret $9 \div \frac{1}{3}$ as how many $\frac{1}{3}$'s are in 9 and $9 \div \frac{2}{3}$ as how many $\frac{2}{3}$'s are in 9. Now it makes sense that it will take twice as much to make $\frac{2}{3}$ as to make $\frac{1}{3}$. So the number you can make will be half as large.

continued on next page

The relationship between the two division problems allows students to relate a whole string of division problems, such as $9 \div \frac{1}{3}$, $9 \div \frac{2}{3}$, $9 \div \frac{3}{3}$, and $9 \div \frac{4}{3}$. Here we think of division of fractions as multiplying by the denominator of the divisor to find how many are in one whole and then dividing by the numerator because that is how many it takes to make a piece of the required size. These two actions are the same as multiplying by the reciprocal.

Key Concept

Multiplying by the denominator and dividing by the numerator of a fraction is the same as multiplying by the reciprocal of a fraction.

Many students are able to see the pattern of multiplying by the denominator and dividing by the numerator of the divisor and explain why it makes sense through the following kind of classroom talk.

> For $\frac{2}{3} \div \frac{3}{4}$, you can find the quotient by multiplying $\frac{2}{3}$ by $\frac{4}{3}$. The way I think about it, multiplying by 4 tells you how many $\frac{1}{4}$'s are in a whole.
>
> Dividing by 3 adjusts this answer by accounting for the fact that it takes 3 of the $\frac{1}{4}$'s to make one object of the size you want.

Multiplying by the Reciprocal

The reciprocal approach may arise when working with a fraction divided by whole number. For example, with the expression $\frac{1}{2} \div 4$, students often draw the following diagram. A sample explanation is shown.

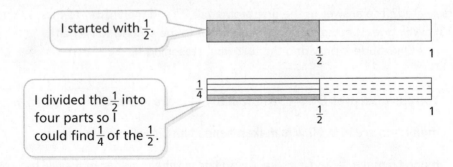

I started with $\frac{1}{2}$.

I divided the $\frac{1}{2}$ into four parts so I could find $\frac{1}{4}$ of the $\frac{1}{2}$.

Here students are relating the expression $\frac{1}{2} \div 4$ to the expression $\frac{1}{2} \times \frac{1}{4}$. This type of reasoning, the diagram that develops it, and the number sentences that support it help students move from a division problem to multiplying by the reciprocal.

UNIT
OVERVIEW

GOALS AND
STANDARDS

▶ MATHEMATICS
BACKGROUND

UNIT
INTRODUCTION

Common-Denominator Approach

Some students intuitively try the same approach for division that worked in addition and subtraction—finding a common denominator. This algorithm nicely links to their whole-number understanding of division. A student explanation appears below.

> In the expression $\dfrac{7}{9} \div \dfrac{1}{3}$, I can rename the fractions. Then I can rewrite the expression, with a common denominator, as $\dfrac{7}{9} \div \dfrac{3}{9}$.
>
> So I have 7 one-ninth-size pieces and I want to find out how many groups of three one-ninth-size pieces I can make.
>
> I compute $7 \div 3$, which equals $2\dfrac{1}{3}$.

This algorithm is used in *Decimal Ops* to develop decimal division.

The common denominator strategy for division of fractions can be modeled using fraction strips and the number line. It also can lead to the algebraic proof of the more traditional rule of "invert and multiply." Using a memorized rule is not in the spirit of CMP, but it is important that teachers understand these mathematical connections. A division problem presented in the introduction of Investigation 3 illustrates this connection.

Suppose you ask, "How many $\frac{1}{2}$'s are in $\frac{2}{3}$?" You can write the question as a division expression, $\frac{2}{3} \div \frac{1}{2}$. This division expression can also be represented by comparing fractions strips, as shown below.

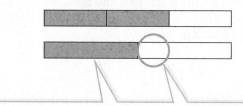

To make $\frac{2}{3}$, you need a full $\frac{1}{2}$ and part of another $\frac{1}{2}$.

continued on next page

To completely solve this problem by comparing fraction strips, both strips in the figure below are divided into equal-sized pieces. This is essentially what the common denominator approach to solving a fraction division problem accomplishes.

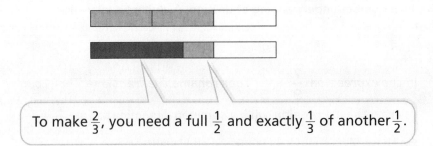

To make $\frac{2}{3}$, you need a full $\frac{1}{2}$ and exactly $\frac{1}{3}$ of another $\frac{1}{2}$.

The expression $\frac{2}{3}\left(\frac{2}{2}\right) \div \frac{1}{2}\left(\frac{3}{3}\right)$ is equivalent to $\frac{4}{6} \div \frac{3}{6}$, and since the pieces are now the same size, we can divide the numerators to get $\frac{4}{3}$, which can be written as the mixed numeral $1\frac{1}{3}$.

Note that in order to solve this problem by comparing fraction strips, we divided each strip into equal sized pieces. This is essentially what the common denominator approach to solving a fraction division problem accomplishes.

Relating Multiplication and Division

In additive situations, those involving addition and subtraction, the quantities are easy to count, measure, combine, and separate. This is because each quantity in an addition or subtraction problem has the same kind of label or is the same type of unit. For example, $3 + 4 = 7$ can be thought of as 3 marbles plus 4 marbles equals 7 marbles. Each quantity is a number of marbles.

In multiplicative situations, those involving multiplication and division, the quantities are not so straightforward. Each number may represent a different kind of unit. For example, if tomatoes cost 87 cents per can, the total cost for 6 cans can be found by multiplying 6 cans × 87 cents. It is hard to imagine a situation where adding tomatoes and money would make sense.

Example

Units of measure do not change in addition.

     marbles + marbles = marbles

Units of measure may change in multiplication.

     cans × dollars per can = dollars

Another challenge is the different kinds of situations that call for multiplication and for division. A multiplication problem may be counting an array, or finding an area, or finding the sum of a repeated addition, and so on. Division may be finding how many groups of a certain size or measure that you can make from a given quantity or how many objects or parts would be in each of a given number of groups.

For example, the number sentence $3 \times 4 = 12$ could represent 3 people, each with 4 candies. The same number sentence could also represent 3 candies given to each of 4 people. The two types of division situations, *sharing* and *grouping*, are related to these two multiplication situations. The diagram below shows the grouping model of division first, followed by the sharing model.

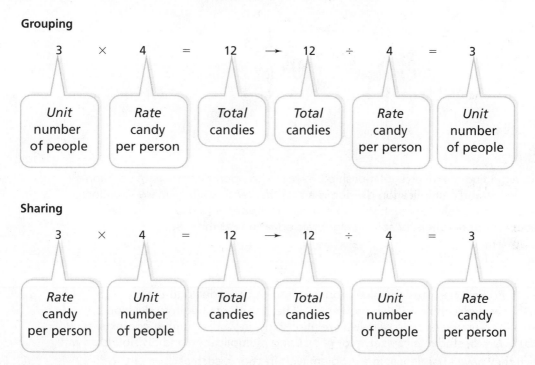

Grouping

$3 \quad \times \quad 4 \quad = \quad 12 \quad \rightarrow \quad 12 \quad \div \quad 4 \quad = \quad 3$

| *Unit* number of people | *Rate* candy per person | *Total* candies | *Total* candies | *Rate* candy per person | *Unit* number of people |

Sharing

$3 \quad \times \quad 4 \quad = \quad 12 \quad \rightarrow \quad 12 \quad \div \quad 4 \quad = \quad 3$

| *Rate* candy per person | *Unit* number of people | *Total* candies | *Total* candies | *Unit* number of people | *Rate* candy per person |

It is important that students develop a sense of the kinds of situations for which each operation is useful. Therefore, you will see attention to meanings and interpretation of the operation in the unit.

Inverse Relationships

Fact families and missing-value problems are used to introduce the inverse relationships of addition and subtraction, and of multiplication and division. In elementary grades, students learn about fact families for whole numbers.

Whole-number fact family for the number sentence $3 + 5 = 8$
$3 + 5 = 8$
$5 + 3 = 8$
$8 - 5 = 3$
$8 - 3 = 5$

continued on next page

In *Let's Be Rational* these ideas are expanded to include fractions. Fact families can contain fractions as well as whole numbers.

Fraction fact family for the number sentence $\frac{7}{10}+\frac{1}{2}=\frac{6}{5}$
$\frac{7}{10}+\frac{1}{2}=\frac{6}{5}$
$\frac{1}{2}+\frac{7}{10}=\frac{6}{5}$
$\frac{6}{5}-\frac{1}{2}=\frac{7}{10}$
$\frac{6}{5}-\frac{7}{10}=\frac{1}{2}$

Understanding the inverse relationship between the operations pairs of addition-subtraction and multiplication-division is a tool that lends itself to many situations, one of which is solving equations. Do not expect students to develop formal procedures or notation for solving algebraic equations at this stage.

In *Let's Be Rational*, missing-value problems introduce students to the use of a variable as a placeholder. Such problems will help students begin to develop a generalized understanding of inverse relationships. In whole-number contexts, such as $20 \div N = 5$, students can solve for N by using multiplication and division facts with which they have experience. In a problem with fractions, such as $\frac{8}{15} \div N = \frac{2}{3}$, this becomes more difficult. Students have to think about which values are the factors in the related multiplication sentences $\frac{2}{3} \times N = \frac{8}{15}$ and $N \times \frac{2}{3} = \frac{8}{15}$.

Missing-Value Problems

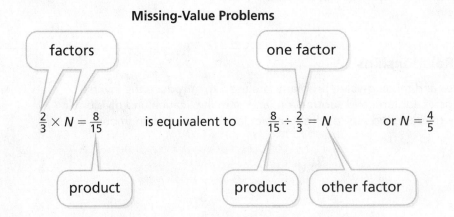

Keep in mind that inverse relationships will be explored in other number contexts such as decimals and integers. Over time, students will start to think beyond the actual numbers to the relationships that exist among the values in fact families. This understanding will be a powerful tool for students to use in other mathematical contexts.

UNIT
OVERVIEW

GOALS AND
STANDARDS

MATHEMATICS
BACKGROUND

▶ UNIT
INTRODUCTION

Unit Introduction

Using the Unit Opener

Discuss the questions posed on the opening page of the Student Edition, which are designed to make students think about the mathematics and the kinds of questions in the Unit. These questions also give you an informal assessment of what students already know about fractions and fraction operations. Don't expect all students to be able to answer correctly at this time. Use this as an opportunity for the class to discuss the questions and to start thinking about what is needed to answer them. You may want to revisit these questions as students learn the mathematical ideas and techniques necessary to find the answers.

Students reason about the mathematics of the Unit by working through problems in contexts. The problems are deliberately sequenced to provide scaffolding for more challenging problems. Contexts, models, estimation, and number sentences help students develop skills, strategies, and algorithms for fraction operations.

Using the Mathematical Highlights

The Mathematical Highlights page in the Student Edition provides information for students, parents, and other family members. It gives a preview of the mathematics and of some overarching questions that students should ask themselves while studying *Let's Be Rational*.

As they work through the Unit, students can refer back to the Mathematical Highlights page to review what they have learned and to preview what is still to come. This page also tells students' families about the mathematical ideas and activities that will be covered during *Let's Be Rational*.

Looking Ahead

Min Ji has a $\frac{7}{8}$-yard strip of balsa wood. Shawn wants to buy half of the balsa wood. **How long** is the strip of wood Shawn wants to buy?

There are 12 rabbits at a pet store. Gabriella has $5\frac{1}{2}$ ounces of parsley to feed the rabbits. **How much** parsley does each rabbit get?

Jimarcus plans to build a fence at the back of his garden. If the fence will be $5\frac{1}{3}$ yards long, **how many** $\frac{2}{3}$-yard sections of fence will he need?

Notes _____

_____

_____

In *Comparing Bits and Pieces*, you learned what fractions, decimals, ratios, and percents mean. You also explored different real-world situations in which these numbers are used.

In *Let's Be Rational*, you will investigate situations such as those described on the previous page. These situations require addition, subtraction, multiplication, or division of fractions, including mixed numbers. You will decide which operation makes sense in each situation.

Knowing strategies for working with all kinds of numbers is very important. If you take part in developing these strategies, they will make more sense to you. You will be able to more easily apply these strategies to other situations.

You may already know some shortcuts for working with fractions. During this Unit, you will think about why those shortcuts, and the strategies you develop with your class, make sense. Remember, it is not enough to answer a problem. The real power is your ability to discuss your ideas and strategies and use them in new situations.

Looking Ahead   3

Notes _____

_____

_____

Mathematical Highlights

Understanding Fraction Operations

In *Let's Be Rational*, you will develop an understanding of the four basic arithmetic operations with fractions, including mixed numbers. You will also describe strategies for using these operations when solving problems involving fractions.

You will learn how to

- Use benchmarks and other strategies to make reasonable estimates for results of operations with fractions, including mixed numbers

- Develop ways to model sums, differences, products, and quotients, including the use of areas, fraction strips, and number lines

- Look for rules to generalize patterns in fraction operations

- Use your knowledge of fractions, equivalence of fractions, and properties of numbers to develop algorithms for adding, subtracting, multiplying, and dividing fractions

- Recognize when addition, subtraction, multiplication, or division is the appropriate operation to solve a problem

- Write fact families to show the inverse relationship between addition and subtraction, and between multiplication and division

- Solve problems using operations on fractions, including mixed numbers

- Find values for variables by using operations on fractions, including mixed numbers

When you encounter a new problem, it is a good idea to ask yourself questions. In this Unit, you might ask questions such as:

What models or diagrams might be helpful in understanding the problem situation and the relationships among quantities?

What models or diagrams might help you decide which operation is useful in solving a problem?

What is a reasonable estimate for the answer?

Notes _____

_____

_____

Common Core State Standards
Mathematical Practices and Habits of Mind

In the *Connected Mathematics* curriculum you will develop an understanding of important mathematical ideas by solving problems and reflecting on the mathematics involved. Every day, you will use "habits of mind" to make sense of problems and apply what you learn to new situations. Some of these habits are described by the *Common Core State Standards for Mathematical Practices* (MP).

MP1 Make sense of problems and persevere in solving them.
When using mathematics to solve a problem, it helps to think carefully about

- data and other facts you are given and what additional information you need to solve the problem;
- strategies you have used to solve similar problems and whether you could solve a related simpler problem first;
- how you could express the problem with equations, diagrams, or graphs;
- whether your answer makes sense.

MP2 Reason abstractly and quantitatively.
When you are asked to solve a problem, it often helps to

- focus first on the key mathematical ideas;
- check that your answer makes sense in the problem setting;
- use what you know about the problem setting to guide your mathematical reasoning.

MP3 Construct viable arguments and critique the reasoning of others.
When you are asked to explain why a conjecture is correct, you can

- show some examples that fit the claim and explain why they fit;
- show how a new result follows logically from known facts and principles.

When you believe a mathematical claim is incorrect, you can

- show one or more counterexamples—cases that don't fit the claim;
- find steps in the argument that do not follow logically from prior claims.

Common Core State Standards   5

Notes _____

MP4 Model with mathematics.

When you are asked to solve problems, it often helps to

- think carefully about the numbers or geometric shapes that are the most important factors in the problem, then ask yourself how those factors are related to each other;
- express data and relationships in the problem with tables, graphs, diagrams, or equations, and check your result to see if it makes sense.

MP5 Use appropriate tools strategically.

When working on mathematical questions, you should always

- decide which tools are most helpful for solving the problem and why;
- try a different tool when you get stuck.

MP6 Attend to precision.

In every mathematical exploration or problem-solving task, it is important to

- think carefully about the required accuracy of results; is a number estimate or geometric sketch good enough, or is a precise value or drawing needed?
- report your discoveries with clear and correct mathematical language that can be understood by those to whom you are speaking or writing.

MP7 Look for and make use of structure.

In mathematical explorations and problem solving, it is often helpful to

- look for patterns that show how data points, numbers, or geometric shapes are related to each other;
- use patterns to make predictions.

MP8 Look for and express regularity in repeated reasoning.

When results of a repeated calculation show a pattern, it helps to

- express that pattern as a general rule that can be used in similar cases;
- look for shortcuts that will make the calculation simpler in other cases.

You will use all of the Mathematical Practices in this Unit. Sometimes, when you look at a Problem, it is obvious which practice is most helpful. At other times, you will decide on a practice to use during class explorations and discussions. After completing each Problem, ask yourself:

- What mathematics have I learned by solving this Problem?
- What Mathematical Practices were helpful in learning this mathematics?

Notes _____

_____

_____

Investigation

1

PLANNING

▶ INVESTIGATION
OVERVIEW

GOALS AND
STANDARDS

Extending Addition and Subtraction of Fractions

▼ Investigation Overview

Investigation Description

Investigation 1 focuses on estimating sums of fractions and decimals, and then moves to finding algorithms for precise computations. It builds on *Comparing Bits and Pieces* by extending skills with benchmarks, equivalent fractions, and the relationship between decimals and fractions.

Students play a game in which they estimate the size of sums. Students also explore estimation as a strategy to reason about contextual situations. They identify whether their estimate is an underestimate or an overestimate.

This Investigation also focuses on developing computational understanding and skill in adding and subtracting fractions. Students are not given algorithms for computation. Instead, students figure out how to add and subtract fractions by being flexible in finding equivalent fractions. This Investigation serves as an important formative assessment of students' understanding of fractions.

In the course of solving the problems, students develop strategies for adding and subtracting fractions and mixed numbers. Through class discussion, these strategies are made more explicit and efficient.

Investigation Vocabulary

- algorithm
- benchmark
- number sentence
- overestimate
- underestimate

Mathematics Background

- Building Proficiency Using Algorithms
- Choosing Appropriate Operations

Planning Chart

Content	ACE	Pacing	Materials	Resources
Problem 1.1	1–21, 54–57, 62–66, 72–74	1 day	**Labsheet 1.1A** Getting Close Fraction Game Cards **Labsheet 1.1B** Getting Close Decimal Game Cards **Labsheet 1.1C** Getting Close Number Squares fraction strips calculators	**Teaching Aid 1.1A** Estimating Sums of Fractions **Teaching Aid 1.1B** Student Strategies for Estimation **Teaching Aid 1.1C** Benchmarks of Sums– Classroom Dialogue Model
Problem 1.2	22–26, 51	1 day	**Labsheet 1ACE:** Exercise 22 (accessibility)	
Problem 1.3	27–29, 52–53, 67–70, 75–76	1 day	**Labsheet 1.3** Land Sections **Labsheet 1ACE:** Exercise 27 (accessibility) colored pencils or markers	**Teaching Aid 1.3A** Land Divided Into 64ths **Teaching Aid 1.3B** Question C– Classroom Dialogue Model • Fraction Game
Problem 1.4	30–50, 58–61, 71, 77	1½ days	**Labsheet 1.4:** Recipe Cards (accessibility) **Labsheet 1ACE:** Exercises 31, 32, 37, 38 (accessibility) containers of spices of different weights	**Teaching Aid 1.4A** Student Strategies **Teaching Aid 1.4B** Student Algorithms
Mathematical Reflections		½ day		
Assessment: Check Up 1		½ day		• Check Up 1

Goals and Standards

Goals

Numeric Estimation Understand that estimation is a tool used in a variety of situations including checking answers and making decisions, and develop strategies for estimating results of arithmetic operations:

- Use benchmarks and other strategies to estimate results of operations with fractions

- Use estimates to check the reasonableness of exact computations

- Give various reasons to estimate and identify when a situation calls for an overestimate or an underestimate

- Use estimates and exact solutions to make decisions

Fraction Operations Revisit and continue to develop meanings for the four arithmetic operations and skill at using algorithms for each:

- Determine when addition, subtraction, multiplication, or division is the appropriate operation to solve a problem

- Develop ways to model sums, differences, products, and quotients with areas, fraction strips, and number lines

- Use knowledge of fractions and equivalence of fractions to develop algorithms for adding, subtracting, multiplying, and dividing fractions

- Write fact families with fractions to show the inverse relationship between addition and subtraction, and between multiplication and division

- Compare and contrast dividing a whole number by a fraction to dividing a fraction by a whole number

- Recognize that when you multiply or divide a fraction, your answer might be less than or more than the numbers you started with

- Solve real-world problems using arithmetic operations on fractions

Variables and Equations Use variables to represent unknown values and equations to represent relationships:

- Represent unknown real-world and abstract values with variables

- Write equations (or number sentences) to represent relationships among real-world and abstract values

- Use fact families to solve for unknown values

Mathematical Reflections

Look for evidence of student understanding of the goals for this Investigation in their responses to the questions in *Mathematical Reflections*. The goals addressed by each question are indicated below.

1. **a.** What are some situations in which estimating a sum or difference is useful? Why is estimation useful in these situations?

   b. When is it useful to overestimate? When is it useful to underestimate?

   Goals
   - Use benchmarks and other strategies to estimate results of operations with fractions
   - Give various reasons to estimate and identify when a situation calls for an overestimate or an underestimate

2. When should you use addition to solve a problem involving fractions? When should you use subtraction?

   Goal
   - Determine when addition, subtraction, multiplication, or division is the appropriate operation to solve a problem

3. Suppose you are helping a student who has not studied fractions. Explain to him or her how to add and subtract fractions. Give an example of the type you think is easiest to explain. Give an example of the type you think is hardest to explain.

   Goal
   - Use knowledge of fractions and equivalence of fractions to develop algorithms for adding, subtracting, multiplying and dividing fractions

Standards

Common Core Content Standards

6.NS.B.3 Fluently add, subtract, multiply, and divide multi-digit decimals using the standard algorithm for each operation. *Problem 1*

6.NS.B.4 Find the greatest common factor of two whole numbers less than or equal to 100 and the least common multiple of two whole numbers less than or equal to 12. Use the distributive property to express a sum of two whole numbers 1–100 with a common factor as a multiple of a sum of two whole numbers with no common factor. *Problems 3 and 4*

Essential for 6.EE.A.2 Write, read, and evaluate expressions in which letters stand for numbers. *Problems 3 and 4*

Essential for 6.EE.A.2b Identify parts of an expression using mathematical terms (sum, term, product, factor, quotient, coefficient); view one or more parts of an expression as a single entity. *Problems 3 and 4*

Essential for 6.EE.A.4 Identify when two expressions are equivalent (i.e., when the two expressions name the same number regardless of which value is substituted into them). *Problem 3*

Essential for 6.EE.B.5 Understand solving an equation or inequality as a process of answering a question: which values from a specified set, if any, make the equation or inequality true? Use substitution to determine whether a given number in a specified set makes an equation or inequality true. *Problems 1 and 2*

Essential for 6.EE.B.6 Use variables to represent numbers and write expressions when solving a real-world or mathematical problem; understand that a variable can represent an unknown number, or, depending on the purpose at hand, any number in a specified set. *Problem 4*

Essential for 6.EE.B.7 Solve real-world and mathematical problems by writing and solving equations of the form $x + p = q$ and $px = q$ for cases in which p, q and x are all nonnegative rational numbers. *Problems 1, 2, and 4*

Facilitating the Mathematical Practices

Students in *Connected Mathematics* classrooms display evidence of multiple Common Core Standards for Mathematical Practice every day. Here are just a few examples where you might observe students demonstrating the Standards for Mathematical Practice during this Investigation.

Practice 1: **Make sense of problems and persevere in solving them.**

Students are engaged every day in solving problems and, over time, learn to persevere in solving them. To be effective, the problems embody critical concepts and skills and have the potential to engage students in making sense of mathematics. Students build understanding by reflecting, connecting, and communicating. These student-centered problem situations engage students in articulating the "knowns" in a problem situation and determining a logical solution pathway. The student-student and student-teacher dialogues help students to not just make sense of the problems, but also to persevere in finding appropriate strategies to solve them. The suggested questions in the Teacher Guides provide the metacognitive scaffolding to help students monitor and refine their problem-solving strategies.

Practice 2: **Reason abstractly and quantitatively.**

Students work on real-world problems throughout the Investigation but transition to abstract and quantitative reasoning in Problem 1.4. During this Problem, students create their own real-world situations to match equations and describe algorithms for finding sums and differences of fractions.

Practice 5: **Use appropriate tools strategically.**

Students use calculators to check the accuracy of their estimates in Problem 1.1. They also use the Fraction Game digital tool as a supplement to Problem 1.3.

Practice 6: **Attend to precision.**

Students make estimates in Problem 1.1, and work to make the estimates increasingly exact throughout the Problem. Students also decide whether estimates are overestimates or underestimates during Problem 1.2. They explore whether estimates are sufficient or exact answers are necessary throughout Investigation 1.

Students identify and record their personal experiences with the Standards for Mathematical Practice during the Mathematical Reflections at the end of the Investigation.

Getting Close
Estimating Sums

▼ Problem Overview

> $\mathcal{F}\text{ocus}\ \mathcal{Q}\text{uestion}$ What are some strategies for estimating the sums of fractions?

Problem Description

In this Problem, students estimate sums of fractions and decimals to determine whether each sum is nearest to 0, 1, 2, or 3.

Students play a game based on estimating sums of fractions and decimals. They begin by estimating sums of fractions, then sums of decimals. Decimal and fraction cards are later mixed together to help students build flexibility in moving between representations. While playing the game, students explore estimation strategies.

The last part of the Summarize introduces the terms **underestimate** and **overestimate**, which are further explored in Problem 1.2. Problem 1.2 asks students to decide if a situation calls for an underestimate or an overestimate. You might find it helpful to read the introduction to Problem 1.2 at this point so that you can see how Problem 1.2 builds off of Problem 1.1.

Problem Implementation

Students may work in groups of 2 to 4 to play the Getting Close game. Students should then work in pairs to solve the Questions within the Problem.

Materials

- **Labsheet 1.1A:** Getting Close Fraction Game Cards (one per group)
- **Labsheet 1.1B:** Getting Close Decimal Game Cards (one per group)
- **Labsheet 1.1C:** Getting Close Number Squares (one per group)
- **Teaching Aid 1.1A:** Estimating Sums of Fractions
- **Teaching Aid 1.1B:** Student Strategies for Estimation
- **Teaching Aid 1.1C:** Benchmarks of Sums–Classroom Dialogue Model

fraction strips (optional)

calculators (optional)

Vocabulary

• benchmark

Mathematics Background

• Choosing Appropriate Operations

At a Glance and Lesson Plan

• At a Glance: Let's Be Rational Problem 1.1
• Lesson Plan: Let's Be Rational Problem 1.1

▼ Launch

Connecting to Prior Knowledge

Use the introduction to review whole number benchmarks and selecting the nearest benchmark for a rational number. Students did a similar activity in *Comparing Bits and Pieces*. Discuss $\frac{3}{8}$ and 0.58 and the whole-number benchmarks closest to these two rational numbers. You might want to provide a few more examples and ask students to describe additional strategies they can use to find the nearest benchmark numbers for these examples.

Suggested Questions

Display a number line from 0 to 2 with each $\frac{1}{4}$-unit marked. Provide students with a fraction or decimal, and ask questions such as the following:

• About where does $\frac{4}{9}$ belong on the number line? How do you know? (Between 0 and 1, but close to $\frac{1}{2}$. Half of 9 is 4.5, or $4\frac{1}{2}$, so 4 out of 9 is close to $\frac{1}{2}$.)

• Is $\frac{4}{9}$ closer to 0 or 1? How do you know? (Since 4.5 out of 9 is equal to $\frac{1}{2}$, then $\frac{4}{9}$ must be a little less than $\frac{1}{2}$. So $\frac{4}{9}$ is closer to 0.)

• How far is $\frac{4}{9}$ from 0? ($\frac{4}{9}$)

• How far is $\frac{4}{9}$ from 1? ($\frac{5}{9}$)

When students are comfortable with estimating the placement of a single rational number on a number line, ask students to estimate the sum of two rational numbers and decide whether the sum is closest to 0, 1, or 2. Display **Teaching Aid 1.1A: Estimating Sums of Fractions** and ask:

• Is the sum of $\frac{1}{2} + \frac{5}{8}$ between 0 and 1 or between 1 and 2? (The sum is between 1 and 2 since one number is exactly $\frac{1}{2}$ and the other number is more than $\frac{1}{2}$.)

- Is the sum closer to 1 or closer to 2? (Closer to 1 because $\frac{5}{8}$, is just an eighth more than $\frac{1}{2}$. When you add $\frac{5}{8}$ to exactly $\frac{1}{2}$, the sum is just an eighth more than 1.)

In addition to these examples, **Teaching Aid 1.1C: Benchmarks of Sums–Classroom Dialogue Model** provides questions that can also be used. These examples use benchmarks from 0 to 3, such as in the game situation, Getting Close.

Presenting the Challenge

When you are confident that the class is thinking about strategies for using benchmarks to estimate sums, explain that they are going to play a game that involves fractions, decimals, estimation, addition, and benchmarks.

Read through the directions for playing the Getting Close game, and make sure that students understand how to play. You might have two students play a couple of rounds in front of the class to demonstrate.

Distribute a set of four number squares (0, 1, 2 and 3) to each student and a set of Getting Close game cards to each group. Be sure that each group has the opportunity to work with fraction game cards, decimal game cards, and a combination of both types. Have each group play the game several times before they begin answering the Questions.

This game works well for two to four people. If students are struggling with the game, remind them that they may use benchmarks, fraction strips, number lines, or diagrams to model the sums.

▼ Explore

Providing for Individual Needs

Have each group play a couple of rounds of Getting Close. Tell them to share their strategies with the other members of their group after each round. As you listen to groups share their strategies, take note of interesting strategies to share in the Summarize.

If students are struggling with the game, remind them that they may use benchmarks, fraction strips, number lines, or diagrams to model the sums.

At some point, have students stop playing the game to answer the Questions.

Going Further

Students who are not challenged enough using 0, 1, 2, and 3 as benchmarks can play a different version of the game called Getting Even Closer. The game follows the same directions, but students use the benchmarks $\frac{1}{2}$, $1\frac{1}{2}$, and $2\frac{1}{2}$, in addition to their original number squares. This version of the game can also be used as a follow-up activity for the whole class.

Planning for the Summary

What evidence will you use in the summary to clarify and deepen understanding of the Focus Question?

What will you do if you do not have evidence?

▼ Summarize

Orchestrating the Discussion

Suggested Questions

Before discussing the strategies students used for estimating sums, you may want to ask the students about other elements of the game.

- What kinds of sums were easy to estimate? (Answers will vary. Have students share their thinking about why some pairs of game cards have sums that are easy to estimate.)

- Were there times that you found the actual sum instead of estimating because it was just as quick? (Students may offer a few examples such as $\frac{2}{5} + \frac{1}{5}$ where the actual sum is $\frac{3}{5}$.)

- Did you find it easier to estimate when the cards were either both decimals or both fractions? (Yes, because then you don't have to convert a fraction into a decimal or a decimal into a fraction before you estimate.)

- Were there any sums that were difficult to estimate? (Students may offer a few examples such as $1\frac{1}{3} + \frac{6}{8}$.)

- What made them difficult? (Answers may vary. Possible answer: The fractions did not have a common denominator, and neither of them is very close to a benchmark number.)

- What did you do when one game card was a fraction and the other was a decimal? (You can think of the fraction as an equivalent decimal or the decimal as an equivalent fraction before you estimate.)

Mention several possible situations from the Getting Close game. Begin by asking students to discuss a reasonable estimate for the sum and their strategies for finding the estimate. For example,

- If your group turned over the game cards $\frac{4}{9}$ and $1\frac{1}{3}$, how would you decide what whole-number benchmark the sum is nearest? (The sum is closest to 2 because $\frac{4}{9}$ is about $\frac{1}{2}$ and $1\frac{1}{3}$ is about $1\frac{1}{2}$ so $\frac{1}{2} + 1\frac{1}{2}$ is 2.)

- Is 2 a reasonable estimate? (Yes.)

- Did someone think about the problem a different way? (Answers will vary. Make note of any differences in strategy.)

After students describe their strategies for a few problems, shift the conversation to introducing overestimation and underestimation, the focus of Problem 1.2.

- For the game cards $\frac{4}{9}$ and $1\frac{1}{3}$, is the actual sum exactly 2, less than 2, or greater than 2? (less than 2)

- How do you know? ($\frac{4}{9}$ is a little less than $\frac{1}{2}$ and $1\frac{1}{3}$ is a little less than $1\frac{1}{2}$. Since the estimates are greater than the actual numbers, the sum of the estimates is greater than the actual sum. This means that the actual sum is less than 2.)

- Suppose two fractions, each less than $\frac{1}{2}$, are added. What can you tell me about the actual sum? (Since $\frac{1}{2} + \frac{1}{2} = 1$, a number less than $\frac{1}{2}$ plus another number less than $\frac{1}{2}$ must be less than 1.)

- If you use $\frac{1}{2} + \frac{1}{2} = 1$ as the estimated sum, but the actual addends are each less than $\frac{1}{2}$, is your estimated sum an overestimate or an underestimate of the actual sum? Why? (The estimate is more than the actual sum, so it is an overestimate.)

- Suppose two fractions, each a little greater than $1\frac{1}{2}$, are added. What can you tell me about the actual sum? How do you know? (Since the actual values are each greater than $1\frac{1}{2}$, and $1\frac{1}{2} + 1\frac{1}{2} = 3$, the actual sum is greater than 3.)

- If you use $1\frac{1}{2} + 1\frac{1}{2} = 3$ as the estimated sum, but the actual addends are both a little greater than $1\frac{1}{2}$, is your estimated sum an overestimate or an underestimate? Why? (The estimated sum is less than the actual sum, so the estimated sum is an underestimate.)

When posing these questions verbally, they can be confusing. It is helpful to display a problem with an estimate. For example, display:

Actual sum: $\frac{2}{3} + \frac{5}{9} = ?$

Estimated sum: $\frac{1}{2} + \frac{1}{2} = 1$

- Is the estimated sum greater than or less than the actual sum? (less than)

- How do you know? (Both $\frac{2}{3}$ and $\frac{5}{9}$ are greater than $\frac{1}{2}$, so the actual sum must be greater than 1.)

- Is the estimated sum an underestimate or an overestimate of the actual sum? (The estimated sum of 1 is less than the actual sum. So the estimated sum is an underestimate of the actual answer.)

Discuss the answers to Questions A–C, which can be found in the Problem's Resources section. Be sure to address the Focus Question by asking,

- What are some strategies you found useful in the game? (Answers will vary. Many students may find the nearest $\frac{1}{2}$ or whole for each addend, and then add. Others may construct a number line to help them model the situation. Students can also think about the distance from one addend to a benchmark, and then see if the second addend pushes the sum past that benchmark number)

Conclude the discussion by asking students to share their strategies for estimating sums of fractions and decimals. It helps to show their answers as number sentences with an *approximately equal* to sign, $\approx$. After the class has finished sharing their own strategies, you can share additional strategies with your students by displaying **Teaching Aid 1.1B: Student Strategies for Estimation**.

Reflecting on Student Learning

Use the following questions to assess student understanding at the end of the lesson.

- What evidence do I have that students understand the Focus Question?
  - Where did my students get stuck?
  - What strategies did they use?
  - What breakthroughs did my students have today?
- How will I use this to plan for tomorrow? For the next time I teach this lesson?
- Where will I have the opportunity to reinforce these ideas as I continue through this Unit? The next Unit?

ACE Assignment Guide

- **Applications:** 1–21
- **Connections:** 54–57, 62–66
- **Extensions:** 72–74

▼ Problem Overview

> *Focus Question* How do you know if your estimate is an underestimate or an overestimate? What information does an underestimate and overestimate tell you?

Problem Description

In Problem 1.2, students learn estimation strategies in contextual situations and consider whether they need to overestimate or underestimate a sum or difference.

When playing the Getting Close game in Problem 1.1, students had to estimate what integer the exact sum was nearest. The context of the game did not require students to think about whether their estimate was greater than the exact answer or less than the exact answer.

When estimating in contextual situations, students need to make decisions based on the information they have. It is not appropriate to say that they can adjust all the values down or up, or to the nearest whole number. The estimation depends on the context of the problem and the specific values in the problem. A good example of this is Question C, which is discussed in the Summarize.

Note: Encourage students to use the phrases **estimated sum** and **actual sum**, instead of *estimate* and *sum*. This will help clarify the intent of the Focus Question and prompt students to think about the overall effect of their estimation.

Problem Implementation

This is a good Problem with which to use a Think-Pair-Share classroom organization. Start the Problem by having students work individually, and then have them pair up with another student to share their reasoning.

You may want to Summarize after students have finished Questions A–C and assign Questions D and E for homework.

Labsheet 1ACE: Exercise 22 (accessibility) is a sample of how ACE Exercises can be modified to help students who would benefit from additional scaffolding.

Materials

• **Labsheet 1ACE:** Exercise 22 (accessibility)

Vocabulary

• overestimate   • underestimate

Mathematics Background

• Choosing Appropriate Operations

At a Glance and Lesson Plan

• At a Glance: Let's Be Rational Problem 1.2
• Lesson Plan: Let's Be Rational Problem 1.2

▼ Launch

Launch Video

In this video, two people are making curtains for a window. One person underestimates how much fabric is needed, and the other overestimates how much fabric is needed. Use this video to give students an example of a scenario where it is important to choose either underestimation or overestimation as a strategy, depending on the situation. You can show this video during the Connecting to Prior Knowledge section, but before discussing specific contexts in which students should overestimate or underestimate. Visit Teacher Place at mathdashboard.com/cmp3 to see the complete video.

Discuss how overestimation/underestimation relates to problem situations. Ask students to provide an example of when underestimating is a good strategy. Then continue with Presenting the Challenge.

Connecting to Prior Knowledge

Explain to students that they are going to practice estimating answers for realistic problems. Students will have to decide whether they need to overestimate or an underestimate.

Suggested Questions

Start with a few estimation questions with numbers but no context to reintroduce the notion of underestimating and overestimating.

• Suppose you want to estimate the sum $1\frac{5}{6} + 1\frac{7}{8}$. What is a good estimate for the actual sum? (4; $1\frac{5}{6} + 1\frac{7}{8}$ is close to $2 + 2$.)

- Is the estimated sum greater than or less than the actual sum? (The estimated sum is greater than the actual sum. This means that the estimated sum is an overestimate of the actual sum since 2 + 2 (the estimated sum) is greater than $1\frac{5}{6} + 1\frac{7}{8}$ (the actual sum).)

- Someone suggests that a reasonable estimate for $1\frac{5}{6} + 1\frac{7}{8}$ can be found by adding $1\frac{1}{2} + 1\frac{1}{2}$. What is this estimated sum? (3)

- Is $1\frac{1}{2} + 1\frac{1}{2} = 3$ an overestimate of the actual sum or an underestimate? (It is an underestimate because the estimated sum, $1\frac{1}{2} + 1\frac{1}{2}$, is less than the actual sum, $1\frac{5}{6} + 1\frac{7}{8}$.)

- What do these two estimates tell you about the actual sum? (It must be somewhere between 3 and 4.)

- Are both estimates reasonable? (Yes.)

- What about the estimate $1\frac{1}{2} + 2 = 3\frac{1}{2}$? Is this estimate closer to or farther from the actual sum? (Since $1\frac{5}{6}$ was reduced and $1\frac{7}{8}$ was increased, it is probably closer to the actual sum.)

- Is this an overestimate of the actual answer or an underestimate? (It is hard to tell. It is probably an underestimate, though, since reducing $\frac{5}{6}$ to $\frac{1}{2}$ is a greater change than increasing $\frac{7}{8}$ to 1.)

- What if you are buying fencing for a small garden and the actual lengths you need are $1\frac{5}{6}$ and $1\frac{7}{8}$? Which of these three estimates is the most useful? Is it best to buy 3 feet, $3\frac{1}{2}$ feet, or 4 feet of fencing? (It is best to overestimate with 4 feet so that you can be sure you have enough fencing. Three feet is an underestimate, and it will not be enough. Using $3\frac{1}{2}$ feet is close, but you chance not having enough fencing. With 4 feet, you can be sure you have enough.)

Tell the students that when they work with only numbers, any of these three types of estimates are reasonable. But in real-life situations, they need to choose a specific type of estimate. This would be a good time to show students the Launch video. Continue by asking the following questions.

- Name some situations where you might want to overestimate. (buying food for a party, getting supplies, bringing money needed for shopping, having enough gas for a trip)

- Name some situations where you might want to underestimate. (trimming off something like hair or fabric, estimating the amount of weight a chair or an elevator can hold, guessing an older person's age)

Introduce Problem 1.2 to your students by saying,

Questions A–E will help you think more about how to overestimate or underestimate and when to use each one.

Presenting the Challenge

Read through Question A with the students to be sure they understand what they are expected to do during the Problem. You may need to explain the context of the Question to them. This will allow them to tackle the other Questions with more confidence.

▼ Explore

Providing for Individual Needs

Some students may need help understanding the context of the Questions. In addition, students may struggle with deciding if they should overestimate or underestimate. You might suggest that they first estimate, and then decide if they correctly overestimated or underestimated.

Suggested Questions

As students work, help them to focus on the actual sum and the estimated sum. Ask questions that let you assess student reasoning, such as the following:

- Is your estimated sum greater than (an overestimate of) or less than (an underestimate of) your actual sum?

- When you rounded the addends to the nearest benchmarks, did you increase or decrease each number to get a benchmark?

- What does the estimated sum tell you about how much you should actually buy?

- What does the estimated sum tell you about how much you have?

At this time in the Investigation, it is not important for students to use an efficient strategy or algorithm. Students might benefit from attempting to solve the problems in parts. Ask questions such as the following:

- What is a reasonable estimate for this problem?

- Now can you rewrite all of the fractions so that they have the same denominator?

- Of what number would 3, 6, 8, and 12 all be a factor? (24)

- How can this help you to rewrite the fractions with the same denominator?

- How do you know if you have too much (an overestimate) or too little (an underestimate)?

When students have completed most of the Questions and seem ready to discuss them, move to the Summarize.

Planning for the Summary

What evidence will you use in the summary to clarify and deepen understanding of the Focus Question?

What will you do if you do not have evidence?

▼ Summarize

Orchestrating the Discussion

Begin by having students share their estimates for Question A. Have them describe why they think it is an underestimate or an overestimate.

Suggested Questions

- Without computing an exact answer, how can you tell how much wood Mrs. Edwards should buy? (First, combine $4\frac{1}{4} + 4\frac{1}{4}$ to get $8\frac{1}{2}$. Then, estimate $5\frac{1}{8} + 8\frac{1}{2}$ by decomposing it into whole-number parts and fractional parts. $5 + 8 = 13$, and $\frac{1}{8} + \frac{1}{2}$ will be less than one, so 14 inches is enough.)

- Is this a situation where you need an underestimate or an overestimate? Why? (You want to overestimate how much material you need to buy so you can be sure to have enough. You can always throw away the extra material or use it for something else.)

Have students share their estimates for Question B and why they think they should overestimate or underestimate.

- Without computing an exact answer, how can you find how much fabric Mr. Cheng should buy? (Possible answers: Round $1\frac{1}{3}$ up to the benchmark $1\frac{1}{2}$ and $1\frac{3}{4}$ up to 2. The estimated sum is then $3\frac{1}{2}$. Or, decompose the expression $1\frac{1}{3} + 1\frac{3}{4}$ to $1 + 1 = 2$, then estimate $\frac{1}{3} + \frac{3}{4}$. This is a little more than one, so the total estimated sum is a little more than 3. Note : both of these estimation strategies indicate that Mr. Cheng needs to buy 4 yards of fabric to have enough to make the curtains.)

- Is this a situation where you need an underestimate or an overestimate? Why? (You want to overestimate how much material you need to get so you can be sure to have enough to make the curtains.)

For Question C, have students share what they thought of Mr. Aleman's budget. Some students may say that the budget is fine, while others will understand that Mr. Aleman is over-budget because the fractions add up to a number that is greater than one.

- Why is it a problem that the fractional parts of the budget add up to be greater than one? (Because each fraction represents a part of one whole budget. If the parts add up to greater than the whole, then Mr. Aleman is over-budget. There will be no money left for next year, and he will not be able to cover the other expenses he listed.)

For Question D, have students share their estimates. In this Question, students may share either an underestimate strategy or an overestimate strategy. For instance, students may underestimate how many quarts of berries Jasmine has, but the converse of this logic is that they are also overestimating how many quarts of berries Jasmine needs. Either approach works.

For Question E, students must underestimate because there is a limit on how much gas the tank will hold. Priya cannot overflow the tank for two reasons: first, she does not want to pollute the lake water; and second, she does not want to waste gas and money.

Close the Summarize by generalizing and describing overestimates and underestimates. Revisit student examples of situations in which an underestimate is needed and some in which an overestimate is needed. This will allow you to assess how well they are making sense of underestimates and overestimates, as well as when each is useful.

- What is an overestimate? (An overestimate occurs when the estimated sum is greater than the actual sum.)

- What are some situations in which you should overestimate? (When you are trying to be sure that you will have more than you actually need or that you have enough. You should overestimate when serving food or buying materials to make something, or when deciding how much money you will need to buy something. So, you often overestimate what you need.)

- What is an underestimate? (An underestimate occurs when the estimated sum is less than the actual sum.)

- For what type of situations are underestimates useful? (When you want to have "about some amount" but you don't want to have any extra. Also, when it is okay to have extra, but you need to be sure you have a certain minimum amount. For instance, when you are making something, you want to underestimate what you already have because this means that you really have more than enough to finish the project.)

Reflecting on Student Learning

Use the following questions to assess student understanding at the end of the lesson.

- What evidence do I have that students understand the Focus Question?
  - Where did my students get stuck?
  - What strategies did they use?
  - What breakthroughs did my students have today?
- How will I use this to plan for tomorrow? For the next time I teach this lesson?
- Where will I have the opportunity to reinforce these ideas as I continue through this Unit? The next Unit?

ACE Assignment Guide

- **Applications:** 22–26, 51
- **Labsheet 1ACE:** Exercise 22 (accessibility)

1.3 Land Sections
Adding and Subtracting Fractions

▼ Problem Overview

> *Focus Question* What are some strategies for adding and subtracting fractions?

Problem Description

In Problem 1.3, students use an area model in the context of buying and selling land to reason about adding and subtracting fractions.

Students first name the fraction of a section each person owns. Next, students explore combining and separating parts of the section. In addition, students are told that each section is equivalent to 640 acres. This allows for questions that discuss the size of the parts of the sections in another way: number of acres owned.

In this Problem and the ones that follow, students write number sentences to represent and symbolize situations. During the Explore phase of the lesson, pay attention to the students' notation in their work. The Summarize is also an excellent opportunity to help students connect their mental computations with the number sentences that symbolize what they have done.

Problem Implementation

This Problem works well in a Think-Pair-Share arrangement. Give students time to tackle the Problem themselves before they share with a partner or larger group.

Materials

- **Labsheet 1.3:** Land Sections (accessibility)
- **Labsheet 1ACE:** Exercise 27 (accessibility)
- **Teaching Aid 1.3A:** Land Divided Into 64ths
- **Teaching Aid 1.3B:** Question C–Classroom Dialogue Model

colored pencils or markers (optional)

Using Technology

If your students have Internet access, you can direct them to the **Fraction Game**, which provides additional support in adding fractions.

Vocabulary

• number sentence

Mathematics Background

• Building Proficiency Using Algorithms
• Choosing Appropriate Operations

At a Glance and Lesson Plan

• At a Glance: Let's Be Rational Problem 1.3
• Lesson Plan: Let's Be Rational Problem 1.3

▼ Launch

Connecting to Prior Knowledge

Before starting Problem 1.3, use the introduction in the Student Edition to review what a number sentence is. Make the students aware that there are several terms that will be used to indicate that they should write a number sentence. These terms include mathematical sentence, addition sentence, subtraction sentence, multiplication sentence, and division sentence.

Presenting the Challenge

Suggested Questions

One way to launch the Problem is to have a conversation with your students about naming amounts with fractions. Display **Labsheet 1.3: Land Sections**. Pose questions such as the following:

• How many sections of land are being discussed in this problem? (2)

• How many acres are in a section? (640)

• How many owners have land in Sections 18 and 19? (12)

• Does anyone own a whole section? (No.)

• What does this tell you about how much land each person owns? (This means that everyone owns a fraction that is less than 1 section.)

• Who owns the largest piece of a section? (Foley or Walker)

• About how much land does Foley own? (Between $\frac{1}{4}$ and $\frac{1}{2}$ of a section, may be $\frac{1}{3}$)

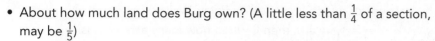

- About how much land does Burg own? (A little less than $\frac{1}{4}$ of a section, may be $\frac{1}{5}$)

- What would be a reasonable estimate for Burg + Foley's land? (about $\frac{1}{2}$ of a section)

  How do you know? (Possible answers: I estimated the sum; or, since they are next to one another, it is easy to estimate how much land they own together. They take up about $\frac{1}{2}$ of Section 19.)

- About how much land does Lapp own? ($\frac{1}{4}$ of a section)

- What does "write a number sentence" in Question B mean? (to model, using addition or subtraction, the problem situations)

  Can you give an example? (Students will not know the exact fractional values, but they can use words in their models. They can replace the words with fractions once they find what the exact values are. For example, Bouck + Lapp = Foley is $\frac{1}{16} + \frac{1}{4} = \frac{5}{16}$)

After students give approximate answers for how much land each person owns, hand out **Labsheet 1.3: Land Sections**. Students can then use other strategies to more accurately identify the amount of land each farmer owns, such as folding or drawing on the Labsheet. Have extra copies of the map on hand for students who make mistakes and are too far along to restart on the same sheet. You may want to have colored pencils or markers on hand so that students can differentiate between the original plot divisions and any lines they may draw during their work.

▼ Explore

Providing for Individual Needs

You may want to check that students have accurately identified how much land each person owns in Question A before they go on to use those values in the rest of the Problem.

Help students who are struggling to write number sentences. It is often helpful for students to write a number sentence with the names of the landowners, and then substitute numerical values. For example,

Bouck + Stewart = total can be rewritten as $\frac{1}{16} + \frac{5}{32} = \frac{7}{32}$.

Be sure to ask students how they chose the operation for their number sentence. It is important that students know which operations apply to which situations.

For Question D parts (1) and (2), encourage students to find more than one number sentence to represent the situation. These questions are good opportunities to review the Distributive Property. If some students find multiple ways to arrive at the answer, be sure to have them share during the Summarize.

Students might add the fractions of a section owned by Foley, Walker, Burg and Krebs ($\frac{5}{16} + \frac{5}{16} + \frac{3}{16} + \frac{1}{32} = \frac{27}{32}$ of a section) and then find out how many acres this is: $\frac{27}{32}$ of 640 acres. Or they may find out how many acres each person owns and add the acres: $\frac{5}{16}$ of 640 acres + $\frac{5}{16}$ of 640 acres + $\frac{3}{16}$ of 640 acres + $\frac{1}{32}$ of 640 acres = 200 acres + 200 acres + 120 acres + 20 acres = 540 acres. Comparing the two strategies brings out that 640 is a common factor in the expressions on the second strategy.

If groups finish early, they can organize their thinking on a clean copy of the map in order to share their work with the class.

Planning for the Summary

What evidence will you use in the summary to clarify and deepen understanding of the Focus Question?
What will you do if you do not have evidence?

▼ Summarize

Orchestrating the Discussion

Start the Summarize by asking the students to discuss how they found the fractional names for each person's part of land. Select groups to show their work and discuss the strategy they used to name the pieces. One of the most common strategies that students use is to divide each section into 64ths as shown in **Teaching Aid 1.3A: Land Divided Into 64ths**.

When asked how they decided to divide each section into 64ths, one student said the following.

> *Heidi* : I didn't know it had to be divided into 64ths when I started. I extended the property lines that were already there until they reached the section borders. I did this for each property line. Then, I looked to see where else I needed to add lines to make each piece in the section the same size, and I drew those lines. When I finished, the pieces were all the same size, and there were 64 pieces in each section. I could just count how many of the pieces each person had out of the 64 pieces.

When asked how she kept the property lines straight, Heidi said that she drew in the new lines with a different color so that it was easy to see where the original property lines were.

In general, have students evaluate each other's strategies. It is not uncommon for students to identify different, but equivalent, values for each person's share of land. Students can reinforce their knowledge of equivalent fractions.

Suggested Questions

After a group has presented their strategy, ask the class questions like the following:

- What do others think about this group's strategy? Does it seem reasonable?

- Did anyone have a different answer or use a different strategy? (This discussion will allow students to share their own ideas while noticing pros and cons of others' strategies.)

In addition, for Questions B–E, ask students to share the number sentences that support their calculations. Continue to emphasize equivalence when discussing the number sentences that students wrote.

After a group has presented its strategy, ask questions like the following:

- What equation represented your solution?

- How does this solution compare to Group B's solution? Are the two equations equivalent? How do you know? (Students should respond to these questions by detailing what they know about fractions and the properties of numbers. Specifically, students should mention renaming fractions with different denominators and the use of the Commutative Property.)

- How do you decide if addition or subtraction will help you solve a problem? (When combining land, you need to add. When separating land, selling land, or finding a difference, you need to subtract.)

- What strategies help you add or subtract fractions? (Answers will vary. Many students will talk about renaming fractions so that the addends have the same denominator. Others will rely on visual representations.)

Question B provides a mixture of addition and subtraction problem situations.

Question C gives students an opportunity to create several possibilities that satisfy the conditions of the two problems. Collect several number sentences that have the same sum even though they represent different combinations. **Teaching Aid 1.3B: Question C–Classroom Dialogue Model** details a conversation that took place in a classroom when talking about Question C.

Have more than one student show their strategy for solving Question D, part (1). Question D, part (2) builds on strategies from part (1). In Question D, we are foreshadowing multiplication with fractions by having students find a fraction of a number other than 1. This is a different skill from their work in Question A where they found a fractional part of a whole, or 1.

Question D, parts (2) and (3) lend themselves to a discussion on multiple strategies.

For part (2), students can add all the land pieces expressed in acres to arrive at a final answer: Foley + Walker + Burg + Krebs = 200 + 200 + 120 + 20 = 540 acres.

Alternatively, students can find the fractional sum and then convert that sum into acres: $(\frac{5}{16} + \frac{5}{16} + \frac{3}{16} + \frac{1}{32})$ of 640 acres = $\frac{27}{32}$ of 640 acres = 540 acres.

For part (3), students can add all the land from Section 19 that is sold to the state, and then subtract that total from 1: $1 - (\frac{5}{16} + \frac{5}{16} + \frac{3}{16}) = 1 - \frac{13}{16} = \frac{3}{16}$.

Alternatively, they can find the names of the owners who did not sell their land (only Theule in this case) and simply add those parts of a section together $(\frac{3}{16})$.

Question E is a practice problem and can be assigned as homework if you do not get to it during class.

Reflecting on Student Learning

Use the following questions to assess student understanding at the end of the lesson.

- What evidence do I have that students understand the Focus Question?
  - Where did my students get stuck?
  - What strategies did they use?
  - What breakthroughs did my students have today?
- How will I use this to plan for tomorrow? For the next time I teach this lesson?
- Where will I have the opportunity to reinforce these ideas as I continue through this Unit? The next Unit?

ACE Assignment Guide

- **Applications:** 27–29
- **Connections:** 52–53, 67–70
- **Extensions:** 75–76
- **Labsheet 1ACE:** Exercise 27 (accessibility)

PROBLEM

1.4

Visiting the Spice Shop
Adding and Subtracting Mixed Numbers

▼ Problem Overview

> *Focus Question*   What are some strategies for adding and subtracting mixed numbers?

Problem Description

In Problem 1.4, students continue to work on addition and subtraction of fractions and mixed numbers using spice recipes as a context.

Questions A–D of Problem 1.4 use the context of mixing spices. Questions E and F ask students to stand back and use what they have learned about adding and subtracting mixed numbers with noncontextual problems.

As students work, they should realize that they need fractions with common denominators in order to add and subtract fractional quantities. When mixed numbers are involved, students may choose to turn each mixed number into an improper fraction, or they may choose to operate on the whole numbers and the fractions separately. The traditional addition and subtraction algorithm expects students to operate on fractions first and whole numbers second. Many students, however, prefer to operate on the whole numbers first, followed by the fractions. Allow students to work in either direction.

Question E includes missing-value problems. These kinds of problems will appear throughout the Unit. The goal is to introduce students to variable notation where the variable is being used as a placeholder. In addition, we want students to explore the role of inverse operations so that they have experience with this type of reasoning and can draw upon it in future algebra work.

This idea will be revisited in other problems, as well as in other units. We do not expect students to develop formal strategies for solving equations. Rather, we would like students to develop strategies that are sensible to them and incorporate what they know about adding and subtracting fractions.

Prior to doing Problem 1.4, you might consider having students share their whole-number subtraction strategies in a class opener so that you and the students can become familiar with various strategies. Students can make connections between regrouping in whole-number subtraction and regrouping in mixed-numbers subtraction.

Problem Implementation

Use a Think-Pair-Share grouping arrangement. If your students need more work in developing the algorithm for adding and subtracting fractions, use **Teaching Aid: Algorithms for Adding and Subtracting Fractions**. This resource gives students additional opportunities to add and subtract fractions and mixed numbers. Students categorize which expressions are easier to solve and which are more difficult to solve. Students then analyze the characteristics of each group enabling them to more accurately identify algorithms for adding and subtracting fractions and mixed numbers.

Labsheet 1ACE: Exercises 31, 32, 37, 38 (accessibility) is a sample of how ACE Exercises can be modified to help students who would benefit from additional scaffolding.

Materials

- **Labsheet 1.4:** Recipe Cards (accessibility)
- **Labsheet 1ACE:** Exercises 31, 32, 37, 38 (accessibility)
- **Teaching Aid 1.4A:** Student Strategies
- **Teaching Aid 1.4B:** Student Algorithms
- **Check Up 1** (one per student)

containers of spices of different weights (optional)

Vocabulary

- algorithm

Mathematics Background

- Building Proficiency Using Algorithms
- Choosing Appropriate Operations

At a Glance and Lesson Plan

- At a Glance: Let's Be Rational Problem 1.4
- Lesson Plan: Let's Be Rational Problem 1.4

Launch

Connecting to Prior Knowledge

You might start with a discussion of spices in general. Find out which spices students like or which spices their parents use. The spice mixes given in the Problem are often used in different ethnic recipes.

Begin Problem 1.4 by setting the context of Reyna's spice shop. Discuss how spices are sold (by weight) with the students. You may want to display **Labsheet 1.4: Recipe Cards** (accessibility) while you read the Problem with the students. It might also be helpful to bring a few spice containers of different weights to class so that students get a sense of how heavy 2 or 3 ounces of various spices feel.

Be sure students understand what is intended in Question E. Students must find the missing value as well as write a story problem to match the number sentence.

Presenting the Challenge

When the class understands what is expected of them, give them a copy of **Labsheet 1.4: Recipe Cards** (accessibility) and let them work on the questions. Students might want to mark the labsheet with equivalent fractions or other notes.

You may want to introduce the Problem with a statement such as this:

> *Many problems we have solved so far have focused on estimation. In this Problem, we will still use estimation to predict and check our answers. The focus of this Problem, however, is to develop strategies for finding exact answers to problems involving fractions.*

▼ Explore

Providing for Individual Needs

Look for different strategies that the students use as they work. These can be discussed in the Summarize. If students are having trouble getting started, remind them of the strategies they used in Problem 1.3, such as renaming fractions as different equivalent fractions. Some students might suggest that fractions be converted to decimals in order to solve problems. While this is not incorrect, the focus of this investigation is to develop strategies for working with fractions. Redirect students to find ways to work with these numbers in fraction form.

Suggested Questions

- What denominator did you use in the Spice Parisienne recipe? (10)

- Why is this a good choice? (You can change the fifths to tenths so that all the denominators are the same.)

- Could you have renamed the fractions as 20ths and solved the problem? (Yes.)

- Why? (5 and 10 are both factors of 20.)

- Why might it be more helpful to use 10 as the denominator instead of 20, even if both are possible approaches? (Using 10 as the denominator will result in the numerators being simpler numbers which are easier to add. Also, simplifying the answer will probably be easier.)

Some students struggle when they have to identify a common denominator for three different denominators in order to find equivalent fractions. This is the case with the Garam Masala recipe in Question C.

- Is there a number of which 2, 3, and 4 are all factors? (12 or 24)

- How can you use that number as the denominator to rename all your fractions? (Multiply a fraction's denominator by a whole number so that the resulting denominator is either 12 or 24. Multiply the numerator by that same whole number. Do this separately for each fraction.)

When students have made sufficient progress, pull them together to discuss strategies and solutions. Depending upon your students, you may want to stop and discuss Questions A–D before having them work on Questions E and F.

For Question B, part (2), be sure that students share their strategies with each other during the Pair-Share portion of the Explore. There are a number of different ways to arrive at the answer, and students should try to understand all approaches.

Question D allows students to practice their skill in converting between units.

Students may need support as they transition from contextual to noncontextual situations. If students struggle with the use of variable notation in Question E, you might suggest they think of the variable N as a question mark.

Planning for the Summary

What evidence will you use in the summary to clarify and deepen understanding of the Focus Question?

What will you do if you do not have evidence?

Summarize

Orchestrating the Discussion

The focus of the Summarize is similar to the focus of the Summarize of Problem 1.3. The computations and the reasoning are equally important. Writing a number sentence does not prove that a sum or difference is correct. As students share their number sentences, help them pull together the mathematics of the problems and generalize their strategies. Use questions that focus on the role of equivalence as well as how they handled adding and subtracting mixed numbers.

Suggested Questions

Have students share their answers for Questions A–D. Ask questions like the following:

- Why did you change the denominators in the Spice Parisienne recipe to tenths? How did that help solve the problem? (Having like denominators makes fractions easy to add and subtract.)

- Why did you choose 12 as the denominator for the Garam Masala recipe? (It is a multiple of 2, 3, and 4.)

- What tells you that a problem requires adding? (a combining situation)

- What are some strategies you have found useful when combining or adding quantities of spices? (Answers may vary: renaming fractions by finding a common denominator, combining fractions with like denominators first, looking for sums of 1 whole to add first.)

A strategy students might use is to combine quantities that add together easily before they rename fractions with common denominators. For example, for Question A, some students might notice that the two $\frac{1}{10}$'s are equivalent to $\frac{1}{5}$ and then work through Question A using $\frac{1}{5}$'s.

In one classroom, three strategies emerged for subtracting mixed numbers in situations when regrouping is needed. After the students have shared all of their own strategies, display **Teaching Aid 1.4A: Student Strategies**.

Discuss the Teaching Aid's approach for addition and any other approaches that students may provide. Check to see if other students understand these strategies.

When students are comfortable with addition of mixed numbers, shift the focus to subtraction.

- How did you subtract the two amounts?

Regrouping or renaming is needed to complete these parts. Help students to see that regrouping is also a way to create equivalent fractions.

- When a student tried to subtract $11\frac{1}{8} - 4\frac{1}{4}$ in Question B, part (2), he changed the 11 to a 10. Why? (He needed extra eighths to complete the subtraction, so he took one away from 11 so that he would have a whole to break up into eighths.)

- Why did he change the $\frac{1}{8}$ to $\frac{9}{8}$? (Because the one whole he took from 11 is equivalent to $\frac{8}{8}$, and $\frac{8}{8} + \frac{1}{8} = \frac{9}{8}$.)
- Is $11\frac{1}{8}$ equivalent to $10\frac{9}{8}$? (Yes.)

In one classroom, three strategies emerged, viewable in **Teaching Aid 1.4A: Student Strategies**, for subtracting mixed numbers in situations when regrouping is needed. After the students have shared all of their own strategies, display **Teaching Aid 1.4A: Student Strategies** to help students visualize these approaches.

Note: If students don't normally use negatives when they subtract with whole numbers, they may be confused by the negative-number strategy within **Teaching Aid 1.4A: Student Strategies** and will need more help in understanding.

Students are not expected to master all of these strategies. They should be able to use the strategies that they find sensible and efficient. What is important is that students try to understand the reasoning behind each offered strategy and decide whether it makes sense or not.

For Question E, have students share their approaches for finding *N* in each part. In part (1), *N* is a placeholder for the sum. This is an opportunity to extend strategies that have emerged for finding sums and differences in noncontextual problems.

Parts (2) and (3) are missing-value problems. Ask students to share how they found their solutions. Students may rewrite the known values with common denominators, and then draw upon their whole-number knowledge to find the numerator of the unknown value.

For example, in part (3), by rewriting $2\frac{2}{3} - N = 1\frac{1}{4}$ as $\frac{32}{12} - \frac{?}{12} = \frac{15}{12}$, students can easily find the missing numerator by solving $32 - ? = 15$, or $32 - 17 = 15$. Now students can see that $N = \frac{17}{12}$, or $1\frac{5}{12}$.

Students may suggest the use of inverse operations as a solution strategy for finding *N*. For example, a student may rewrite $N + \frac{3}{4} = 1\frac{1}{2}$ as $1\frac{1}{2} - \frac{3}{4} = N$. He or she might reason that if adding $\frac{3}{4}$ to *N* results in $1\frac{1}{2}$, then to get back to *N*, he or she has to subtract $\frac{3}{4}$ from $1\frac{1}{2}$. If this strategy does arise here, that is fine.

It is okay if students are struggling to make sense of missing-value problems. Strategies are more likely to emerge throughout the remainder of the Unit when these types of problems will be revisited.

Use Question F to explicitly summarize strategies. The explanations in **Teaching Aid 1.4B: Student Algorithms** represent some students' explanations.

Note: While some students think the negative-number algorithm (Student Algorithm 4) is hard to understand at first, the students who use the strategy are usually very proficient in using and explaining it.

Reflecting on Student Learning

Use the following questions to assess student understanding at the end of the lesson.

- What evidence do I have that students understand the Focus Question?
  - Where did my students get stuck?
  - What strategies did they use?
  - What breakthroughs did my students have today?
- How will I use this to plan for tomorrow? For the next time I teach this lesson?
- Where will I have the opportunity to reinforce these ideas as I continue through this Unit? The next Unit?

ACE Assignment Guide

- **Applications:** 30–50
- **Connections:** 58–61, 71
- **Extensions:** 77
- **Labsheet 1ACE:** Exercises 31, 32, 37, 38 (accessibility)

▼ Mathematical Reflections

Possible Answers to Mathematical Reflections

1. **a.** Answers will vary. Estimating a sum or difference is useful when buying materials for a project. You may not be able to buy exactly what you need, but you can estimate so that you buy enough. That way, you won't have to return to the store to purchase more. Estimating is also useful when earning money. If you want to buy something at the end of the week, you can estimate how much additional money you have to earn in order to have enough money for the purchase.

   b. Answers will vary. Overestimating is useful when estimating the cost of groceries. You don't want to arrive at the cash register with less money than the total bill. Underestimating is useful when you are trying to determine the amount of money you have to create a budget. This will safeguard you from budgeting with money you don't have.

2. You use addition when asked to combine parts to find the sum or the total. You use subtraction when asked to separate parts to find the difference or find "how much more" or "how much is left".

3. Answers may vary. When adding or subtracting, the fraction needs to have equally partitioned parts, (a common denominator). Rewrite each fraction as an equivalent fraction with that common denominator. When working with mixed numbers, it may be easiest to work with the whole numbers first and then the fractional parts. The easiest type to explain is addition of two fractions less than one, where the denominators are already the same and where the sum is also less than one. For example $\frac{1}{8} + \frac{5}{8} = \frac{6}{8}$. This is the easiest type because the denominator remains the same, and you just add the numerators to find the numerator of the sum. The hardest type to explain is the difference of two mixed numbers where regrouping the first mixed number is helpful to allow subtraction of the fractional parts, for example $3\frac{1}{2} - 1\frac{3}{4} = 2\frac{3}{2} - 1\frac{3}{4} = 2\frac{6}{4} - 1\frac{3}{4} = 1\frac{3}{4}$. This is the most difficult type to explain because you need to rename $3\frac{1}{2}$ as $2\frac{6}{4}$ in order to complete the subtraction in a simple way.

Possible Answers to Mathematical Practices Reflections

Students may have demonstrated all of the eight Common Core Standards for Mathematical Practice during this Investigation. During the class discussion, have students provide additional Practices that the Problem cited involved and identify the use of other Mathematical Practices in the Investigation.

One student observation is provided in the Student Edition. Here is another sample student response.

"In this Investigation, we solved a lot of problems that described different situations. We had to understand what was happening in the problem in order to estimate the amounts and solve the problem. For Problem 1.2, I had to learn what a budget is to help me solve the problem. Sometimes we drew diagrams of fractions to solve the problems. We estimated and then compared our exact answers with the estimates. We needed to find the fraction of the section that Bouck and Stewart owned together in Problem 1.3. We used the Labsheet to figure out that Bouck's part was $\frac{1}{16}$ of a section. We knew this because we divided the section into pieces. It took cutting up the section into 16 equal pieces before the size of each piece was the size of Bouck's land. Stewart's part was even harder to find. We kept dividing each section into smaller and smaller pieces. We drew extra lines in each section until there were 32 parts in each. Stewart owned five of those parts, so his part is $\frac{5}{32}$ of a section. Then we got confused for a while because we did not know how to combine these two parts. Then Joe came up with the idea that we could divide Bouck's part into smaller pieces too. That way we could use $\frac{1}{32}$ as the main unit. We found that, together, Bouck and Stewart have $\frac{7}{32}$ of the section."

MP1: Make sense of problems and persevere in solving them

Investigation 1

Extending Addition and Subtraction of Fractions

Knowing how to combine and separate quantities is helpful in understanding the world around you. The mathematical names for combining and separating quantities are *adding* and *subtracting*. The result of addition is called a *sum*; the result of subtraction is called a *difference*.

Sometimes when you need to find a sum or difference, you do not need an exact answer. In these situations, making a reasonable estimate is good enough. It is *always* a good idea to estimate, even when you want an exact answer. You can check your exact answer by comparing it to an estimate.

- What is a good estimate for $198 + 605$?

- What is a good estimate for $7.9 - 1.04$?

- How do these estimates help you check the exact sum and difference?

....

Common Core State Standards

6.NS.B.4 Find the greatest common factor of two whole numbers less than or equal to 100 and the least common multiple of two whole numbers less than or equal to 12. . .

6.EE.B.7 Solve real-world and mathematical problems by writing and solving equations of the form $x + p = q$ and $px = q$ for cases in which p, q and x are all nonnegative rational numbers.

Also 6.EE.A.2, 6.EE.A.2b, 6.EE.B.5, 6.EE.B.6

Investigation 1   **Extending Addition and Subtraction of Fractions**   7

Notes

1.1 Getting Close
Estimating Sums

Getting Close is a game that will sharpen your estimating skills by using **benchmarks.** A benchmark is a reference number that can be used to estimate the size of other numbers. Examine this set of benchmarks.

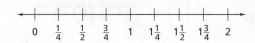

- Which fraction benchmark is $\frac{3}{8}$ closest to?

Raul says that $\frac{3}{8}$ is exactly halfway between $\frac{1}{4}$ and $\frac{1}{2}$. He reasons that $\frac{3}{8}$ is less than $\frac{1}{2}$ because it is less than $\frac{4}{8}$. However, $\frac{3}{8}$ is greater than $\frac{1}{4}$ because it is greater than $\frac{2}{8}$.

- Which benchmark is 0.58 closest to?

Desiree says that since $\frac{1}{2}$ is equal to 0.50, 0.58 is greater than $\frac{1}{2}$. Also, 0.58 is less than 0.75, which equals $\frac{3}{4}$. So 0.58 is between $\frac{1}{2}$ and $\frac{3}{4}$, but it is closer to $\frac{1}{2}$.

- Is Desiree correct?

- Is there another way to find the closest benchmark?

Cetera wonders if she can use benchmarks to estimate the sum of two fractions, such as the sum below.

$$\frac{1}{2} + \frac{5}{8}$$

- Is the sum between 0 and 1 or between 1 and 2?

- Is the sum closest to 0, to 1, or to 2?

You can practice using benchmarks and other strategies to estimate the sum of two numbers during the Getting Close game.

8   Let's Be Rational

Notes

_____

_____

_____

Getting Close Game

Two to four players can play Getting Close.

Materials

- Getting Close fraction or decimal game cards (one set per group)
- A set of four number squares (0, 1, 2, and 3) for each player

Directions

1. All players hold their 0, 1, 2, and 3 number squares in their hand. The game cards are placed facedown in a pile in the center of the table.

2. One player turns over two game cards from the pile. Each player mentally estimates the sum of the numbers on the two game cards.

3. Each player then selects a number square (0, 1, 2, or 3) closest to their estimate and places it facedown on the table.

4. After each player has played a number square, the players turn their number squares over at the same time.

5. Each player calculates the actual sum by hand or with a calculator. The player whose number square is closest to the actual sum gets the two game cards.
   Note: If there is a tie, all players who tied get one game card. Players who have tied may take a game card from the deck if necessary.

6. Players take turns turning over the two game cards.

7. When all game cards have been used, the player with the most game cards wins.

Notes _____

_____

Problem **1.1**

Play Getting Close several times. Keep a record of the estimation strategies you find useful. Use these estimation strategies to answer the questions below.

Ⓐ Suppose you played Getting Close with only these game cards:

1. Which two cards have the greatest sum? How do you know? Estimate the sum.

2. Which two cards have the least sum? How do you know? Estimate the sum.

Ⓑ Suppose you played Getting Close with only these game cards:

1. Which two cards have the greatest sum? How do you know? Estimate the sum.

2. Which two cards have the least sum? How do you know? Estimate the sum.

Ⓒ Suppose you played Getting Close with only these game cards:

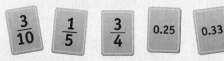

1. Which two cards have the greatest sum? The least sum? How do you know? Estimate the greatest sum and the least sum.

2. How can you estimate the sum of two game cards when one game card is a decimal and one game card is a fraction?

Ⓓ Estimate each sum to the nearest whole number. Explain how you made each estimate.

1. $\frac{2}{3} + \frac{1}{5}$ 2. $2\frac{1}{3} + 3\frac{2}{3}$ 3. $\frac{3}{4} + \frac{4}{3}$

Ⓐ Ⓒ Ⓔ Homework starts on page 18.

Notes

_____

_____

_____

1.2 Estimating Sums and Differences

It is important to know how to find exact sums and differences. It is also important to be able to make good estimates. If an exact answer is not necessary, you can solve problems more quickly by estimating. Estimates help you know whether or not an answer is reasonable.

- What are some situations in which you can estimate a sum or difference instead of finding an exact answer?

Sometimes you should **overestimate,** or give an estimate that is a bit bigger than the actual value. Overestimate to make sure you have enough. Sometimes you should **underestimate,** or give an estimate that is a bit smaller than the actual value. Underestimate to stay below a certain limit.

Problem 1.2

For Questions A–E,

- Answer the question by using estimation. Explain your reasoning.

- Explain how confident you are in your answer.

- For each estimate you make, tell whether it is an overestimate or an underestimate. Explain why you chose to overestimate or underestimate.

A Mrs. Edwards is building a dollhouse for her children. She needs to buy wood for the railing on the balcony.

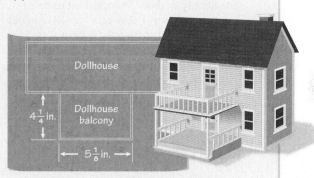

The wood is available in 12-inch, 14-inch, and 16-inch lengths. She does not want to waste wood. What length should she buy?

continued on the next page >

Notes

Problem **1.2** *continued*

B Mr. Cheng is making shades for his office. One window needs $1\frac{1}{3}$ yards of material and the other window needs $1\frac{3}{4}$ yards of material. The fabric store only sells whole-number lengths of this material. How many yards of material should Mr. Cheng buy?

C Mr. Aleman is the treasurer for his local scouting troop. He makes a budget for the troop. He suggests that they spend $\frac{1}{2}$ of their money on field trips, $\frac{1}{3}$ of their money on events, and $\frac{1}{4}$ of their money on scholarships. He wants to save the rest of the troop's money for next year. What do you think of Mr. Aleman's budget?

D Jasmine is making jam to enter in the state fair.

    1. Jasmine's raspberry jam recipe calls for $4\frac{1}{3}$ quarts of raspberries. She has picked $3\frac{1}{2}$ quarts of raspberries. About how many more quarts of raspberries should she pick?

    2. Jasmine's mixed berry jam recipe calls for $6\frac{2}{3}$ quarts of berries. She has $3\frac{1}{3}$ quarts of strawberries and $2\frac{7}{8}$ quarts of blackberries. Does Jasmine have enough berries? If not, about how many more quarts of berries does she need to pick?

E The gas tank on Priya's pontoon boat can hold 5 gallons. It is completely empty. Priya needs a full tank for the day's activities. She adds $2\frac{1}{4}$ gallons from a gas canister and then takes the boat to a nearby marina to fill it up. She has to pay ahead. Priya wants the tank as full as possible but does not want to overpay. How many gallons should Priya ask for?

A C E Homework starts on page 18.

Notes _____

_____

_____

1.3 Land Sections
Adding and Subtracting Fractions

When Tupelo Township was founded, the land was divided into sections that could be farmed. Each section is a square that is 1 mile long on each side. In other words, each section is 1 square mile of land. There are 640 acres of land in one square-mile section.

Over time, the owners of the sections have bought and sold land, so each section is owned by several owners. You can use **number sentences** to find how much land each owner has.

If a farmer owns 2 acres of land and buys another $1\frac{1}{2}$ acres of land, she will have $2 + 1\frac{1}{2}$, or $3\frac{1}{2}$, acres of land. The number sentence that shows this relationship is

$$2 + 1\frac{1}{2} = 3\frac{1}{2}$$

The *sum* of the parts is the total land the farmer owns, $3\frac{1}{2}$ acres.

If a farmer has $2\frac{1}{2}$ acres of land and then sells $\frac{1}{2}$ of an acre of land, she will own $2\frac{1}{2} - \frac{1}{2}$, or 2, acres of land. The number sentence that shows this relationship is:

$$2\frac{1}{2} - \frac{1}{2} = 2$$

The *difference* is the land the farmer still owns, 2 acres.

Investigation 1   **Extending Addition and Subtraction of Fractions**   13

Notes _____

_____

This Problem requires you to add and subtract fractions to find exact answers. Remember to estimate to make sure that your answers are reasonable. As you work, use what you know about fractions and finding *equivalent fractions*. Write number sentences to communicate your strategies for solving the Problem.

The diagram below shows two sections of land that are *adjacent,* or side by side, in Tupelo Township. Several people share ownership of each section. The diagram shows the part of a section each person owns.

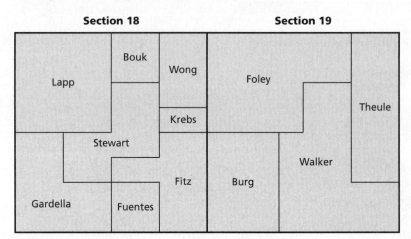

- Who owns the most land in Section 18? In Section 19?

Problem 1.3

(A) What fraction of a section does each person own? Explain how you know.

For Questions B and C,

- Find an approximate answer using estimation.
- Write a number sentence and answer the question.
- Compare your answer to your estimate to make sure your answer is reasonable.
- Identify the meaning of each number and symbol in your number sentence.

(B) **1.** Stewart and Bouck combine their land. What fraction of a section do they now own together?

2. Foley and Burg combine their land. What fraction of a section do they now own together?

3. How much more land does Lapp own than Wong?

(C) **1.** Name a set of owners whose combined land equals $1\frac{1}{2}$ sections.

2. Name a set of owners whose combined land equals $1\frac{3}{4}$ sections.

(D) **1.** Each section of land is one square mile. One square mile is equal to 640 acres. How many acres of land does each person own? Explain your reasoning.

2. Foley, Walker, Burg, and Krebs sell their land for a state park. How many acres are covered by the state park? Explain.

3. After Foley, Walker, Burg, and Krebs sell their land, what fraction of Section 19 remains in private ownership? Explain.

(E) **1.** Which set of owners' combined land does this number sentence represent?

$$1 + \frac{1}{4} + \frac{3}{16} + \frac{1}{16} = 1\frac{1}{2}$$

2. Explain how you know that this sum of fractions is exactly equal to $1\frac{1}{2}$.

(A)(C)(E) Homework starts on page 18.

Investigation 1 **Extending Addition and Subtraction of Fractions**   15

Notes

1.4 Visiting the Spice Shop
Adding and Subtracting Mixed Numbers

All over the world, cooks use spices to add flavor to foods. Because recipe ingredients are often measured using fractions, cooking can involve operating with fractional quantities.

Reyna owns a spice shop in Tupelo Township. Some of her recipes are shown below.

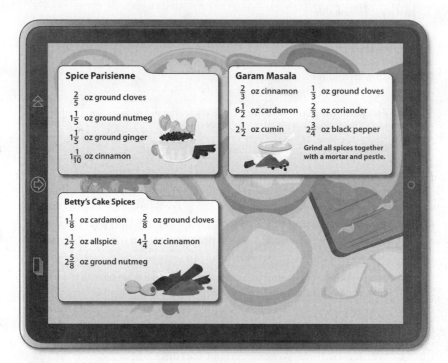

Spice Parisienne

$\frac{2}{5}$ oz ground cloves

$1\frac{1}{5}$ oz ground nutmeg

$1\frac{1}{5}$ oz ground ginger

$1\frac{1}{10}$ oz cinnamon

Garam Masala

$\frac{2}{3}$ oz cinnamon $\frac{1}{3}$ oz ground cloves

$6\frac{1}{2}$ oz cardamon $\frac{2}{3}$ oz coriander

$2\frac{1}{2}$ oz cumin $2\frac{3}{4}$ oz black pepper

Grind all spices together with a mortar and pestle.

Betty's Cake Spices

$1\frac{1}{8}$ oz cardamon $\frac{5}{8}$ oz ground cloves

$2\frac{1}{2}$ oz allspice $4\frac{1}{4}$ oz cinnamon

$2\frac{5}{8}$ oz ground nutmeg

- Which makes a greater amount of spice mix, Betty's Cake Spices recipe, or the Garam Masala recipe? How much more spice mix?

Notes _____

_____

_____

Problem 1.4

(A) **1.** Latisha buys spices to make one batch of Spice Parisienne. Use estimation to decide whether she buys more or less than 4 ounces of spices. Explain your reasoning.

2. Use estimation to decide which weighs more, one batch of Betty's Cake Spices or one batch of Garam Masala. About how much more does it weigh? Explain.

For Questions B and C,

• Decide which operation you will use to solve each problem.

• Find an approximate answer using estimation.

• Write a number sentence and answer the question.

(B) Betty buys spices for her famous cake.

1. How many ounces of spice does Betty buy?

2. Tevin is allergic to cinnamon. If Betty removes cinnamon from the recipe for him, how many ounces of spice does she buy?

(C) Ms. Garza buys spices to make one batch of Garam Masala. When she weighs her spices at home, she only has $10\frac{11}{12}$ ounces of spice. Which spice did Ms. Garza forget?

(D) Renuka has two pounds of pepper in her cupboard. She knows that there are 16 ounces in one pound. After Renuka makes one batch of Garam Masala, how many ounces of pepper does Renuka have left in her cupboard?

(E) For each number sentence below, write a spice story. Then find the value for N that makes the sentence true.

1. $3\frac{1}{6} - 1\frac{3}{4} = N$ **2.** $N + \frac{3}{4} = 1\frac{1}{2}$ **3.** $2\frac{2}{3} - N = 1\frac{1}{4}$

(F) **1.** Describe a strategy for estimating sums and differences of fractions, including mixed numbers.

2. An **algorithm** (AL guh rith um) is a plan, or a series of steps, for doing a computation. Each step in an algorithm should be clear and precise. Describe an algorithm for finding sums and differences of fractions, including mixed numbers.

ACE Homework starts on page 18.

Notes _____

Applications

For Exercises 1–6, determine whether the number is closest to 0, $\frac{1}{2}$, or 1. Explain your reasoning.

1. $\frac{10}{9}$ **2.** $\frac{9}{16}$ **3.** $\frac{5}{6}$

4. $\frac{48}{100}$ **5.** 0.67   **6.** 0.0009999

For Exercises 7–12, determine whether the sum of the two Getting Close game cards is closest to 0, 1, 2, or 3. Explain.

7. $\frac{7}{8}$ and $\frac{4}{9}$ **8.** $1\frac{3}{4}$ and $\frac{1}{8}$ **9.** $1\frac{1}{3}$ and 1.3

10. 0.25 and $\frac{1}{8}$ **11.** 1.352 and 0.84   **12.** $1\frac{4}{10}$ and 0.375

For Exercises 13–15, you are playing a game called Getting Even Closer. In this game, you have to estimate sums to the nearest $\frac{1}{2}$ or 0.5. Decide if the sum of the two game cards turned up is closest to 0, 0.5, or 1. Explain.

13.   **14.**   **15.**

16. Four students were asked the following question: "Can you find two fractions with a sum greater than $\frac{3}{4}$?" Explain whether or not each answer below is correct.

     a. $\frac{1}{8} + \frac{2}{4}$ **b.** $\frac{3}{6} + \frac{2}{4}$ **c.** $\frac{5}{12} + \frac{5}{6}$ **d.** $\frac{5}{10} + \frac{3}{8}$

For Exercises 17–20, find two fractions with a sum that is between the two given numbers.

17. 0 and $\frac{1}{2}$ **18.** $\frac{1}{2}$ and 1   **19.** 1 and $1\frac{1}{2}$ **20.** $1\frac{1}{2}$ and 2

Notes

21. A new set of Getting Close Cards contains the following numbers:

$$1.05 \qquad 0.7 \qquad \frac{3}{5} \qquad \frac{1}{4} \qquad \frac{9}{10}$$

a. Which two cards have the greatest sum?

b. Which two cards have the least sum?

22. Julio is at the grocery store. He has $10.00. Here is a list of the items he would like to buy.

Milk	$2.47
Eggs	$1.09
Cheese	$1.95
Bread	$0.68
Honey	$1.19
Cereal	$3.25
Avocado	$0.50
Chipotles	$1.29

Use mental computation and estimation to answer parts (a)–(c).

a. Can Julio buy all the items with the money he has? Explain your reasoning.

b. If Julio only has $5.00, what can he buy? Give two possible combinations.

c. What different items can he buy to come as close as possible to spending $5.00?

23. Many sewing patterns have a $\frac{5}{8}$-inch border for sewing the seam. Is a $\frac{5}{8}$-inch border closest to 0, $\frac{1}{2}$, or 1 inch? Explain your reasoning.

24. Soo needs 2 yards of molding to put around the bottom of a stand. He has two pieces of molding. One piece is $\frac{7}{8}$ of a yard long. The other is $\frac{8}{7}$ yards long. Estimate whether or not he has enough molding. Explain.

Investigation 1   Extending Addition and Subtraction of Fractions   19

Notes

25. Reggie picked $3\frac{3}{4}$ quarts of blueberries and $4\frac{1}{3}$ quarts of raspberries at a fruit farm. *About* how many total quarts of berries did he pick?

26. You mix $\frac{5}{8}$ of a cup of wheat flour with $1\frac{3}{4}$ cups of white flour. Do you have enough flour for a recipe that calls for $2\frac{1}{2}$ cups of flour? Explain.

27. The Langstons planted a big garden with flowers.

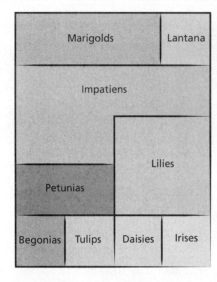 

a. About what fraction of the garden is planted with each type of flower?

b. How much more of the garden is planted with lilies than daisies?

c. The Langstons replace the daisies and irises with lilies. What fraction of the garden is planted with lilies? Write a number sentence.

d. In the following sentence, the name of each type of flower represents the fraction of the garden in which the flower is planted.

Marigolds − Begonias = Petunias + Tulips

Use fractions to explain whether the sentence is correct or incorrect.

e. Look at the original garden plan. Find three different combinations of plots that total the fraction of the garden planted with impatiens. Write a number sentence for each combination.

Notes _____

_____

_____

For Exercises 28–30, use the sample magazine page shown.

28. A local magazine sells space for ads. It charges advertisers according to the fraction of a page purchased.

    Sample Magazine Page

    a. Advertisers purchase $\frac{1}{8}$ and $\frac{1}{16}$ of page 20. What fraction of the page is used for ads?

    b. What fraction of page 20 remains available for other uses? Explain.

29. The Cool Sub Shop is having its grand opening. The owner buys three $\frac{1}{4}$-page ads, four $\frac{1}{8}$-page ads, and ten $\frac{1}{16}$-page ads. What is the total amount of ad space that the owner buys?

30. A local concert promoter purchases $2\frac{3}{4}$ pages of ads. When one of the concerts is canceled, the promoter cancels $1\frac{5}{8}$ pages of ads. How much advertising space is the concert promoter actually using?

31. Rico and his friend eat some lasagna. Rico eats $\frac{1}{9}$ of the lasagna, and his friend eats $\frac{1}{18}$ of the lasagna. How much of the lasagna is left?

32. Sonia finds a $\frac{3}{4}$-full small bag of chips. She eats the rest of the chips in the bag. Then she opens another small bag of chips. Sonia eats $\frac{1}{8}$ of those chips. What fraction of a small bag of chips does Sonia eat altogether?

For Exercises 33–36, find each sum or difference.

33. $1\frac{2}{5} + 1\frac{1}{3}$

34. $2\frac{1}{8} + 3\frac{3}{4} + 1\frac{1}{2}$

35. $11\frac{1}{2} - 2\frac{2}{3}$

36. $8\frac{11}{12} - 2\frac{3}{4}$

For Exercises 37–38, determine which sum or difference is greater. Show your work.

37. $\frac{2}{3} + \frac{5}{6}$ or $\frac{3}{4} + \frac{4}{5}$

38. $\frac{7}{6} - \frac{2}{3}$ or $\frac{3}{5} - \frac{5}{10}$

Notes

For Exercises 39–44, find each sum or difference.

39. $2\frac{5}{6} + 1\frac{1}{3}$ **40.** $15\frac{5}{8} + 10\frac{5}{6}$ **41.** $4\frac{4}{9} + 2\frac{1}{5}$

42. $6\frac{1}{4} - 2\frac{5}{6}$ **43.** $3\frac{1}{2} - 1\frac{4}{5}$ **44.** $8\frac{2}{3} - 6\frac{5}{7}$

For Exercises 45–50, find each sum. Describe any patterns that you see.

45. $\frac{1}{2} + \frac{1}{4}$ **46.** $\frac{1}{3} + \frac{1}{6}$ **47.** $\frac{1}{4} + \frac{1}{8}$

48. $\frac{1}{5} + \frac{1}{10}$ **49.** $\frac{1}{6} + \frac{1}{12}$ **50.** $\frac{1}{7} + \frac{1}{14}$

51. Tony works at a pizza shop. He cuts two pizzas into eight equal sections each. Customers then eat $\frac{7}{8}$ of each pizza. Tony says that $\frac{7}{8} + \frac{7}{8} = \frac{14}{16}$, so $\frac{14}{16}$ of all of the pizza was eaten. Is Tony's addition correct? Explain.

Connections

52. The rectangle shown represents 150% of a whole. Draw 100% of the same whole.

53. The beans shown represent $\frac{3}{5}$ of the total beans on the kitchen counter. How many total beans are there on the counter?

Notes _____

_____

_____

54. The following fractions occur often in our lives. It is useful to quickly recall their decimal and percent equivalents.

$$\frac{1}{2} \quad \frac{1}{3} \quad \frac{1}{4} \quad \frac{2}{3} \quad \frac{3}{4} \quad \frac{1}{6} \quad \frac{1}{5} \quad \frac{1}{8}$$

a. For each of these important fractions, give the decimal and percent equivalents.

b. Draw a number line. On your number line, mark the point that corresponds to each fraction shown above. Label each point with its fraction and decimal equivalent.

55. Multiple Choice Which set of decimals is ordered from least to greatest?

A. 5.603   5.63   5.096   5.67   5.599

B. 5.63   5.67   5.096   5.599   5.603

C. 5.096   5.63   5.67   5.603   5.599

D. 5.096   5.599   5.603   5.63   5.67

56. In which of the following groups of fractions can *all* of the fractions be renamed as a whole number of hundredths? Explain your reasoning for each group.

a. $\frac{3}{2}, \frac{3}{4}, \frac{3}{5}$

b. $\frac{7}{10}, \frac{7}{11}, \frac{7}{12}$

c. $\frac{2}{5}, \frac{2}{6}, \frac{2}{8}$

d. $\frac{11}{5}, \frac{11}{10}, \frac{11}{20}$

57. Suppose you select a number in the interval from $\frac{1}{2}$ to $\frac{3}{4}$ and a number in the interval from $\frac{3}{4}$ to $1\frac{1}{4}$. (Note: The numbers $\frac{1}{2}$ and $\frac{3}{4}$ are included in the interval from $\frac{1}{2}$ to $\frac{3}{4}$. The numbers $\frac{3}{4}$ and $1\frac{1}{4}$ are included in the interval from $\frac{3}{4}$ to $1\frac{1}{4}$.)

a. What is the least possible sum for these two numbers? Explain your reasoning.

b. What is the greatest possible sum for these two numbers? Explain your reasoning.

Notes

For a number sentence, the word *solve* means to find the value that makes the number sentence true. Solve Exercises 58–61.

58. $\frac{3}{12} = \frac{N}{8}$

59. $\frac{N}{4} = \frac{6}{8}$

60. $\frac{N}{12} = \frac{2}{3}$

61. $\frac{5}{12} = \frac{10}{N}$

In Exercises 62–64, paint has spilled on the page, covering part of the fraction strips. You can identify important information about each set of strips by looking at what is shown. The question marks indicate equivalent fractions of the strips. Name the equivalent fractions indicated by the question marks.

62.

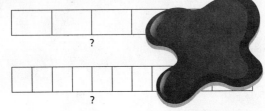

63.

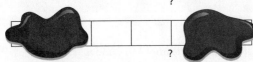

64.

Notes _____

_____

_____

For Exercises 65 and 66, copy each pair of numbers.
Insert $<$, $>$, or $=$ to make a true statement.

65. 18.156 ▓ 18.17

66. 4.0074 ▓ 4.0008

For Exercises 67 and 68, use the map of Tupelo Township.

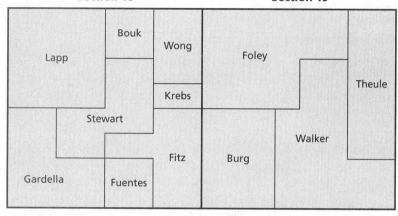

Section 18   Section 19

67. **Multiple Choice** Choose the combination of landowners who
together own exactly one hundred percent of a section.

   F. Burg, Lapp, Wong, Fuentes, and Bouck

   G. Burg, Lapp, Fuentes, Bouck, Wong, Theule, and Stewart

   H. Lapp, Fitz, Foley, and Walker

   J. Walker, Foley, Fitz, and Fuentes

68. Find two different combinations of landowners whose total
land is equal to 1.25 sections. Write number sentences to
show your solutions.

Notes

69. The figure below represents $\frac{1}{3}$ of a whole.

Use the figure to name the amounts shown in parts (a) and (b).

a.

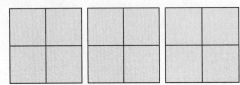

b.

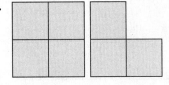

70. The following figure represents one whole.

    a. Draw a picture to represent $1\frac{1}{3} + \frac{1}{6}$.

    b. Draw a picture to represent $2\frac{2}{3} - \frac{4}{3}$.

71. When adding $\frac{7}{15} + \frac{2}{10}$, Maribel writes $\frac{70}{150} + \frac{30}{150}$.

    a. Show why $\frac{70}{150} + \frac{30}{150}$ is equivalent to $\frac{7}{15} + \frac{2}{10}$.

    b. Write two more addition problems that are equivalent to $\frac{7}{15} + \frac{2}{10}$.

    c. Consider the three problems, Maribel's problem and the two you wrote. Which is the easiest to use to find the sum? Why?

Notes _____

_____

_____

Extensions

For Exercises 72–74, use the number line below.

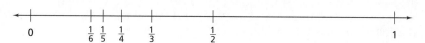

72. Name a fraction between $\frac{1}{3}$ and $\frac{1}{2}$.

73. Name a fraction between $\frac{1}{4}$ and $\frac{1}{3}$.

74. For Exercises 72 and 73, can you find another fraction in each interval? Explain.

75. *The Spartan* magazine charges $160 for each full page of advertising.

   a. Identify the cost for each ad size shown below.

   $\frac{1}{32}$-page, $\frac{1}{16}$-page, $\frac{1}{8}$-page, $\frac{1}{4}$-page, $\frac{1}{2}$-page, 1-page

   b. Use the costs you found. What is the bill for the Cool Sub Shop if the owner purchases three $\frac{1}{4}$-page ads, four $\frac{1}{8}$-page ads, and one $\frac{1}{16}$-page ad?

   c. The senior class is raising money for a trip. They have $80 to spend on advertising. Can they purchase two $\frac{1}{8}$-page ads and four $\frac{1}{16}$-page ads? Explain.

   d. Find four different sets of ad sizes that the senior class can purchase for $80. Show why your answers are correct.

76. It takes 8 people to clear an acre of weeds in 4 hours.

   a. How many acres can 16 people clear in 4 hours?

   b. How many acres can 2 people clear in 4 hours?

   c. How many people are needed to clear 3 acres in 4 hours?

   d. How many people are needed to clear 3 acres in 2 hours?

77. a. Find a number for each *denominator* to make the number sentence below true. If necessary, you may use a number more than once.

$$\frac{1}{\blacksquare} - \frac{1}{\blacksquare} = \frac{1}{\blacksquare}$$

   b. Find a different solution for part (a).

Notes _____

_____

_____

Mathematical Reflections

1

In this Investigation, you developed strategies for estimating the sum or difference of fractions and decimals. You then found exact sums and differences of fractions and mixed numbers. The following questions will help you summarize what you have learned.

Think about these questions. Discuss your ideas with other students and your teacher. Then write a summary of your findings in your notebook.

1. **a.** **What** are some situations in which estimating a sum or difference is useful? **Why** is estimation useful in these situations?

   b. **When** is it useful to overestimate? **When** is it useful to underestimate?

2. **When** should you use addition to solve a problem involving fractions? **When** should you use subtraction?

3. Suppose you are helping a student who has not studied fractions. **Explain** to him or her how to add and subtract fractions. Give an example of the type you think is easiest to explain. Give an example of the type you think is hardest to explain.

Notes _____

_____

_____

Common Core Mathematical Practices

As you worked on the Problems in this Investigation, you used prior knowledge to make sense of them. You also applied Mathematical Practices to solve the Problems. Think back over your work, the ways you thought about the Problems, and how you used Mathematical Practices.

Shawna described her thoughts in the following way:

For Problem 1.1, my group knew that the sum $\frac{3}{4} + \frac{4}{3}$ was closest to the benchmark number 2. We knew this because $\frac{3}{4}$ is a little less than 1, and $\frac{4}{3}$ is a little more than 1. But, we did not know if the sum was greater than 2 or less than 2.

After a while, Mia said that $\frac{4}{3}$ is $\frac{1}{3}$ of a unit away from 1. If you add $\frac{1}{3}$ to $\frac{3}{4}$, it is greater than 1. So $\frac{1}{3} + \frac{3}{4} + \frac{3}{3}$ must be greater than 2.

Common Core Standards for Mathematical Practice
MP6 Attend to precision.

• What other Mathematical Practices can you identify in Shawna's reasoning?

• Describe a Mathematical Practice that you and your classmates used to solve a different Problem in this Investigation.

Notes _____

_____

_____

Building on Multiplication With Fractions

▼ Investigation Overview

Investigation Description

Investigation 2 focuses on developing computational skill with and understanding of fraction multiplication. Various contexts and models are introduced to help students make sense of when multiplication is appropriate.

In Problem 2.1 students develop an understanding of multiplication with simple fractions. Problems 2.2 and 2.3 focus on multiplication with fraction, mixed-number, and whole-number combinations.

Estimation is used across the Problems so that students can determine the reasonableness of their answers. Also, students develop the idea that multiplication does not always lead to a larger product. Within these Problems, students form a general algorithm for fraction multiplication.

Investigation Vocabulary

• reciprocal

Mathematics Background

• Building Proficiency Using Algorithms
• Multiplication of Rational Numbers
• Developing a Multiplication Algorithm

Planning Chart

Content	ACE	Pacing	Materials	Resources
Problem 2.1	1–2, 28–29	1 day	**Labsheet 2.1A:** Brownie Pans (accessibility) **Labsheet 2.1B** Extra Brownie Pan Problems colored pencils	**Teaching Aid 2.1** $\frac{1}{2}$ of $\frac{2}{3}$
Problem 2.2	3–12, 30–38, 54–55	1 day	**Labsheet 2ACE:** Exercise 33 (accessibility)	
Problem 2.3	13–27, 39–53, 56–57	1 day		**Teaching Aid 2.3A** Takoda's and Yuri's Strategies **Teaching Aid 2.3B** Student Model of Problem 2.3 **Teaching Aid 2.3C** Diagrams for Question B, part (3)
Mathematical Reflections		½ day		
Assessment: Partner Quiz		½ day		• Partner Quiz

▼ Goals and Standards

Goals

Numeric Estimation Understand that estimation is a tool used in a variety of situations including checking answers and making decisions, and develop strategies for estimating results of arithmetic operations

- Use benchmarks and other strategies to estimate results of operations with fractions

- Use estimates to check the reasonableness of exact computations

- Give various reasons to estimate and identify when a situation calls for an overestimate or an underestimate

- Use estimates and exact solutions to make decisions

Fraction Operations Revisit and continue to develop meanings for the four arithmetic operations and skill at using algorithms for each

- Determine when addition, subtraction, multiplication, or division is the appropriate operation to solve a problem

- Develop ways to model sums, differences, products, and quotients with areas, fraction strips, and number lines

- Use knowledge of fractions and equivalence of fractions to develop algorithms for adding, subtracting, multiplying, and dividing fractions

- Write fact families with fractions to show the inverse relationship between addition and subtraction, and between multiplication and division

- Compare and contrast dividing a whole number by a fraction to dividing a fraction by a whole number

- Recognize that when you multiply or divide a fraction, your answer might be less than or more than the numbers you started with

- Solve real-world problems using arithmetic operations on fractions

Mathematical Reflections

Look for evidence of student understanding of the goals for this Investigation in their responses to the questions in *Mathematical Reflections*. The goals addressed by each question are indicated below.

1. Explain and illustrate what "of" means when you find a fraction of another number. What operation do you use when you find parts of parts?

   Goals
   - Use knowledge of fractions and equivalence of fractions to develop algorithms for adding, subtracting, multiplying, and dividing fractions
   - Determine when addition, subtraction, multiplication, or division is the appropriate operation to solve a problem
   - Solve real-world problems using arithmetic operations on fractions

2. **a.** If you forgot the algorithm for multiplying fractions, how might you use rectangular models to help you multiply fractions?

   b. Describe an algorithm for multiplying any two fractions.

   c. Describe when it might be useful to provide an estimate for a product.

Goals
- Develop ways to model sums, differences, products, and quotients with areas, fraction strips, and number lines
- Use knowledge of fractions and equivalence of fractions to develop algorithms for adding, subtracting, multiplying, and dividing fractions
- Use benchmarks and other strategies to estimate results of operations with fractions
- Give various reasons to estimate and identify when a situation calls for an overestimate or an underestimate
- Use estimates and exact solutions to make decisions

3. Use examples to explain the following statement:

   When you multiply a fraction by another fraction, your answer might be less than both factors, more than one of the factors, or more than both factors.

Goals
- Recognize that when you multiply or divide a fraction, your answer might be less than or more than the numbers you started with
- Solve real-world problems using arithmetic operations on fractions

Standards

Common Core Content Standards

6.EE.A.3 Apply the properties of operations to generate equivalent expressions. *Problems 2 and 3*

Essential for 6.NS.A.1 Interpret and compute quotients of fractions, and solve word problems involving division of fractions by fractions, e.g., by using visual fraction models and equations to represent the problem. *Problems 1, 2, and 3*

Facilitating the Mathematical Practices

Students in *Connected Mathematics* classrooms display evidence of multiple Common Core Standards for Mathematical Practice every day. Here are just a few examples where you might observe students demonstrating the Standards for Mathematical Practice during this Investigation.

Practice 1: Make sense of problems and persevere in solving them.

Students are engaged every day in solving problems and, over time, learn to persevere in solving them. To be effective, the problems embody critical concepts and skills and have the potential to engage students in making sense of mathematics. Students build understanding by reflecting, connecting, and communicating. These student-centered problem situations engage students in articulating the "knowns" in a problem situation and determining a logical solution pathway. The student-student and student-teacher dialogues help students to not just make sense of the problems, but also to persevere in finding appropriate strategies to solve them. The suggested questions in the Teacher Guides provide the metacognitive scaffolding to help students monitor and refine their problem-solving strategies.

Practice 3: Construct viable arguments and critique the reasoning of others.

Students analyze two different sample strategies in Problem 2.3. Students examine two different strategies for multiplication, using the Distributive Property and converting factors into improper fractions. They then are required to critique sample work and use these strategies in their own multiplication.

Practice 4: Model with mathematics.

Students use brownie-pan models and other drawings to support their thinking in Problems 2.1, 2.2, and 2.3. They use these drawings to visualize fraction multiplication as well as to prove their answers.

Practice 5: Use appropriate tools strategically.

Students may use colored pencils to indicate fractions of a whole, of a part, or of more than one whole in Problems 2.1, 2.2, and 2.3 so as to illustrate rational products.

Practice 7: Look for and make use of structure.

Students find patterns when multiplying fractions in Problem 2.1. They find relationships between the numerators of factors and products and the denominators of factors and products. By doing this, students are able to develop an algorithm for multiplying proper fractions.

Students identify and record their personal experiences with the Standards for Mathematical Practice during the Mathematical Reflections at the end of the Investigation.

PROBLEM

2.1

How Much of the Pan Have We Sold?
Finding Parts of Parts

▼ Problem Overview

Focus Question How does an area model relate to multiplying fractions?

Problem Description

Students work with an area model for fractions within the context of finding parts of brownie pans.

For Questions A–C, students should find ways to make sense of the problem by using brownie pan models. They do not need to develop a deep understanding of the multiplication algorithm at this stage. Instead, students should think about what it means to find a "part of a part." In fact, the "× " symbol is not introduced until Problem 2.2.

In Question D, students examine area models and write corresponding number sentences. This gives them more opportunities to notice patterns within the number sentences. Also, it requires students to connect visual models with number sentences in the opposite direction from Questions A–C.

Question E specifically targets how the diagrams relate to the denominators and numerators of a fraction multiplication problem. Students connect multiplication to a "part of a part" by explaining patterns they see in the number sentences. This helps students understand when multiplication will help solve a problem in other situations.

Problem Implementation

Students should work in pairs or in small groups for this Problem. Have students put their work on poster paper to use in the Summarize.

If students need more practice with these types of problems, provide them with **Labsheet 2.1B: Extra Brownie Pan Problems** in which students draw additional brownie pan models to match given number sentences.

Materials

- **Labsheet 2.1A:** Brownie Pans (accessibility)
- **Labsheet 2.1B:** Extra Brownie Pan Problems (optional)
- **Teaching Aid 2.1:** $\frac{1}{2}$ of $\frac{2}{3}$

poster paper (one per group)

colored pencils (optional)

Vocabulary

There are no new glossary terms introduced in this Problem.

Mathematics Background

- Building Proficiency Using Algorithms
- Multiplication of Rational Numbers
- Developing a Multiplication Algorithm

At a Glance and Lesson Plan

- At a Glance: Let's Be Rational Problem 2.1
- Lesson Plan: Let's Be Rational Problem 2.1

▼ Launch

Launch Video

This video can be shown instead of reading through the Problem's introduction in the Student Edition to help them understand the Problem situation. This Launch video introduces the situation of selling fractions of a pan of brownies. In this video, your students will see an example of the area model that they will be using throughout Problem 2.1. Play the video during Presenting the Challenge after asking the suggested questions. Visit Teacher Place at mathdashboard.com/cmp3 to see the complete video.

Finish Presenting the Challenge, and have students begin working on the Problem.

Connecting to Prior Knowledge

Explain to students that in this Investigation, they will work with fractions using another operation, multiplication.

Suggested Questions

- Can you describe some situations in which multiplication is used? (Answers will vary. Allow students to provide a few different examples.)

- What characteristics do all these situations have in common? (They involve equally sized groups of items.)

Direct students to look at the Investigation's introduction in the Student Edition. Discuss the football packaging problem to find out what students already know about fraction multiplication situations. Notice whether or not students have a sense of how big or small the products are.

- What strategies could you use to answer this problem? (Draw a model; estimate using rounding; find the number of footballs in the full boxes first and then find the number of footballs in the half-full box.)

Presenting the Challenge

Engage students in thinking about area models by discussing Paulo and Shania's brownie booth problem.

Suggested Questions

- Think back to when we made fraction bars out of paper. What does it mean to find $\frac{1}{2}$ of $\frac{1}{3}$? (Split the $\frac{1}{3}$ section of a fraction bar into two pieces.)

- When you find $\frac{1}{2}$ of $\frac{1}{3}$, should you get something greater than or less than $\frac{1}{3}$? (Less than $\frac{1}{3}$ since that fraction is being broken into two pieces. Each piece will be smaller than $\frac{1}{3}$.)

These questions are intended to make students think about what happens when fractions are split into equally sized parts.

Read through the Problem's introduction with your class, or show your students the Launch video. Point out that they are to figure out what part, or fraction, of the whole brownie pan is being bought.

- As you work on this Problem, think about how large or small the answer should be when you are finding a part of a part. Questions A, B, and C ask you to draw models. First, you should show how the brownie pan might look before a customer buys some brownies. It is not full. Then, you need to mark the part of the brownie pan that shows how much the customer buys.

Give students **Labsheet 2.1A: Brownie Pans** (accessibility) to draw the models.

▼ Explore

Providing for Individual Needs

As you circulate, ask students what it means to find a fraction of something, such as $\frac{1}{2}$ of $\frac{3}{4}$. Be sure they make drawings for Questions A–C. Note whether or not students are naming the fraction *of the whole pan* that is being bought. Some students may have a misconception that they are to name the fraction of the amount of brownie originally in the pan.

Suggested Questions

- How does your drawing help someone see the part of the whole pan that is bought? (Answers will vary. Students should be able to identify the portion of the pan being bought and the portion of the pan that will be left over when the customer leaves.)

- What could you do in your drawing to make this clearer? (Use different colors or textures to show the difference between the portion the customer is buying and the portion left over; or, represent one fraction with horizontal lines and one fraction with vertical lines.)

For Questions A and B, notice how students transition from finding a fraction of a fraction to finding a fraction of $12. Ask them to compare these strategies.

- What strategies do you use to find the fraction of a pan of brownies that a customer buys? (Look at the brownie pan model. Find the number of pieces and the size of the pieces in the entire brownie pan and then find out how many pieces the customer bought.)

- What strategies do you use to find how much money the customer owes? (Once you know what fraction of the pan has been bought you use this fraction to determine the cost. Divide $12 by the denominator and then multiply by the numerator. For example, $\frac{1}{4} \times$ of $12 is the same as $12 \div 4$, which is $3. If you want to find $\frac{3}{4}$ of $12, you just multiply $3 by 3, which is $9.)

While working on Questions A–D, students may notice that they can multiply the numerators to find the numerator of the product and multiply the denominators to find the denominator of the product. Ask them to use their drawings to show why they think this works. This is further explored in Question E. Students may relate the visual of the brownie pan model to what they already know about multiplication with whole numbers, since the brownie pan mimics an array.

Planning for the Summary

What evidence will you use in the Summarize to clarify and deepen understanding of the Focus Question?

What will you do if you do not have evidence?

Summarize

Orchestrating the Discussion

For Questions A–C, have groups share their solutions and strategies. Focus the conversation on taking a "part of a part." Help them connect the drawing to the situation of the problem.

Suggested Questions

- How did you decide what fraction of the whole pan is being bought? (Sample answers for Question A: I had two thirds and I broke each of them in half. A half of a third is a sixth, so I had two sixths. Or, I had two pieces, and each piece was a third. So, if I take half of that amount, I get one third.)

- Can someone share a way to mark the brownie pan so that it is easy to see what part of the whole pan is bought? (Here is an opportunity to suggest that using horizontal and vertical lines make it easier to keep track of what is happening. If someone does not suggest this approach, do so yourself.)

- What number sentence did you write for Question A? ($\frac{1}{2}$ of $\frac{2}{3} = \frac{2}{6}$, which is the same as $\frac{1}{3}$; $\frac{1}{3}$ of \$12 = \$4.)

It is helpful to write the number sentence next to the models. By doing this, students typically notice that you can multiply the numerators and denominators to find the numerator and denominator of the product. If students raise this idea, push them to explain why it works.

- Why does multiplying the numerators and multiplying the denominators work?

Students may point out that the numbers give the right answer. If students do, direct them to consider both the numbers and the brownie pans to figure out the math behind this method.

- For Question A, how did you first mark your brownie pan? (split it into thirds)

- When you took half of the thirds, you broke each third into two parts. How many parts were in the whole pan after you did this? (six)

- What part of your fractions told you to make thirds and then halves? (the denominators)

- What does the denominator of a fraction tell you? (how many parts are in the whole)

- What part of your drawing in Question A shows the denominator? (The number of parts the whole pan is divided into. The drawing marks a 2-by-3 array with 6 sections in all.)

So multiplying the denominators gives the number of pieces that the whole pan contains.

- Your numerators are 2 and 1. Where do you see this on the brownie pan drawing? (It is two of the pieces. The pan was originally $\frac{2}{3}$ full, so we shaded two parts of the pan out of three equal parts. We then cut each of these two pieces into halves and shaded one of the two halves in each case, that is the "1" in the numerator.)

- Can you see that the common shaded area is 2 of the total parts? What does the numerator of a fraction tell you? (How many parts of the whole are being bought. This is a 1-by-2 array, or 2 parts of the whole.)

After the discussion, consider having a student display his or her work, or show **Teaching Aid 2.1: $\frac{1}{2}$ of $\frac{2}{3}$**. This may help students to visualize what was discussed.

Students may not grasp the math behind the models right away, but continue to ask about it when appropriate. Students need to realize that there is a logical reason behind multiplying the numerators and multiplying the denominators to find the product.

Once students seem comfortable in finding the portions of the brownie pan that were purchased, discuss the cost of the brownies in Questions A and B. Ask students to explain how they arrived at their answers. Students may have drawn another picture to find the cost, or they may have related taking a fraction of $12 to dividing the $12 by the denominator. For example, one sixth of $12 is the same as $12 ÷ 6 , or $2.

In Question D, students analyze brownie pan area models and write corresponding number sentences. Sometimes students have difficulty determining what the "whole" of the fraction is. This Question is designed to highlight that issue by making students recognize that the whole is the brownie pan in this case. In addition, students will need to visualize the whole brownie pan divided into sections. In the images provided, section lines are intentionally missing from the part of the pan that is already empty. Some students may need to use an additional copy of **Labsheet 2.1A: Brownie Pans** (accessibility) to draw these representations.

- In Question D, what is the whole in the picture? (the brownie pan)

For each part, ask,

- How much of the brownie pan was full at the beginning of the problem? (Note the colors in the directions of the Student Edition. part (1): $\frac{1}{2}$ of the pan; part (2): $\frac{3}{4}$ of the pan; part (3): $\frac{2}{4}$ of the pan; part (4): $\frac{4}{6}$ of the pan.)

- What fraction of that portion was purchased? (Note the colors in the directions of the Student Edition. Part (1): $\frac{3}{5}$ of $\frac{1}{2}$; part (2): $\frac{1}{4}$ of $\frac{3}{4}$; part (3): $\frac{3}{5}$ of $\frac{2}{4}$; part (4): $\frac{2}{3}$ of $\frac{4}{6}$ of the pan.)

- What number sentences are represented? (part (1): $\frac{3}{5}$ of $\frac{1}{2} = \frac{3}{10}$; part (2): $\frac{1}{4}$ of $\frac{3}{4} = \frac{3}{16}$; part (3): $\frac{3}{5}$ of $\frac{2}{4} = \frac{6}{20}$; part (4): $\frac{2}{3}$ of $\frac{4}{6} = \frac{8}{18}$.)

Note that parts (1) and (3) of Question D are designed to highlight both equivalent fractions and the fact that the horizontal and vertical orientation of the area models does not affect the outcome of the final answer. This second concept relates to the application of the Commutative Property of Multiplication.

Question E explicitly asks students to make connections between number sentences and the algorithm for multiplying fractions.

If students need more practice on brownie pan problems, give them a copy **Labsheet 2.1B: Extra Brownie Pan Problems**.

Reflecting on Student Learning

Use the following questions to assess student understanding at the end of the lesson.

- What evidence do I have that students understand the Focus Question?
  - Where did my students get stuck?
  - What strategies did they use?
  - What breakthroughs did my students have today?
- How will I use this to plan for tomorrow? For the next time I teach this lesson?
- Where will I have the opportunity to reinforce these ideas as I continue through this Unit? The next Unit?

ACE Assignment Guide

- **Applications:** 1–2
- **Connections:** 28–29

Modeling Multiplication Situations

▼ Problem Overview

> **𝐹𝑜𝑐𝑢𝑠 𝑄𝑢𝑒𝑠𝑡𝑖𝑜𝑛** What strategies can you use to multiply all combinations of factors including whole numbers, fractions, and mixed numbers?

Problem Description

Students extend their understanding of multiplication by modeling situations that involve fractions, mixed numbers, and whole numbers.

In Question A, students multiply fractions within real-world contexts. They estimate the product, create a model or diagram for the situation, and write a number sentence to solve each problem.

In Question B, students work in the opposite direction of Question A. Students identify contextual situations to match given number sentences.

Students evaluate a generalization about fractions in Question C: "When you multiply with fractions, the product is less than each of the two factors."

Question D asks students to describe their strategy for multiplying any two fractions.

Problem Implementation

Working in pairs or in small groups is appropriate for this Problem. Have students put their work on poster paper to use in the Summarize.

Some students may need extra help in working through some of the ACE Exercises. **Labsheet 2ACE: Exercise 33** (accessibility) provides an example of how you might modify an ACE exercise.

Materials

• **Labsheet 2ACE:** Exercise 33 (accessibility)
• **Teaching Aid 2.2:** Display of Problem Answers
poster paper (one per group)

Vocabulary

There are no new glossary terms introduced in this Problem.

Mathematics Background

- Building Proficiency Using Algorithms
- Multiplication of Rational Numbers
- Developing a Multiplication Algorithm

At a Glance and Lesson Plan

- At a Glance: Let's Be Rational Problem 2.2
- Lesson Plan: Let's Be Rational Problem 2.2

▼ Launch

Connecting to Prior Knowledge

The introduction text to Problem 2.2 reviews the use of the word *of* in multiplication of whole numbers as well as fractions.

Note: Students often overgeneralize the link between the word *of* and multiplication. They occasionally think that word problems that contain *of* anywhere in the problem require multiplication. You may want to discuss specific examples of when this link is accurate (e.g., "groups of" or "a $\frac{1}{4}$ of" another number) as well as specific examples when this connection does not necessarily work (e.g., a fraction of an item may involve any operation). In the situation "a recipe calls for $\frac{3}{4}$ of a cup of butter and $\frac{1}{3}$ of a cup of milk," the word *of* does not imply multiplying the two given quantities.

Suggested Questions

- How can you draw a picture to show $6\frac{1}{4}$ groups of 8? (Draw 6 groups of 8 and then $\frac{1}{4}$ of 8, which is 2.)
- What number sentence would match this drawing? ($6\frac{1}{4} \times 8 = N$)

Presenting the Challenge

Tell students that they will work with multiplication problems that use fractions, whole numbers, and mixed numbers. Remind students that estimating products, drawing models, and writing number sentences for each problem will help them understand why multiplication is the proper operation to use for these problems. Discuss the content and questions contained in the Problem's introduction in the Student Edition.

Suggested Questions

- Do you think the fraction multiplication strategies you used in Problem 2.1 will work for all kinds of fractions? (Students may be ready to answer this question at this point; however, the Problem provides the proper context to fully respond.)

▼ Explore

Providing for Individual Needs

Students may struggle at first when they try to model the problem situations in Question A. If they are unsure, reread the problem to them. You might ask questions like the following:

Suggested Questions

- For Question A, part (1), what does $\frac{2}{3}$ represent? (the part of the bag that is needed for the recipe)

- What does 16 represent? (the size of the chocolate chips bag)

- What does "$\frac{2}{3}$ of a 16-ounce bag" mean? (that only a part of the bag will be used)

- How do you find $\frac{2}{3}$ of something? (You can multiply $\frac{2}{3}$ by the original size, or you can divide the original size into three parts, then count two of the parts.)

Look for various models for students to present in the Summarize. When they present, ensure that groups write number sentences for the problems. They should explain how these number sentences relate to their diagrams.

Students are likely to struggle with Question B. It might be helpful for students to rewrite the expression using the word *of*.

- $\frac{5}{6}$ of one what? What can you take $\frac{5}{6}$ of? (Sample answers: a pizza, a chocolate bar, a length of wood)

- When might you take $\frac{5}{6}$ of something? (Sample answers: when you want to save a part for later, if you only need a part)

- How can you find $\frac{5}{6}$ of something? (split the object into six equal parts, and then count five of those parts)

Students may be tempted to overgeneralize as Jacinta does in her statement, especially after working through Problem 2.1. Encourage students to examine the problems in Question B. See if they can think of a pattern using those problems.

Planning for the Summary

What evidence will you use in the summary to clarify and deepen understanding of the Focus Question?

What will you do if you do not have evidence?

▼ Summarize

Orchestrating the Discussion

For each Question, begin by discussing the estimates that students made. Ask them to describe how they decided upon their estimates. When students share their models and number sentences, focus the reasoning behind these answers.

Suggested Questions

After a solution is presented, ask questions like the following:

- Do you agree with this answer and the reasoning supporting it? Explain.
- Does the exact answer seem reasonable given the estimate?
- Does anyone have a different way to think about the problem?

Students generally come up with two strategies for solving Question A, part (3). Some will convert both fractions to improper fractions and use the algorithm they developed in 2.1, multiplying numerators and denominators. Some will use the Distributive Property, which can be done in a couple of different ways. Be sure to discuss these in class. Having the student work on posters will help. Refer to **Teaching Aid 2.2: Display of Problem Answers** for possible solutions that students might share.

When students share their contexts for the number sentences in Question B, focus on their reasoning.

After a context for a number sentence is presented, ask questions like:

- How does the context match the number sentence?
- Do you agree with this answer and the reasoning? Explain.
- Does anyone have a different context to relate to this number sentence?

Refer to **Teaching Aid 2.2: Display of Problem Answers** or possible solutions that students might share.

For Question C, students may over-generalize to agree with Jacinta. Questions A and B contains problems that are counterexamples to Jacinta's statement. Ask students if the problems in Questions A and B support Jacinta's statement.

- Is Jacinta correct? Why or Why not? (No; Jacinta is not correct. For most of these problems, the product is less than one factor, but greater than the other factor.)

- Do all of the problems in Questions A and B support Jacinta's statement? (No.)

- Which problems do? Which problems do not? (None of the answers to the parts in Questions A and B follow Jacinta's rule. However, all of the answers to Problem 2.1 followed Jacinta's rule.)

- Are there any patterns that you see? (For most of the problems, the product is less than one factor, but greater than the other factor. The only part where this isn't true is Question A, part (3). The product is bigger than both factors for that problem.)

The actual rule is that the product will always be less than either of the factors if the factors are both proper fractions (as in each of the questions in Problem 2.1). The product will be greater than one factor and less than one factor if one factor is less than 1 and one factor is greater than 1. The product will be greater than both factors if both factors are greater than 1. Problem 2.3 provides more examples to solidify this understanding.

Ask students to describe the strategies they found in Question D to multiply any two fractions. Refer to **Teaching Aid 2.2: Display of Problem Answers** or possible solutions that students might share.

Reflecting on Student Learning

Use the following questions to assess student understanding at the end of the lesson.

- What evidence do I have that students understand the Focus Question?
  - Where did my students get stuck?
  - What strategies did they use?
  - What breakthroughs did my students have today?
- How will I use this to plan for tomorrow? For the next time I teach this lesson?
- Where will I have the opportunity to reinforce these ideas as I continue through this Unit? The next Unit?

ACE Assignment Guide

- **Applications:** 3–12
- **Connections:** 30–38, 54–55
- **Labsheet 2ACE:** Exercise 33 (accessibility)

PROBLEM

2.3

Changing Forms
Multiplication With Mixed Numbers

▼ Problem Overview

> *Focus Question*   How can you number properties and equivalent fractions to multiply rational numbers?

Problem Description

Students explore two multiplication strategies for fractions and mixed numbers in this Problem.

Takoda's strategy involves changing the form of any mixed numbers into equivalent improper fractions. This way, students can multiply the factors in the same way as when both factors are proper fractions.

Yuri's strategy uses the Distributive Property when multiplying fractions and mixed numbers. Whether or not Yuri's strategy is useful depends upon the actual quantities of each factor in the multiplication problem. Also, this Distributive Property strategy can be useful for estimation.

Do not promote the Distributive Property strategy as the only approach to multiplying mixed numbers, but it is a reasonable approach. In addition, many students use the Distributive Property intuitively, and sometimes apply it incorrectly, so it is important to have conversations with students about this strategy.

Each of these strategies can be applied as an algorithm. Students should have a strong, efficient algorithm with which to multiply fractions and mixed numbers. The important concept within this Problem is that the efficiency of these two algorithms are case-specific depending on the values of the factors.

Problem Implementation

Working in pairs or in small groups is appropriate for this Problem.

If students need further work on developing a general algorithm for multiplication of fractions and mixed numbers, provide students with **Teaching Aid: Writing a Multiplication Algorithm**. This provides students with additional practice in multiplying fractions, mixed numbers, and whole numbers. Students will consider which products are easier or more difficult to compute and be required to identify why they are easier or more difficult to compute.

Materials

- **Teaching Aid 2.3A:** Takoda's and Yuri's Strategies
- **Teaching Aid 2.3B:** Student Model of Problem 2.3
- **Teaching Aid 2.3C:** Diagrams for Question B, part (3)
- **Partner Quiz** (one per pair)

Vocabulary

- reciprocal

Mathematics Background

- Building Proficiency Using Algorithms
- Multiplication of Rational Numbers
- Developing a Multiplication Algorithm

At a Glance and Lesson Plan

- At a Glance: Let's Be Rational Problem 2.3
- Lesson Plan: Let's Be Rational Problem 2.3

▼ Launch

Connecting to Prior Knowledge

Students should be familiar with both converting mixed numbers to improper fractions and the Distributive Property. Ask questions such as the following to set the tone for this Problem:

Suggested Questions

- How would you rewrite $4\frac{5}{6}$ as an improper fraction? $\left(\frac{29}{6}\right)$
- In the number $4\frac{5}{6}$, what does each number represent? (The 4 stands for 4 wholes. The 6 stands for the size of each part. Each part is $\frac{1}{6}$ big. There are 5 parts in addition to the 4 wholes.)
- In the number $\frac{29}{6}$, what does each number represent? (The 29 stands for how many pieces there are. The 6 stands for what size each piece is. Each piece is $\frac{1}{6}$ big.)
- $(5 \times 7) + (5 \times 3)$ is a sum of two products. Can you use the Distributive Property to rewrite this sum as a product of two factors? $(5 \times (7 + 3))$

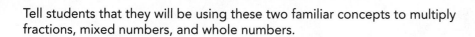

Tell students that they will be using these two familiar concepts to multiply fractions, mixed numbers, and whole numbers.

Presenting the Challenge

Use Question A to introduce the two strategies that students frequently use to multiply different combinations of fractions, mixed numbers, and whole numbers.

Suggested Questions

Display **Teaching Aid 2.3A: Takoda's and Yuri's Strategies**. Read through Question A and pose the following questions.

- What do you think about Takoda's strategy? Is his problem equivalent to the original problem? (Yes. $2\frac{2}{3}$ and $\frac{8}{3}$ are equivalent. $2\frac{2}{3}$ is a mixed number and $\frac{8}{3}$ is an improper fraction.)

- What is the product of $\frac{8}{3} \times \frac{1}{2}$? ($1\frac{1}{3}$)

- What do you think of Yuri's strategy? Is his problem equivalent to the original problem? (Yes. Yuri used the Distributive Property to rewrite the problem as a sum of two products.)

- In Problem 2.2, we drew models to multiply with mixed numbers. Take a few minutes and draw a model for this problem. (Give students time to draw a model. An example is shown in **Teaching Aid 2.3B: Student Model of Problem 2.3**.)

- Who can use their model to prove that the answer $1\frac{1}{3}$ is sensible? (Have a student present a model, such as the one in Teaching Aid 2.3B: Student Model of Problem 2.3, and pose the following questions.)

- How can this model show Takoda's thinking? How can it show Yuri's thinking? (It shows Takoda's thinking because there are eight $\frac{1}{3}$s that are shaded. Taking half of each of these $\frac{1}{3}$s results in eight $\frac{1}{6}$s, which is equal to $1\frac{1}{3}$ ($\frac{1}{2}$ of $\frac{8}{3} = \frac{8}{6}$). It shows Yuri's thinking because there are two wholes and two $\frac{1}{3}$s shaded. Taking half of each of the two wholes results in 1 since $\frac{1}{2} + \frac{1}{2} = 1$. Taking half of each $\frac{1}{3}$ results in $\frac{2}{6}$, or $\frac{1}{3}$($\frac{1}{2}$ of $\frac{1}{3} = \frac{1}{6}$, and $\frac{1}{6} + \frac{1}{6} = \frac{2}{6}$). So, the final answer is $1\frac{1}{3}$.))

  For Yuri's strategy, students may shade the diagrams differently. Instead of finding $\frac{1}{2}$ of each whole separately, getting $\frac{1}{2} + \frac{1}{2}$, students may think of $\frac{1}{2}$ of 2 as 1.

Then, have students work on the Problem by saying:

> In Question A, part (3), you will use both strategies to solve the problem and draw a picture.

> In Question B, you are going to use what you know about these strategies to solve multiplication problems. Estimate the product first. This will help you to decide if your computation makes sense.

▼ Explore

Providing for Individual Needs

For Question A, part (3), discuss with the students in each group which strategy, Takoda's or Yuri's, they find more efficient. Ask them to identify why they think the strategy they chose is more efficient.

The purpose of Question B is to further explore the efficiency of the strategies. Students will begin to recognize that the efficient use of the strategies depends upon the values of the factors and whether you are estimating or finding an exact answer.

In general, it is most efficient to use the equivalent fraction algorithm; however, students should not apply this strategy without understanding why it works. Parts (2) and (6) in particular are more easily solved using the equivalent fractions algorithm because a whole number is one of the factors.

Both algorithms can be applied to all of the problems, but in particular, parts (1), (3), (4), and (5) lend themselves to the use of both strategies.

For students who struggle to understand what Question C is suggesting, help them make sense of Yuri's strategy from Question A. This question is written to address a common error students make when using the Distributive Property. Have the students compare Yuri's strategy with what Lisa writes in order to find Lisa's error.

Note that the Summarize of Question B, part (3) provides some additional questions that you can ask during the Explore phase of the lesson as well as during the Summarize.

Planning for the Summary

What evidence will you use in the summary to clarify and deepen understanding of the Focus Question?
What will you do if you do not have evidence?

▼ Summarize

Orchestrating the Discussion

Have each group present their estimation and computation work for a part of Question B. Then, ask questions such as those below.

Suggested Questions

- What is a reasonable estimate for $2\frac{1}{2} \times 1\frac{1}{6}$? (a little more than $2\frac{1}{2}$)

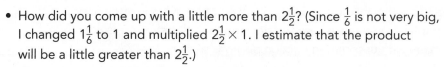

- How did you come up with a little more than $2\frac{1}{2}$? (Since $\frac{1}{6}$ is not very big, I changed $1\frac{1}{6}$ to 1 and multiplied $2\frac{1}{2} \times 1$. I estimate that the product will be a little greater than $2\frac{1}{2}$.)

- Would the estimate of $2\frac{1}{2}$ be an underestimate or an overestimate? (It would be an underestimate because I rounded $1\frac{1}{6}$ down to 1.)

- Did anyone estimate a different way? (Have students share any remaining estimates.)

- How did you multiply $2\frac{1}{2} \times 1\frac{1}{6}$? (I changed each mixed number to an improper fraction, and then I multiplied the numerators with one another and the denominators with one another. I got $\frac{5}{2} \times \frac{7}{6} = \frac{35}{12} = 2\frac{11}{12}$.)

- Did anyone use a different strategy? (I used the Distributive Property to multiply the two numbers because it is easy to find that $2 \times 1\frac{1}{6} = 2\frac{2}{6}$ and that $\frac{1}{2} \times 1\frac{1}{6}$ gives you $\frac{1}{2} + \frac{1}{12}$. Then I found common denominators and added it all up to get $2\frac{4}{12} + \frac{6}{12} + \frac{1}{12} = 2\frac{11}{12}$.)

- Did anyone make a diagram of this problem that they can share? (Display **Teaching Aid 2.3C: Diagrams for Question B, part (3).**)

- Does the picture you drew result in the same product? (Have students explain their diagrams. Be sure that students talk about how the pictures prove that the computation makes sense.)

As you work though the different multiplication problems in Question B, continue to link the estimates and the two strategies for computations with the diagrams. Eventually, return to the question posed in Question A.

- Do you think Takoda's strategy of rewriting the mixed numbers as fractions is sensible? (Yes.)

Ask students to think about when using the Distributive Property would be a useful strategy.

- Would you want to use the Distributive Property strategy on part (2)? Why or why not? (Part (2) has a proper fraction and a whole numbers. There are not any factors that make sense to break apart, so the Distributive Property would not make sense for part (2).)

Some students might suggest that the 16 can be broken up into 10 and 6 since you can take $\frac{3}{4}$ of 10 and $\frac{3}{4}$ of 6. You might point out that finding $\frac{3}{4}$ of 10 and 6 is not much easier than finding $\frac{3}{4}$ of 16.

- Would you want to use the Distributive Property with a problem like $3\frac{7}{8} \times 2\frac{5}{6}$? Why or why not? (Probably not. Trying to multiply $2\frac{5}{6}$ by 3 and $2\frac{5}{6}$ by $\frac{7}{8}$ is probably more work than rewriting the mixed numbers as improper fractions in order to multiply.)

Again, emphasize that some multiplication strategies are case-specific. The Distributive Property strategy works well in a problem where common fractions such as $\frac{1}{2}$ are embedded within mixed numbers. This type of problem is often easy to multiply and the partial products are easy to add. However, this strategy is not as efficient for a problem with uncommon fraction portions such as $3\frac{7}{8} \times 2\frac{5}{6}$.

Finally, we want to determine an efficient algorithm for multiplying fractions.

- Can the equivalent fractions strategy and the Distributive Property strategy be considered algorithms? (Both can be considered algorithms, but the equivalent fractions strategy is easier to apply in most situations.)

Be sure to discuss the Did You Know text at the end of Problem 2.3. This discussion of **reciprocals** will give important background for one of the common strategies when dividing fractions.

Going Further

In Problem 2.1 it was established that when a fraction less than 1 is multiplied by another fraction less than 1, the product is less than either factor. This leads to the interesting questions:

- When does multiplication lead to a product greater than either factor? (This happens when both factors are greater than 1.)

- Find two factors whose product lies between the two factors on a number line. Explain what kind of factors these must be and why. (Multiply a fraction less than 1 by a fraction greater than 1. The product will be greater than the factor that is less than 1, and less than the factor that is greater than 1. This is because there is more than 1 group of the lesser factor, so the product will be greater than the lesser factor. There is less than 1 group of the greater factor, so the product will be less than the greater factor.)

Reflecting on Student Learning

Use the following questions to assess student understanding at the end of the lesson.

- What evidence do I have that students understand the Focus Question?
  - Where did my students get stuck?
  - What strategies did they use?
  - What breakthroughs did my students have today?
- How will I use this to plan for tomorrow? For the next time I teach this lesson?
- Where will I have the opportunity to reinforce these ideas as I continue through this Unit? The next Unit?

ACE Assignment Guide

- **Applications:** 13–27
- **Connections:** 39–53
- **Extensions:** 56–57

Mathematical Reflections

Possible Answers to Mathematical Reflections

1. When you take a fraction of another number, you are taking a part of that number. This shows grouping because you are counting equally sized groups. Having these equal groups implies that you need to multiply. When multiplying with whole numbers, you make whole groups of some amount. When multiplying with fractions, you are taking a part of some amount.

2. **a.** You can use a simple example, such as $\frac{2}{3} \times \frac{4}{5}$. This is the same as finding $\frac{2}{3}$ of $\frac{4}{5}$. You can draw a brownie pan to show $\frac{2}{3}$ of a pan that is $\frac{4}{5}$ full. First, you draw a pan that is divided into fifths, and you shade four of the fifths in one color. Next, you divide each fifth into three pieces. Use a different color to shade two of these three pieces for each fifth. This shows $\frac{2}{3}$ of each fifth. There are now fifteen small pieces in the pan, which explains why you multiply the denominators, 3×5. Of the fifteen small pieces, twelve are shaded in the first color to show that we started with $\frac{4}{5}$, or $\frac{12}{15}$, of a pan. Eight small pieces, or 2×4, are shaded in the second color to show the final answer, $\frac{8}{15}$. This explains why we multiply the numerators. This process of drawing a picture reminds you that, to multiply two fractions, you find the product of the numerators and the product of the denominators.

   b. Answers will vary depending on which of the two strategies in Problem 2.3 students find easier to use. Many students will settle on $\frac{a}{b} \times \frac{c}{d} = \frac{ac}{bd}$ because this strategy can be applied to both products of proper fractions and products of mixed numbers (after rewriting the mixed numbers as improper fractions).

   c. Students might say they use estimation to check the reasonableness of a product or to estimate an answer where an exact answer is not required, for example when deciding how much of a spice to buy for a recipe.

3. When you multiply a proper fraction by a proper fraction, you are finding a part of a part. You can model the problem $\frac{1}{4} \times \frac{1}{2}$ with a brownie pan to think about this. You have a half-full pan of brownies, and then you take one fourth of that half of a pan. This will give you a part of the half, one eighth, which is less than both of the factors.

   If you multiply a proper fraction by a mixed number, the answer will be greater than the proper fraction but less than the mixed number. For example, $\frac{1}{2} \times 4\frac{1}{2}$ is $\frac{1}{2}$ of $4\frac{1}{2}$, so the product will be less than $4\frac{1}{2}$. But, if you think of this as $4\frac{1}{2}$ groups of $\frac{1}{2}$, then the answer must be greater than $\frac{1}{2}$.

   If you multiply a mixed number by a mixed number, then the product is greater than both. For example, $2\frac{1}{2} \times 4\frac{1}{2}$ is more than 2 groups of $4\frac{1}{2}$, which is greater than $4\frac{1}{2}$. It is also more than 4 groups of $2\frac{1}{2}$, so the product will be greater than $2\frac{1}{2}$.

Possible Answers to Mathematical Practices Reflections

Students may have demonstrated all of the eight Common Core Standards for Mathematical Practice during this Investigation. During the class discussion, have students provide additional Practices that the Problem cited involved and identify the use of other Mathematical Practices in the Investigation.

One student observation is provided in the Student Edition. Here is another sample student response.

> In Problem 2.3, we examined Takoda's and Yuri's strategies for multiplying fractions and mixed numbers. We had to decide if each strategy works and explain how we knew whether or not they work. We also looked at how the two strategies are the same and how they are different. We thought that Takoda's strategy is quicker. But we also agreed that they are both correct.
>
> **MP3: Construct viable arguments and critique the reasoning of others**

Notes _____

2

Building on Multiplication With Fractions

Sometimes, instead of adding or subtracting numbers, you need to multiply them. For example, suppose you take inventory at a sporting goods store. There are thirteen full boxes and one half-full box of footballs in the storeroom. Twelve footballs fit in each full box.

- How can you find the total number of footballs without opening the boxes? Why does multiplication make sense in this situation?

In this Investigation, you will use multiplication to solve problems involving fractions. Remember, to make sense of a situation, you can draw a model or change a fraction to an equivalent form. You can also estimate to see if your answer makes sense.

2.1 How Much of the Pan Have We Sold?
Finding Parts of Parts

Paulo and Shania work at the brownie booth at the school fair. Sometimes they have to find a fractional part of another fraction. For example, a customer might ask to purchase $\frac{1}{3}$ of the brownies in a pan that is $\frac{2}{3}$ full.

- How much is $\frac{1}{3}$ of $\frac{2}{3}$?

Common Core State Standards

6.EE.A.3 Apply the properties of operations to generate equivalent expressions.

Essential for 6.NS.A.1 Interpret and compute quotients of fractions, and solve word problems involving division of fractions by fractions, e.g., by using visual fraction models and equations to represent the problem.

30   Let's Be Rational

Notes _____

_____

_____

Problem 2.1

All of the pans of brownies are square. A pan of brownies costs $12. You can buy any fractional part of a pan of brownies and pay that fraction of $12. For example, $\frac{1}{2}$ of a pan costs $\frac{1}{2}$ of $12, or $6. We can write this as a number sentence using *of*: $\frac{1}{2}$ of 12 = 6.

A Mr. Williams asks to buy $\frac{1}{2}$ of a pan of brownies that is $\frac{2}{3}$ full.

1. Use a copy of the brownie pan model shown at the right. Draw a picture to show how the brownie pan might look before Mr. Williams buys his brownies.

Model of a Brownie Pan

2. On the same model, use a different color to show the part of the brownies that Mr. Williams buys. Note that Mr. Williams buys a *part of a part* of the brownie pan.

3. What fraction of a whole pan of brownies does Mr. Williams buy? How much does he pay? Write number sentences using *of* to show your thinking.

B Serena buys $\frac{3}{4}$ of another pan that is half full.

1. Draw a picture to show how the brownie pan might look before Serena buys her brownies.

2. Use a different color to show the part Serena buys.

3. What fraction of a whole pan of brownies does Serena buy? How much does she pay? Write number sentences using *of* to show your thinking.

C Draw a brownie pan picture for each example below. Then write a number sentence using *of* for each. Find the part of a whole brownie pan that results.

1. $\frac{1}{3}$ of $\frac{1}{4}$ of a brownie pan

2. $\frac{1}{4}$ of $\frac{1}{3}$ of a brownie pan

3. $\frac{1}{3}$ of $\frac{3}{4}$ of a brownie pan

4. $\frac{3}{4}$ of $\frac{2}{5}$ of a brownie pan

continued on the next page >

Notes

Problem 2.1 continued

D The pictures below are models of brownie pan problems. Consider *orange* to be the portion of the brownie pan that is purchased. Consider *blue* to be the portion of the brownie pan that is left in the pan. For each picture, write a number sentence using *of* to describe what fraction of the brownie pan is purchased.

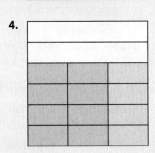

1.

2.

3.

4.

E **1.** Draw pictures to check that each of the following number sentences is correct.

   a. $\frac{3}{4}$ of $\frac{1}{2} = \frac{3}{8}$

   b. $\frac{2}{5}$ of $\frac{4}{5} = \frac{8}{25}$

2. What pattern do you notice in the denominators? How does this pattern relate to your drawings?

3. What pattern do you notice in the numerators? How does this pattern relate to your drawings?

4. Paulo says that when you find a *part of a part*, your answer will always be less than either of the original parts. Is this true? Explain your reasoning.

A C E Homework starts on page 37.

32   Let's Be Rational

Notes _____

_____

_____

2.2 Modeling Multiplication Situations

You have used *of* in multiplication statements with whole numbers. For example:

$$2 \text{ groups } of \, 12 = 2 \times 12 = 24$$

In Problem 2.1, you wrote number sentences such as:

$$\tfrac{3}{4} \, of \, \tfrac{1}{2} = \tfrac{3}{8}$$

Mathematicians use multiplication to rewrite number sentences involving fractions. When you multiply a fraction by a fraction, you are finding part of a part:

$$\tfrac{3}{4} \times \tfrac{1}{2} = \tfrac{3}{8}$$

- What strategy helps you multiply two fractions that are each less than one?

You can also model multiplication situations that involve mixed numbers.

$$2\tfrac{1}{2} \text{ groups } of \, 12 = 2 \text{ groups } of \, 12 \, and \, \tfrac{1}{2} \text{ group } of \, 12$$
$$= 2 \times 12 + \tfrac{1}{2} \times 12$$
$$= 24 + 6$$
$$= 30$$

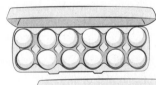

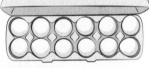

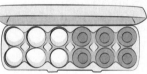

 Do you think these multiplication strategies will work for all kinds of fractions?

Notes _____

_____

_____

In this Problem, you will work with multiplication situations that use fractions, whole numbers, and mixed numbers.

Problem 2.2

A For parts (1)–(3):

- Estimate the answer.
- Draw a model or a diagram to find the exact answer.
- Write a number sentence.

    1. A recipe calls for $\frac{2}{3}$ of a 16-ounce bag of chocolate chips. How many ounces are needed?

    2. Mr. Flansburgh buys a $2\frac{1}{2}$-pound block of cheese. His family eats $\frac{1}{3}$ of the block. How much cheese has Mr. Flansburgh's family eaten?

    3. Malik and Erin run the corn harvester for Mr. Avery. Malik and Erin harvest about $2\frac{1}{3}$ acres' worth of corn each day. They only have $10\frac{1}{2}$ days to harvest the corn. How many acres' worth of corn can they harvest for Mr. Avery?

B For each number sentence below, write a story problem and find the answer.

    1. $\frac{5}{6} \times 1$

    2. $\frac{3}{7} \times 2$

    3. $\frac{1}{2} \times \frac{9}{3}$

    4. $\frac{9}{10} \times \frac{10}{7}$

C Jacinta notices a pattern when she multiplies fractions. Her pattern is written below.

> When you multiply with fractions, the product is less than each of the two factors.

Is Jacinta's pattern correct for the fractions you worked with in Questions A and B? Explain your reasoning.

D Describe a strategy for multiplying any two fractions.

A C E Homework starts on page 37.

34 Let's Be Rational

Notes _____

_____

_____

2.3 Changing Forms
Multiplication With Mixed Numbers

You have developed some strategies for modeling multiplication and finding products of fractions. This Problem will give you a chance to formulate your strategies into algorithms. Before you begin a problem, always ask yourself:

- About how large will the product be?

Problem 2.3

A **1.** Takoda and Yuri are computing $\frac{1}{2} \times 2\frac{2}{3}$. What is a reasonable estimate for this product?

2. Takoda and Yuri each use a different strategy.

Takoda's Strategy		Yuri's Strategy

Takoda's Strategy

I used what I know about fractions to rewrite $2\frac{2}{3}$ as $\frac{8}{3}$ to make the problem easier to solve.

$$\frac{1}{2} \times 2\frac{2}{3} = \frac{1}{2} \times \frac{8}{3}$$
$$= \frac{8}{6}$$
$$= 1\frac{2}{6}$$
$$= 1\frac{1}{3}$$

OR

Yuri's Strategy

I wrote $2\frac{2}{3}$ as $\left(2 + \frac{2}{3}\right)$ and used the Distributive Property to make the problem easier to solve.

$$\frac{1}{2} \times 2\frac{2}{3} = \frac{1}{2} \times \left(2 + \frac{2}{3}\right)$$
$$= \left(\frac{1}{2} \times 2\right) + \left(\frac{1}{2} \times \frac{2}{3}\right)$$
$$= 1 + \frac{2}{6}$$
$$= 1\frac{2}{6}$$
$$= 1\frac{1}{3}$$

a. Does each strategy work? How do you know?

b. How are the strategies similar? How are they different?

3. Use both strategies to solve $1\frac{1}{3} \times \frac{4}{5}$. Then check your answer with a drawing.

continued on the next page >

Investigation 2 **Building on Multiplication With Fractions** 35

Notes

Problem 2.3 *continued*

B For each problem below:

- Estimate the product.
- Use a multiplication strategy to find the exact product.
- Be sure to show your work.

1. $3\frac{4}{5} \times \frac{1}{4}$ **2.** $\frac{3}{4} \times 16$

3. $2\frac{1}{2} \times 1\frac{1}{6}$ **4.** $1\frac{1}{3} \times 3\frac{6}{7}$

5. $1\frac{1}{5} \times 2\frac{1}{4}$ **6.** $12 \times 4\frac{4}{9}$

C **1.** Lisa tries to use Yuri's strategy to find $4\frac{1}{2} \times 1\frac{1}{3}$. She writes:

$$4 \times 1 + \frac{1}{2} \times \frac{1}{3} = 4\frac{1}{6}$$

Yuri says that $4\frac{1}{6}$ is too small. Do you agree with Lisa or Yuri? Explain your reasoning.

2. Yuri tries to help Lisa. Yuri writes:

$$4 \times 1\frac{1}{3} + \frac{1}{2} \times 1\frac{1}{3}$$

How is this different from what Lisa wrote?

D Describe an algorithm for multiplying any two fractions, including mixed numbers.

A C E Homework starts on page 37.

Did You Know?

When you reverse the placement of the numbers in the numerator and the denominator of a fraction, a new fraction is formed. This new fraction is the **reciprocal** of the original. For example, $\frac{8}{7}$ is the reciprocal of $\frac{7}{8}$, and $\frac{12}{17}$ is the reciprocal of $\frac{17}{12}$, or $1\frac{5}{12}$. Notice that the product of a fraction and its reciprocal is 1. Why is this?

Notes _____

Applications

1. A pan of brownies is $\frac{7}{10}$ full. Tyreese buys $\frac{2}{5}$ of the brownies.

   a. Draw a picture of how the brownie pan looks before and after Tyreese buys his brownies.

   b. What fraction of a whole pan of brownies does Tyreese buy?

2. a. Draw brownie-pan models to show whether or not $\frac{2}{3}$ of $\frac{3}{4}$ of a pan of brownies is the same amount as $\frac{3}{4}$ of $\frac{2}{3}$ of a pan of brownies.

   b. If the brownie pans are the same size, how do the amounts of brownies from part (a) compare?

   c. Describe the relationship between $\frac{2}{3}$ of $\frac{3}{4}$ and $\frac{3}{4}$ of $\frac{2}{3}$.

3. Ms. Vargas owns $\frac{4}{5}$ of an acre of land in Tupelo Township. She wants to sell $\frac{2}{3}$ of her land to her neighbor.

   a. What fraction of an acre does Ms. Vargas want to sell? Draw a picture to illustrate your thinking.

   b. Write a number sentence that can be used to solve the problem.

4. Find each answer.

   a. $\frac{1}{2}$ of $\frac{1}{3}$

   b. $\frac{1}{2}$ of $\frac{1}{4}$

   c. $\frac{1}{2}$ of $\frac{2}{3}$

   d. $\frac{1}{2}$ of $\frac{3}{4}$

   e. Describe any patterns that you see in parts (a)–(d).

5. Answer each part without finding the exact answer. Explain your reasoning.

   a. Is $\frac{3}{4} \times 1$ greater than or less than 1?

   b. Is $\frac{3}{4} \times \frac{2}{3}$ greater than or less than 1?

   c. Is $\frac{3}{4} \times \frac{2}{3}$ greater than or less than $\frac{2}{3}$?

   d. Is $\frac{3}{4} \times \frac{2}{3}$ greater than or less than $\frac{3}{4}$?

Notes

For Exercises 6–9, write a number sentence. Use a fraction that is both positive and less than 1.

6. a fraction and a whole number with a whole number product

7. a fraction and a whole number with a product less than 1

8. a fraction and a whole number with a product greater than 1

9. a fraction and a whole number with a product between $\frac{1}{2}$ and 1

10. Shonice is making snack bags for her daughter's field hockey team. She puts $\frac{3}{4}$ cup of pretzels, $\frac{2}{3}$ cup of popcorn, $\frac{1}{3}$ cup of peanuts, and $\frac{1}{4}$ cup of chocolate chips in each bag.

    a. She wants to make 12 snack bags. How much of each ingredient does she need?

    b. Shonice decides that she would like to make snack bags for her card club. There are 15 people in the card club. How much of each ingredient will she need?

11. a. When Sierra gets home, $\frac{3}{4}$ of a sandwich is left in the refrigerator. She cuts the remaining part into three equal parts and eats two of them. What fraction of the whole sandwich did she eat?

    b. Write a number sentence to show your computation.

12. Mr. Jablonski's class is making fudge for a bake sale. Mr. Jablonski has a recipe that makes $\frac{3}{4}$ pound of fudge. There are 21 students in the class. Each student uses the recipe to make one batch of fudge. How many pounds of fudge do the students make?

13. Estimate each product. Explain your reasoning.

    a. $\frac{2}{3} \times 8\frac{5}{6}$ b. $\frac{2}{3} \times 14\frac{1}{2}$ c. $2\frac{1}{2} \times \frac{2}{3}$

14. Esteban is making turtle brownies. The recipe calls for $\frac{3}{4}$ bag of caramel squares. One bag has 24 caramel squares in it.

    a. How many caramel squares should Esteban use to make one batch of turtle brownies?

    b. Esteban decides to make two batches of turtle brownies. Write a number sentence to show how many bags of caramel squares he will use.

Notes _____

_____

_____

15. Isabel is adding a sun porch onto her house. She finds that covering the entire floor requires 12 rows of tiles with $11\frac{1}{3}$ tiles in each row. Write a number sentence to show how many tiles Isabel needs.

16. Judi is making a frame for a square painting. The square painting is $11\frac{3}{8}$ inches on each side.

$11\frac{3}{8}$ in.

To make sure that she has enough wood, Judi wants to buy two extra inches of wood for each corner. How much wood should Judi buy?

17. Find each product.

   a. $\frac{1}{3} \times 18$

   b. $\frac{2}{3} \times 18$

   c. $\frac{5}{3} \times 18$

   d. $1\frac{2}{3} \times 18$

   e. What patterns do you see in these products?

18. Carolyn is making cookies. The recipe calls for $1\frac{3}{4}$ cups of brown sugar. If she makes $2\frac{1}{2}$ batches of cookies, how much brown sugar does she need?

Notes _____

For Exercises 19–27, use an algorithm for multiplying fractions to determine each product.

19. $\frac{5}{12} \times 1\frac{1}{3}$ **20.** $\frac{2}{7} \times \frac{7}{8}$ **21.** $3\frac{2}{9} \times \frac{7}{3}$

22. $2\frac{2}{5} \times 1\frac{1}{15}$ **23.** $10\frac{3}{4} \times 2\frac{2}{3}$ **24.** $1\frac{1}{8} \times \frac{4}{7}$

25. $\frac{11}{6} \times \frac{9}{10}$ **26.** $\frac{9}{4} \times 1\frac{1}{6}$ **27.** $\frac{5}{2} \times \frac{8}{11}$

Connections

28. Bianca and Yoko work together to mow the lawn. Suppose Yoko mows $\frac{5}{12}$ of the lawn and Bianca mows $\frac{2}{5}$ of the lawn. How much lawn still needs to be mowed?

29. Joe and Ashanti need $2\frac{2}{5}$ bushels of apples to make applesauce. Suppose Joe picks $1\frac{5}{6}$ bushels of apples. How many more bushels need to be picked?

30. Roshaun and Lea go to an amusement park. Lea spends $\frac{1}{2}$ of her money, and Roshaun spends $\frac{1}{4}$ of his money. Is it possible for Roshaun to have spent more money than Lea? Explain your reasoning.

31. Min Ji uses balsa wood to build airplane models.

After completing a model, she has a strip of balsa wood measuring $\frac{7}{8}$ yard left over. Shawn wants to buy half of the strip from Min Ji. How long is the strip of wood Shawn wants to buy?

Notes _____

_____

_____

32. Aran has a bag of pretzels for a snack. He gives half of the pretzels to Jon. Then, Jon gives Kiona $\frac{1}{3}$ of his portion. What fraction of the bag of pretzels does each person get?

33. Mr. Mace's class is planning a field trip, and $\frac{3}{5}$ of his students want to go to Chicago. Of those who want to go to Chicago, $\frac{2}{3}$ want to go to Navy Pier. What fraction of the class wants to go to Navy Pier?

34. In Vashon's class, three fourths of the students are girls. Four fifths of the girls in the class have brown hair.

   a. What fraction represents the girls in Vashon's class with brown hair?

   b. How many students are in Vashon's class? Explain your reasoning.

35. Violeta and Mandy are making beaded necklaces. They have beads of various colors and sizes. As they design patterns, they want to find out how long the final necklace will be. They have the following bead widths to work with:

Widths of Beads

Bead	Width
Small Trade Neck	$\frac{1}{4}$ inch
Medium Trade Neck	$\frac{3}{8}$ inch
Large Trade Neck	$\frac{7}{16}$ inch

   a. Mandy makes the necklace below. She uses 30 small Trade Neck beads, 6 medium Trade Neck beads, and 1 large Trade Neck bead. How long is Mandy's necklace?

   b. Violeta wants to make a 16-inch necklace by alternating medium and large Trade Neck beads. She only has 8 medium Trade Neck beads. If she uses 8 medium Trade Neck beads and 8 large Trade Neck beads, will her necklace be 16 inches long?

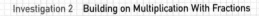

Notes _____

_____

_____

36. **Multiple Choice** Which of the numbers below, when multiplied by $\frac{4}{7}$, will be greater than $\frac{4}{7}$?

    A. $\frac{1}{7}$　　　　**B.** $\frac{7}{7}$　　　　**C.** $\frac{17}{7}$　　　　**D.** $\frac{4}{7}$

37. **Multiple Choice** Which of the numbers below, when multiplied by $\frac{4}{7}$, will be less than $\frac{4}{7}$?

    F. $\frac{1}{7}$　　　　**G.** $\frac{7}{7}$　　　　**H.** $\frac{17}{7}$　　　　**J.** $\frac{8}{7}$

38. **Multiple Choice** Which of the numbers below, when multiplied by $\frac{4}{7}$, will be exactly $\frac{4}{7}$?

    A. $\frac{1}{7}$　　　　**B.** $\frac{7}{7}$　　　　**C.** $\frac{17}{7}$　　　　**D.** $\frac{4}{7}$

For Exercises 39–42, find each product.

39. $\frac{1}{3}$ of $\frac{2}{3}$

40. $\frac{5}{6}$ of 3

41. $\frac{2}{3}$ of $\frac{5}{6}$

42. $\frac{2}{5}$ of $\frac{5}{8}$

43. **a.** How many minutes are in 1 hour?

    b. How many minutes are in $\frac{1}{2}$ hour?

    c. How many minutes are in 0.5 hour?

    d. How many minutes are in 0.1 hour?

    e. How many minutes are in 1.25 hours?

    f. How many hours are in 186 minutes? Express this as a mixed number and as a decimal.

Notes

44. Terry wants to make $\frac{1}{2}$ of a batch of chocolate chip cookies. Rewrite her recipe so that she only needs $\frac{1}{2}$ as much of each ingredient.

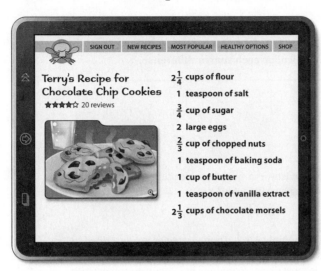

Terry's Recipe for Chocolate Chip Cookies
★★★★☆ 20 reviews

$2\frac{1}{4}$ cups of flour
1 teaspoon of salt
$\frac{3}{4}$ cup of sugar
2 large eggs
$\frac{2}{3}$ cup of chopped nuts
1 teaspoon of baking soda
1 cup of butter
1 teaspoon of vanilla extract
$2\frac{1}{3}$ cups of chocolate morsels

45. Terry finds a recipe for chewy brownie cookies.

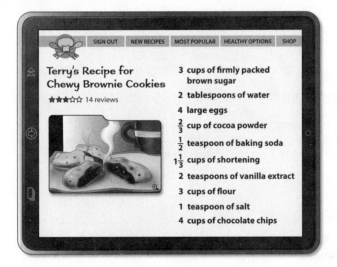

Terry's Recipe for Chewy Brownie Cookies
★★★☆☆ 14 reviews

3 cups of firmly packed brown sugar
2 tablespoons of water
4 large eggs
$\frac{2}{3}$ cup of cocoa powder
$\frac{1}{2}$ teaspoon of baking soda
$1\frac{1}{3}$ cups of shortening
2 teaspoons of vanilla extract
3 cups of flour
1 teaspoon of salt
4 cups of chocolate chips

She wants to bake only $\frac{1}{4}$ of the number of cookies the recipe will make. Rewrite her recipe so that it will make $\frac{1}{4}$ as many chewy brownie cookies.

Investigation 2   **Building on Multiplication With Fractions**   43

Notes _____

46. Estimate each product to the nearest whole number (1, 2, 3, ...).

a. $\frac{1}{2} \times 2\frac{9}{10}$ **b.** $1\frac{1}{2} \times 2\frac{9}{10}$ **c.** $2\frac{1}{2} \times \frac{4}{7}$ **d.** $3\frac{1}{4} \times 2\frac{11}{12}$

e. For each of parts (a)-(d), will the actual product be greater than or less than your whole-number estimate? Explain.

For Exercises 47–52, calculate each sum or difference.

47. $2\frac{2}{3} + 3\frac{5}{6}$

48. $2\frac{8}{10} + 2\frac{4}{5} + 1\frac{1}{2}$

49. $4\frac{3}{10} + 2\frac{2}{6}$

50. $5\frac{5}{8} - 2\frac{2}{3}$

51. $6\frac{7}{10} - 3\frac{4}{5}$

52. $8 - 3\frac{14}{15}$

53. Multiple Choice How many tiles are needed to make a rectangle that is $4\frac{1}{3}$ tiles long by $\frac{1}{2}$ tile wide?

A. $2\frac{1}{3}$ **B.** $2\frac{1}{6}$ **C.** 2 **D.** $2\frac{1}{4}$

54. Three students multiply $6 \times \frac{1}{5}$. Their strategies are described below. The students' answers are $\frac{6}{5}$, 1.2, and $1\frac{1}{5}$. Match each answer to the strategy that is most likely to produce it. Explain your reasoning.

a. Fala draws six shapes, each representing $\frac{1}{5}$, and fits them together.

b. Jorell writes $\frac{6}{1} \times \frac{1}{5}$.

c. Hiroshi writes 6×0.2.

55. Multiple Choice John is making bows to put on wreaths. Each bow uses $2\frac{1}{3}$ yards of ribbon. A spool contains 15 yards of ribbon. How many whole bows can John make from one spool?

F. 6 **G.** 7 **H.** 12 **J.** 35

Extensions

For Exercises 56 and 57, find each product.

56. $\frac{2}{3} \times \frac{1}{2} \times \frac{3}{4}$

57. $\frac{5}{8} \times \frac{1}{2} \times \frac{2}{3}$

Notes _____

Mathematical Reflections 2

In this Investigation, you explored situations that required you to multiply fractions. You also developed an algorithm for multiplying fractions. The following questions will help you summarize what you have learned.

Think about these questions. Discuss your ideas with other students and your teacher. Then write a summary of your findings in your notebook.

1. **Explain** and **illustrate** what *of* means when you find a fraction *of* another number. What operation do you use when you find parts of parts?

2. **a.** If you forget the algorithm for multiplying fractions, **how** might you use rectangular models to help you multiply fractions?

   b. Describe an algorithm for multiplying any two fractions.

   c. Describe when it might be useful to estimate a product.

3. Use examples to **explain** the following statement:

   When you multiply a fraction by another fraction, your answer might be less than both factors, more than one of the factors, or more than both factors.

Notes _____

_____

_____

Common Core Mathematical Practices

As you worked on the Problems in this Investigation, you used prior knowledge to make sense of them. You also applied Mathematical Practices to solve the Problems. Think back over your work, the ways you thought about the Problems, and how you used Mathematical Practices.

Nick described his thoughts in the following way:

In Problem 2.1, we used a square brownie pan model to show what $\frac{3}{4}$ of $\frac{1}{2}$ looks like. We used the picture to find how much $\frac{3}{4}$ of $\frac{1}{2}$ is. We wrote the number sentence '$\frac{3}{4}$ of $\frac{1}{2} = \frac{3}{8}$' to represent the amount of brownies that we were finding.

This is called an area model for multiplication. The length marked along one side of the pan stands for one fraction. The length along a perpendicular side stands for the second fraction being multiplied. The answer is the area of overlap inside the pan.

Common Core Standards for Mathematical Practice
MP4 Model with mathematics.

- What other Mathematical Practices can you identify in Nick's reasoning?
- Describe a Mathematical Practice that you and your classmates used to solve a different Problem in this Investigation.

Notes _____

_____

_____

Investigation **3**

PLANNING

INVESTIGATION
OVERVIEW

GOALS AND
STANDARDS

Dividing With Fractions

▼ Investigation Overview

Investigation Description

Investigation 3 explores the operation of division. Problem 3.1 emphasizes estimation. The context involves measurements that provide a familiar setting for the first interpretation of division. Students are asked to consider *How much of this is in that?* using fractional dividends and divisors. Everyday situations are used to help students make sense of when division is an appropriate operation. The first two Problems in the Investigation involve the measuring interpretation of division, and the third involves the sharing interpretation. The last Problem uses presorted division problems to develop a general algorithm for fraction division.

Investigation Vocabulary

There are no new glossary terms introduced in this Investigation.

Mathematics Background

- Building Proficiency Using Algorithms
- Division of Rational Numbers
- Developing a Division Algorithm

Planning Chart

Content	ACE	Pacing	Materials	Resources
Problem 3.1	1–2, 36–39	1 day		**Teaching Aid 3.1A** Dividing With Fractions **Teaching Aid 3.1B** Student Strategies **Teaching Aid 3** Understanding Division Situations
Problem 3.2	3–12, 40, 54	1 day	**Labsheet 3ACE:** Exercise 6 (accessibility) poster paper	
Problem 3.3	13–19, 49–53, 55–59	1 day		
Problem 3.4	20–35, 41–48	1 day	**Labsheet 3.4:** Algorithms for Dividing Fractions (accessibility) poster paper	
Mathematical Reflections		½ day		
Assessment: Check Up 2		½ day		

Goals and Standards

Goals

Numeric Estimation Understand that estimation is a tool used in a variety of situations including checking answers and making decisions, and develop strategies for estimating results of arithmetic operations

- Use benchmarks and other strategies to estimate results of operations with fractions

- Use estimates to check the reasonableness of exact computations

- Give various reasons to estimate and identify when a situation calls for an overestimate or an underestimate

- Use estimates and exact solutions to make decisions

Fraction Operations Revisit and continue to develop meanings for the four arithmetic operations and skill at using algorithms for each

- Determine when addition, subtraction, multiplication, or division is the appropriate operation to solve a problem

- Develop ways to model sums, differences, products, and quotients with areas, fraction strips, and number lines

- Use knowledge of fractions and equivalence of fractions to develop algorithms for adding, subtracting, multiplying, and dividing fractions

- Write fact families with fractions to show the inverse relationship between addition and subtraction, and between multiplication and division

- Compare and contrast dividing a whole number by a fraction to dividing a fraction by a whole number

- Recognize that when you multiply or divide a fraction, your answer might be less than or more than the numbers you started with

- Solve real-world problems using arithmetic operations on fractions

Mathematical Reflections

Look for evidence of student understanding of the goals for this Investigation in their responses to the questions in *Mathematical Reflections*. The goals addressed by each question are indicated below.

1. When solving a problem, how do you recognize when division is the operation you need to use?

   Goals
   - Determine when addition, subtraction, multiplication, or division is the appropriate operation to solve a problem
   - Use estimates and exact solutions to make decisions

2. **a.** How is dividing a whole number by a fraction similar to or different from dividing a fraction by a whole number?

   b. Explain your strategy for dividing one fraction by another fraction. Does your strategy also work for divisions where the dividend or divisor is a whole number or a mixed number? Explain.

   Goals
   - Compare and contrast dividing a whole number by a fraction to dividing a fraction by a whole number
   - Use knowledge of fractions and equivalence of fractions to develop algorithms for adding, subtracting, multiplying, and dividing fractions
   - Develop ways to model sums, differences, products, and quotients with areas, fraction strips, and number lines

3. When you divide two whole numbers, neither of which is zero, your answer is always less than the dividend. For example, $15 \div 3 = 5$, and 5 is less than 15 (the dividend). Use examples to help explain the following statement: When you divide a fraction by another fraction, your answer might be greater than the dividend or less than the dividend.

   Goals
   - Recognize that when you multiply or divide a fraction, your answer might be less than or more than the numbers you started with
   - Use estimates to check the reasonableness of exact computations
   - Use estimates and exact solutions to make decisions
   - Develop ways to model sums, differences, products, and quotients with areas, fraction strips, and number lines

Standards

Common Core Content Standards

6.NS.A.1 Interpret and compute quotients of fractions, and solve word problems involving division of fractions by fractions, e.g., by using visual fraction models and equations to represent the problem. *Problems 1, 2, 3, and 4*

6.EE.A.2b Identify parts of an expression using mathematical terms (sum, term, product, factor, quotient, coefficient); view one or more parts of an expression as a single entity. *Problem 1*

Facilitating the Mathematical Practices

Students in *Connected Mathematics* classrooms display evidence of multiple Common Core Standards for Mathematical Practice every day. Here are just a few examples where you might observe students demonstrating the Standards for Mathematical Practice during this Investigation.

Practice 1: Make sense of problems and persevere in solving them.

Students are engaged every day in solving problems and, over time, learn to persevere in solving them. To be effective, the problems embody critical concepts and skills and have the potential to engage students in making sense of mathematics. Students build understanding by reflecting, connecting, and communicating. These student-centered problem situations engage students in articulating the "knowns" in a problem situation and determining a logical solution pathway. The student-student and student-teacher dialogues help students to not just make sense of the problems, but also to persevere in finding appropriate strategies to solve them. The suggested questions in the Teacher Guides provide the metacognitive scaffolding to help students monitor and refine their problem-solving strategies.

Practice 2: Reason abstractly and quantitatively.

Students investigate cooking in Problem 3.2. They represent pizzas and blocks of cheese with appropriate quantities (whole numbers and fractions) and reason through the problem abstractly.

Practice 8: Look for and express regularity in repeated reasoning.

In Problem 3.4, students use repeating patterns they had found in division problems to devise two algorithms for dividing fractions. The first algorithm is to represent both divisor and dividend as fractions with a common denominator and then divide the numerators. The second algorithm is to multiply the dividend by the reciprocal of the divisor.

Students identify and record their personal experiences with the Standards for Mathematical Practice during the Mathematical Reflections at the end of the Investigation.

Preparing Food
Dividing a Fraction by a Fraction

▼ Problem Overview

> *Focus Question* What does it mean to divide a fraction by a fraction? What strategies help you divide a fraction by a fraction?

Problem Description

Problem 3.1 presents fractions divided by fractions in the context of preparing food. In Question A, teachers preparing hamburgers of different sizes demonstrates dividing fractions with equivalent denominators. In Question B, students encounter problems in which the denominators of the fractions are different, but multiples of each other. Finally, students are asked to articulate the strategies they used to solve these problems. Then they can begin the development of an algorithm for dividing fractions. Students will formalize the algorithm later in this Investigation, but not at this time. The emphasis is on beginning strategies and understanding what the answer to a division problem means.

Problem Implementation

Have students work on their own for about 5 minutes and then work with a partner to discuss their solutions.

Have students put their work on poster paper to use in the Summarize. If you need more student work to use in the Summarize, you can use the four examples of student work that are provided for students to discuss. A gallery walk might be appropriate for helping students clarify their understanding.

If needed, you can use **Teaching Aid 3: Understanding Division Situations** (an optional supplemental Problem) to review the meaning of division with whole numbers.

Materials

- **Teaching Aid 3:** Understanding Division Situations
- **Teaching Aid 3.1A:** Dividing With Fractions
- **Teaching Aid 3.1B:** Student Strategies

Vocabulary

There are no new glossary terms introduced in this Problem.

Mathematics Background

• Division of Rational Numbers

At a Glance and Lesson Plan

• At a Glance: Let's Be Rational Problem 3.1
• Lesson Plan: Let's Be Rational Problem 3.1

▼ Launch

Launch Video

Show this video before asking the Suggested Questions in Presenting the Challenge in order to bring real-world context to the discussion of dividing fractions. In this Launch video, grillers make two sizes of burgers: 2-pound burgers and $\frac{1}{4}$-pound burgers. The character grilling 2-pound burgers is given 8 more pounds of burger, allowing him to make 4 more burgers. The character grilling $\frac{1}{4}$-pound burgers is given another $\frac{1}{2}$ pound of burger meat. The whole-number segment of the video helps students link division to the situation at hand, preparing them to divide with fractions. Visit Teacher Place at mathdashboard.com/cmp3 to see the complete video.

After showing the video, continue with the Suggested Questions in Presenting the Challenge.

Connecting to Prior Knowledge

Use the introduction to Problem 3.1 to connect and shift the focus from whole number to fraction division situations.

Suggested Questions

• When you do the division 12 ÷ 5, what does the answer mean? (How many fives are in 12 wholes.)

• Five does not go into 12 an equal, or whole, number of times. Can we use a fraction to show how many times 5 goes into 12? ($12 \div 5 = 2\frac{2}{5}$)

• What does the fraction part of the answer mean? (We are making groups of five. We can make two whole groups and $\frac{2}{5}$ of another group.)

Presenting the Challenge

You may want to use **Teaching Aid 3: Understanding Division Situations**, in which students make sense of the idea of division situations involving whole numbers. Then ask students to think about how these ideas apply to division problems involving fractions. This would be a good time to show the Launch video.

Suggested Questions

- How would you write a division number sentence for "How many $\frac{1}{4}$'s are in $\frac{1}{2}$?" ($\frac{1}{2} \div \frac{1}{4}$)

- You are going to work on problems such as "How many $\frac{1}{4}$'s are in $\frac{1}{2}$?" Before you start, what is a reasonable estimate for how many times will $\frac{1}{4}$ go into $\frac{1}{2}$? (2)

- How can you draw a model to show this? (Draw two fraction strips, one to show $\frac{1}{2}$ and another to show $\frac{1}{4}$'s.)

You may refer to **Teaching Aid 3.1A: Dividing With Fractions**

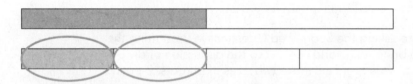

- How does the diagram help you think about finding the quotient for $\frac{1}{2} \div \frac{1}{4}$? (When you compare the two fraction strips, you can see that two fourths are in one half.)

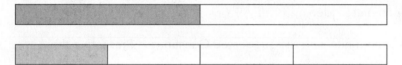

- What does the answer to this division problem mean? (There are two fourths in one half.)

Problem 3.1 involves fractions. Students use what they know about whole-number computation and about fractions to answer these questions.

Explore

Providing for Individual Needs

Circulate as the class works, paying attention to how students are thinking about the problems and where they are having difficulty. Encourage students to draw pictures or diagrams to model the problems. Also, encourage students to write number sentences that represent their pictures and reflect how they solved the problem.

Suggested Questions

- What are the quantities? (They are fractions of a pound.)

- What do you know and what are you trying to find? (You know how much of something you have, and you want to find how many servings you can make.)

- Is this a grouping or a sharing problem? Explain. (This is a grouping problem. You know what the whole is, and you need to find out how many groups you can form.)

- What kind of diagram will help? (Sample answer: Fraction strips will help.)

- Is there a shortcut for doing this problem that makes sense to you? (Make sure that students can explain whey their shortcuts work.)

You might want to have students who used diagrams for the various problems organize their work to share with the class on a clean sheet of paper for the Summarize.

Planning for the Summary

What evidence will you use in the summary to clarify and deepen understanding of the Focus Question?

What will you do if you do not have evidence?

Summarize

Orchestrating the Discussion

Begin the Summarize by asking students if the hamburger and chocolate problems are grouping or sharing problems. The problems used are examples of grouping problems. In each case you know how much meat or chocolate you have and how much is needed for each group (hamburger or cup of chocolate). You do not know how many groups you can make.

As the discussion progresses, you can have students present their strategies or use some of the student strategies provided (see **Teaching Aid 3.1B: Student Strategies**). Questions related to each strategy are provided below.

Suggested Questions

- Are these sharing or grouping problems? (grouping)

For an example of a student strategy for part (1) of Question A, you may refer to **Teaching Aid 3.1B: Student Strategies**. Have a student group display their work. Then ask,

- What is the size of the hamburger patties? ($\frac{1}{8}$ of a pound)
- What does the 7 mean in the answer? (seven $\frac{1}{8}$-pound patties)

For an example of a student strategy for part (2) of Question A, you may refer to **Teaching Aid 3.1B: Student Strategies**. Have a student group display their work. Then ask,

- How do this problem and its answer compare to part (1)? (The size of the patties, or groups, is twice as large, so the answer will be half as big.)
- How much hamburger do you have? ($\frac{7}{8}$ of a pound)
- What is the size of the hamburger patties? ($\frac{2}{8}$ of a pound)
- What is the division number sentence? ($\frac{7}{8} \div \frac{2}{8} = 3\frac{1}{2}$)
- What does the 3 in the answer stand for? (three $\frac{2}{8}$-pound patties)
- What does the $\frac{1}{2}$ stand for? (one half of a $\frac{2}{8}$-pound patty)

For an example of a student strategy for part (3) of Question A, you may refer to **Teaching Aid 3.1B: Student Strategies**. Have a student group display their work. Then ask,

- How does this problem compare to the first two questions? (The size of the total is bigger, greater than one, so the diagram includes two whole pounds and $\frac{3}{4}$ of a pound.)
- How much hamburger do we have? ($2\frac{3}{4}$ or $\frac{11}{4}$ of a pound)
- What is the size of the hamburger patties? ($\frac{1}{4}$ of a pound)
- What is the division number sentence? ($2\frac{3}{4} \div \frac{1}{4} = 11$ or $\frac{11}{4} \div \frac{1}{4} = 11$)
- What does the 11 in the answer stand for? (eleven $\frac{1}{4}$-pound patties)

For an example of a student strategy for Question B you may refer to **Teaching Aid 3.1B: Student Strategies**. Have a student group display their work. Then ask,

- Which was harder, Question A or Question B? Explain. (Question A already had common denominators, so the problems were easier. In Question B, we needed to find common denominators.)
- Did your strategies change for Question B? (Not really, but in Question B we had to do more steps, to find common denominators)

Reflecting on Student Learning

Use the following questions to assess student understanding at the end of the lesson.

- What evidence do I have that students understand the Focus Question?
  - Where did my students get stuck?
  - What strategies did they use?
  - What breakthroughs did my students have today?
- How will I use this to plan for tomorrow? For the next time I teach this lesson?
- Where will I have the opportunity to reinforce these ideas as I continue through this Unit? The next Unit?

ACE Assignment Guide

- **Applications:** 1–2
- **Connections:** 36–39

Into Pieces
Whole Numbers or Mixed Numbers Divided by Fractions

▼ Problem Overview

> *Focus Question* What does it mean to divide a whole number or mixed number by a fraction? What strategies help you divide a whole number or mixed number by a fraction?

Problem Description

Students divide whole numbers by fractions to decide how many servings can be prepared from a given amount of food. Question A uses patterns in the numerator and denominator to help students understand dividing by a fraction. Question B asks students to write questions to match division problems with fractions, and then to solve the problems. Question C asks students to extend their thinking about dividing a whole number by a fraction to dividing a mixed number by a fraction. Question D asks students to articulate their strategies for solving division problems involving fractions.

Students' ideas may still be developing at this time, and students may continue to rely on drawings to solve theses problems. This is acceptable at this point. A formal algorithm will be developed later in this Investigation.

Problem Implementation

Have students work on their own for about 5 minutes and then work with a partner to discuss their solutions. You may want to stop and summarize after Question A and B before students move on to Questions C and D.

Materials

• **Labsheet 3ACE:** Exercise 6 (accessibility)

poster paper (optional)

Vocabulary

There are no new glossary terms introduced in this Problem.

Mathematics Background

• Division of Rational Numbers

At a Glance and Lesson Plan

• At a Glance: Let's Be Rational Problem 3.2
• Lesson Plan: Let's Be Rational Problem 3.2

▼ Launch

Connecting to Prior Knowledge

Remind students that in Problem 3.1, they explored how to divide a fraction by a fraction. Point out that in Problem 3.2, they are still dividing with fractions, but this time they are dividing a whole number by a fraction.

Presenting the Challenge

Use the introduction to Problem 3.2 in the Student Edition to introduce situations with whole numbers divided by fractions. Remind students that drawing a picture is a good way to help think through each situation.

Suggested Questions

• How would you write a division sentence for "How many $\frac{3}{4}$'s are in 14?" ($14 \div \frac{3}{4}$)

• You are going to work on situations such as this in Problem 3.2. Before you start, what is a reasonable estimate for how many times $\frac{3}{4}$ will go into 14? Remember that you know that $14 \div 1 = 14$. (If you can make 14 groups of 1, you should be able to make at least 14 groups of $\frac{3}{4}$ since they are smaller groups. Maybe 16 or even 20 would be reasonable.)

• How can you use a number line to represent $14 \div \frac{3}{4}$? How does this help you find the quotient? (Give students time to think about this question. They may have different strategies. Most will continue to mark off $\frac{3}{4}$ units on the number line and then count how many they have. Have one or two students present their number lines to the class.)

Parts of Problem 3.2 involve fractions. Tell students they can use what they know about whole-number computation and about fractions to find ways to answer these questions.

▼ Explore

Providing for Individual Needs

Circulate as the class works, paying attention to how students are thinking about the problems and where they are having difficulty. Encourage students to draw pictures or diagrams to model the problems. Also, encourage students to write number sentences that represent their pictures and reflect how they solved the problems. Ask whether the problems are about sharing something equally or about how many groups or things of a certain kind can be made.

You might want to have students who used diagrams for the various problems put them on poster paper so you can display them in the Summarize.

Planning for the Summary

What evidence will you use in the summary to clarify and deepen understanding of the Focus Question?
What will you do if you do not have evidence?

▼ Summarize

Orchestrating the Discussion

Begin the Summarize by asking students if the pizza problems are grouping or sharing problems. The problems used are examples of grouping problems. In each case it is known how much cheese is available and how much is needed for each group (pizza). They do not know how many groups (pizzas) they can make.

A Teaching Aid is provided for Problem 3.2: **Sample Student Work 3.2**.

As you go over the parts (1.a) through (1.c) of Question A, have students who drew diagrams share their drawings.

The diagram below represents $\frac{27}{3} \div \frac{1}{3}$. For a sample student discussion of the diagram, you may refer to **Sample Student Work 3.2**. If students do not bring up a similar strategy on their own, display this strategy for class discussion.

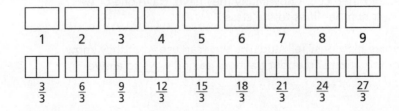

Suggested Questions

Ask questions such as the following:

- What number sentence represents how many $\frac{1}{3}$'s are in 9? ($9 \div \frac{1}{3} = 27$)

- Your solution sounds like you used the number sentence $9 \times 3 = 27$. Do you agree? (Yes. Since each cup has 3 thirds, I can find how many pizzas can be made by multiplying 9 by 3.)

Throughout the discussion of the parts (1.a) through (1.c) of Question A, continue to attach notation to students' reasoning. Students who use common denominators may reason this way. $9 \div \frac{1}{3}$ is the same as $\frac{27}{3} \div \frac{1}{3}$. This means how many thirds are in 27 thirds.

- How would you represent this approach? ($\frac{27}{3} \div \frac{1}{3} = 27$)

- What does the $\frac{27}{3}$ represent? (9 wholes)

- What does the division problem $\frac{27}{3}$ divided by $\frac{1}{3}$ ask? (How many $\frac{1}{3}$'s are in 27 thirds.)

- Why did the 9 get rewritten as $\frac{27}{3}$? (So you can think about the division problem as 27 thirds and try to find out how many $\frac{1}{3}$'s are in $\frac{27}{3}$.)

- What could a diagram for this approach look like? (It could look like the diagram used earlier to represent $9 \div \frac{1}{3}$. The second row of the diagram shows the 9 wholes as $\frac{27}{3}$.)

As you move through the Summarize for Question A, be sure to touch on both of these approaches. You will need to suggest an approach if students do not bring it up.

Student drawings and explanations show that there are two number sentences that make sense for problems such as $9 \div \frac{1}{3}$.

$9 \times 3 = 27$ and $\frac{27}{3} \div \frac{1}{3} = 27$

Once these two ideas and their notation are brought out, and students seem to have a good grasp of what is happening in each situation, move the conversation to parts (1.d) through (1.f) of Question A. As you discuss each of the parts (1.d) through (1.f), ask questions that help students to generalize a strategy for dividing a whole number by a unit fraction and dividing a whole number by a nonunit fraction. Students may need help writing number sentences that model their explanations.

In parts (1.d) through (1.f) of Question A, students use what they know about dividing whole numbers by unit fractions to make sense of problems in which the numerator of the divisor is greater than 1. For example, they can use what they did to solve $9 \div \frac{1}{3}$ to solve the problem $9 \div \frac{2}{3}$ and the other problems.

Have a group share its diagram for $9 \div \frac{2}{3}$.

For a diagram and student discussion, you may refer to **Sample Student Work 3.2**. If students do not bring up a similar strategy on their own, display this strategy for class discussion.

- What are you trying to find out in the problem $9 \div \frac{2}{3}$? (How many $\frac{2}{3}$'s are in 9 wholes.)

- Where did the 13 and the $\frac{1}{2}$ come from? (There are 13 complete $\frac{2}{3}$'s and half of a $\frac{2}{3}$ in 9. After doing as many sets of $\frac{2}{3}$ as possible, there was $\frac{1}{3}$ left. $\frac{1}{3}$ is half of $\frac{2}{3}$. So there are $13\frac{1}{2}$ groups of $\frac{2}{3}$'s in 9 wholes.)

- How does this problem compare to $9 \div \frac{1}{3}$? (You still divide each rectangle into thirds. But groups of $\frac{2}{3}$ are twice as big as groups of $\frac{1}{3}$. Since they are twice as big, only half as many will fit. That is why you get $13\frac{1}{2}$. It is half of 27, or $27 \div 2$.)

- So you are saying that you can use the answer from $9 \div \frac{1}{3}$ to find the answer to $9 \div \frac{2}{3}$. When you solved $9 \div \frac{1}{3}$, you wrote that $9 \div \frac{1}{3} = 9 \times 3$. What would you write as a number sentence for $9 \div \frac{2}{3}$? (To find $9 \div \frac{2}{3}$, you would find $9 \times 3 \div 2 = 13\frac{1}{2}$, which means $13\frac{1}{2}$ groups of $\frac{2}{3}$.)

- Why are you dividing by 2? (It takes $\frac{2}{3}$ of a block to make a pizza. Since each block has 3 thirds in it, we can multiply 9×3 to find out how many thirds are in 9 wholes. Since it takes 2 of the thirds for each pizza, we need to divide by 2.)

Have students look at the other two cases, $\frac{3}{3}$ and $\frac{4}{3}$, and see if the same reasoning works.

Work on writing out number sentences for each of the cases for thirds.

- So, how can you divide any whole number by a fraction? (Multiply by the denominator and divide by the numerator of the divisor.)

Also discuss the common denominator approach.

- Did anyone try using common denominators as we did when we rewrote $9 \div \frac{1}{3}$ as $\frac{27}{3} \div \frac{1}{3}$? (Yes; the common denominator is also 3.)

- How would you use a diagram to show $\frac{27}{3} \div \frac{2}{3}$? (You can use the same diagram as you used for the multiply-by-denominator-and-divide by-numerator approach)

- Why does this approach work? (You are rewriting 9 as $\frac{27}{3}$. $\frac{27}{3}$ is the number of thirds in 9 wholes. When you divide by $\frac{2}{3}$, it means that each pizza uses $\frac{2}{3}$ of a block of cheese, and you are finding how many sets of 2 thirds are in 27 thirds.)

As you move through the Summarize for Question A, compare both approaches and compare the equations for unit fractions and those for non-unit fractions. Your drawings and explanations show that there are two number sentences that make sense for problems such as $9 \div \frac{1}{3}$.

$$9 \times 3 = 27 \text{ and } \frac{27}{3} \div \frac{1}{3} = 27$$

Your drawings and explanations show that there are two number sentences that make sense for problems such as $9 \div \frac{2}{3}$.

$$9 \times 3 \div 2 = 13\frac{1}{2} \text{ and } \frac{27}{3} \div \frac{2}{3} = 13\frac{1}{2}$$

- How are these equations the same? How are they different? (The result is the same, but the operations represent different ways of thinking about the problem.)

Try this approach on several problems to be sure it works.

Question B provides a place for students to use the approaches developed in Question A and for you to informally assess students' progress. Question C asks students to express the relationship between dividing a whole number by a fraction to dividing a mixed number by a fraction.

In Question D, discuss student strategies. Some students may see that dividing by a fraction is the same as multiplying by its reciprocal. Others may feel more comfortable with saying that you multiply the dividend by the denominator of the divisor and then divide the product by the numerator of the divisor. Still others may prefer to make common denominators and then divide the numerators.

Ask students to justify their answers and share any drawings they did to make sense of the problem.

Have each pair of students exchange the problems they created with another pair of students and give them time to work each other's problems. Then have the writers of some of the problems show their drawings and explain what type the problem is: sharing or grouping. Discuss with the class whether they agree with each writer.

Check for Understanding

- Naylah has nine blocks of cheese. How many pizzas can Naylah make if each pizza takes $\frac{1}{5}$ block of cheese? (45)
- If each pizza takes $\frac{2}{5}$ block of cheese? ($22\frac{1}{2}$)
- If each pizza takes $\frac{3}{5}$ block of cheese? (15)
- If each pizza takes $\frac{4}{5}$ block of cheese? ($11\frac{1}{4}$)
- If each pizza takes $\frac{5}{5}$ block of cheese? (9)
- If each pizza takes $\frac{6}{5}$ block of cheese? ($7\frac{1}{2}$)

Reflecting on Student Learning

Use the following questions to assess student understanding at the end of the lesson.

- What evidence do I have that students understand the Focus Question?
  - Where did my students get stuck?
  - What strategies did they use?
  - What breakthroughs did my students have today?
- How will I use this to plan for tomorrow? For the next time I teach this lesson?
- Where will I have the opportunity to reinforce these ideas as I continue through this Unit? The next Unit?

ACE Assignment Guide

- **Applications:** 3–12, 21
- **Connections:** 40
- **Extensions:** 54
- **Labsheet 3ACE:** Exercise 6 (accessibility)

Sample Student Work

- **Sample Student Work 3.2**

Sharing a Prize
Dividing a Fraction by a Whole Number

▼ Problem Overview

Focus Question What does it mean to divide a fraction by a whole number?
What strategies help you divide a fraction by a whole number?

Problem Description

The Problems in this Investigation are organized to help students build on their
ideas from Problems 3.1 and 3.2 to see a pattern that will lead to an algorithm
for dividing a fraction by a whole number. Problem 3.3 has four questions, two
of which give a different situation with several parts. In Question A, all of the
problems involve sharing a fractional amount of peanuts. In Question B, the parts
all involve dividing a non-unit fraction by a whole number. In Question C, students
firm up their understanding by writing problems that fit the computation $\frac{8}{3} \div 4$.
In Question D, students summarize their strategies for dividing a fraction by a
whole number.

Problem Implementation

Have students work in pairs or small groups on this Problem.

Examples of student work are provided to use in the Summarize if needed to
develop the desired understanding (see **Sample Student Work 3.3**).

Materials

• **Sample Student Work 3.3**

Vocabulary

There are no new glossary terms introduced in this Problem.

Mathematics Background

• Division of Rational Numbers

At a Glance and Lesson Plan

• At a Glance: Let's Be Rational Problem 3.3
• Lesson Plan: Let's Be Rational Problem 3.3

▼ Launch

Connecting to Prior Knowledge

In Problem 3.2, students explored how to divide a whole number by a fraction. In Problem 3.3, they are still dividing with fractions, but this time, they are dividing a fraction by a whole number.

Suggested Questions

• Who can tell me how to change $\frac{3}{5}$ into a decimal? (Divide the 5 into the 3.)

• Why does that make sense? (because $\frac{3}{5}$ means $3 \div 5$)

• So a fraction can be thought of as another way to show division. This means that $\frac{2}{3}$ can be thought of as $2 \div 3$. If you divide 2 by 3, you get $\frac{2}{3}$. What is a situation in which $2 \div 3$ would be an appropriate interpretation of a fraction? (Three people order two pizzas to share equally. How much does each get? The answer can be obtained by computing $2 \div 3$, which gives $\frac{2}{3}$. Another situation is when you want to convert a fraction to a decimal. Dividing 2 by 3 with or without a calculator gives you the decimal approximation for $\frac{2}{3}$.)

• In Investigation 2 you looked at products of two numbers that give exactly 1 as the answer. Some examples are $\frac{1}{2} \times 2 = 1$; $3 \times \frac{1}{3} = 1$; $\frac{2}{3} \times \frac{3}{2} = 1$. What do you call these pairs of numbers whose product is exactly 1? (You call them reciprocals.)

• What is the reciprocal of $\frac{3}{5}$? $\left(\frac{5}{3}\right)$

• What is the reciprocal of 7? $\left(\frac{1}{7}\right)$

• Think about a mixed number such as $4\frac{1}{3}$. What is its reciprocal? (First you have to write $4\frac{1}{3}$ as a fraction. This would be $\frac{13}{3}$. Then the reciprocal is $\frac{3}{13}$ because $\frac{13}{3} \times \frac{3}{13} = 1$.)

Presenting the Challenge

Today students have a Problem about peanuts to solve. Tell them that as they read the Problem, they should pay attention to what is different from what they worked with in Problem 3.1 and Problem 3.2 and what is the same.

Read Question A with your students and remind them of things such as the following.

- Drawing a diagram is often very helpful.
- Label your answer so that you know that the number you get is telling you about the situation.

Suggested Questions

- What are the numbers (quantities) given in the Problem? (pounds of peanuts)
- What do you need to find? (fractions of a pound of peanuts)
- What does the answer tell you? (the share for each member of the team)

Have the students work on Questions A and B individually and then in pairs to compare solutions and strategies. If you are pressed for time, assign Questions C and D for homework and discuss them the next day.

▼ Explore

Providing for Individual Needs

As students work, walk around and ask questions to make sure that they notice the types of problems that make up Question A. As students work on Question B, it may be helpful for them to refer back to the problems and their work for Question A.

You may need to help students share their ideas and drawings for these problems. The drawings are related to those done earlier, but now they are working with a fractional part of something and they need to share it equally among a whole number of entities or people.

Suggested Questions

- Are these grouping or sharing problems? (sharing)

Push students to think about patterns and short cuts.

- Do you see a pattern that would give you a short way of finding the answer? (The quotient is a fraction with a denominator equal to the product of the fraction's denominator and the whole number.)

Planning for the Summary

What evidence will you use in the summary to clarify and deepen understanding of the Focus Question?

What will you do if you do not have evidence?

▼ Summarize

Orchestrating the Discussion

Review Question A with the students. Call on students to illustrate how they did the divisions called for in Question A.

Suggested Questions

- Who can give me an answer for Question A, part (1), and explain why you think you are correct?

Call on two students (or more) to get different diagrams. Remind them that the word *sharing* appears in Question A.

If you need more student work for Question A, or the work in class is not sufficient to develop the desired understanding, use these three examples of student work: **Sample Student Work 3.3** The first two examples deal with part (1), and the third deals with part (3).

Student Response, Student 1 Capitalize on student responses to point out that the problem called for the computation $\frac{1}{2} \div 4$. Student 1's diagram shows that $\frac{1}{2} \div 4$ is the same as $\frac{1}{2} \times \frac{1}{4}$, which is $\frac{1}{8}$.

- The diagrams I see remind me of the brownie pan problems you did in Investigation 2. What multiplication problem would this model represent? ($\frac{1}{2} \times \frac{1}{4} = \frac{1}{8}$)
- Why does it make sense that $\frac{1}{2} \div 4$ is the same as $\frac{1}{2} \times \frac{1}{4}$, which is $\frac{1}{8}$? (Dividing something into four parts is the same as taking one quarter of that thing.)

Student Response, Student 2 The other student diagram shows the same result, but with a different representation. Each of these diagrams helps students move from the division problem to multiplying by the reciprocal. Continue with the rest of the parts of Question A. Look at other approaches that students took to make sense of the problems.

Move on to parts (3) and (4), in which the fractional parts given are not unit fractions. For part (3), you can display **Sample Student Work 3.3**.

- Who can tell me how these problems in parts (3) and (4) are different from those in parts (1) and (2)? (They have non-unit fraction parts to be shared.)

- Who can tell me how they thought about part (3)? (I thought about the problem just like the part (2). First I worked it for $\frac{1}{4}$ of a pound of peanuts and then multiplied my answer by 3. Here were my steps: $\frac{1}{4} \div 2 = \frac{1}{4} \times \frac{1}{2} = \frac{1}{8}$. But I have 3 of these eighths to share, so each person gets $3 \times \frac{1}{8} = \frac{3}{8}$ of a pound of peanuts.)

- Did anyone think about part (3) a different way? (I started with $\frac{3}{4}$. Each person gets half of the $\frac{3}{4}$, or $\frac{3}{8}$ of a pound of peanuts. This is the same as $\frac{3}{4} \times \frac{1}{2} = \frac{3}{8}$.)

- What do others think about this? Is $\frac{3}{4} \div 2 = \frac{3}{8}$ the same as $\frac{3}{4} \times \frac{1}{2} = \frac{3}{8}$? Is dividing by 2 the same as multiplying by $\frac{1}{2}$? (Yes.)

- What would be a reasonable estimate for how much each person will get in part (3)? (Each person will get less than a half, because you have three halves altogether and you have to share among four people.)

- Who can tell me their strategy for finding the answer to part (3)? (You have $1\frac{1}{2}$, which is equivalent to $\frac{3}{2}$, to share among four people. So you need to find $\frac{3}{2} \div 4$. I drew a diagram and found that each person gets $\frac{3}{8}$.)

- Is $\frac{3}{8}$ less than $\frac{1}{4}$? ($\frac{1}{4}$ is equal to $\frac{2}{8}$, so $\frac{3}{8}$ is more.)

- Did anyone use common denominators? (I wrote $\frac{3}{2} \div 4 = \frac{3}{2} \div \frac{8}{2} = \frac{3}{8}$.)

Some students may write this one as $\dfrac{(1\frac{1}{2})}{4}$. If they do, help them to see that this means $1\frac{1}{2} \div 4$, which is equivalent to $1\frac{1}{2} \times \frac{1}{4}$. Then they can write $1\frac{1}{2}$ as $\frac{3}{2}$ and have $\frac{3}{2} \times \frac{1}{4}$. Look for opportunities to express students' ideas as number sentences. Ask questions such as the following:

- Is $\frac{2}{5} \div 3$ equivalent to $\frac{2}{5} \times \frac{1}{3}$? (Yes.)

- Is $\frac{2}{5} \div 3$ equivalent to $\frac{2}{5} \times \frac{15}{5}$? (No.)

Have students present their solutions and models for Question C. Use Question D to summarize an algorithm for dividing any fraction by any whole number. Some will see that multiplying by the reciprocal makes sense and works in both kinds of problems they have studied so far. Others will see this as multiplying by the denominator and dividing by the numerator of the divisor. Others may prefer to create common denominators and divide. Some will still need to draw pictures to help think through a problem.

Reflecting on Student Learning

Use the following questions to assess student understanding at the end of the lesson.

- What evidence do I have that students understand the Focus Question?
  - Where did my students get stuck?
  - What strategies did they use?
  - What breakthroughs did my students have today?
- How will I use this to plan for tomorrow? For the next time I teach this lesson?
- Where will I have the opportunity to reinforce these ideas as I continue through this Unit? The next Unit?

ACE Assignment Guide

- **Applications:** 13–19
- **Connections:** 49–53
- **Extensions:** 55–59

Sample Student Work

- Sample Student Work 3.3

PROBLEM

3.4

Examining Algorithms for Dividing Fractions

▼ Problem Overview

Focus Question What is an efficient algorithm for division problems involving fractions and mixed numbers?

Problem Description

In Question A, students are asked to estimate and then solve several division problems. In Question B, students are asked to sort the problems into two groups:

- Group 1: Problems that require little work to solve
- Group 2: Problems that require much work to solve

As students sort the problems into these two groups, they will notice differences in the problems that will help them to write a general algorithm for division problems involving fractions or mixed numbers.

Question C asks students to write additional problems for each group. Question D consolidates the work students have done in this Investigation. It asks them to write an algorithm to find quotients for problems involving fractions and mixed numbers.

Problem Implementation

Have students work in small groups. On **Labsheet 3.4: Algorithms for Dividing Fractions** (accessibility), students can carry out their calculations to answer Question A in the spaces provided. They can then cut up the pages to create cards and sort them into groups for Question B.

Groups can put their work for the sorting on poster paper to use in the Summarize.

Question E can be done individually as an informal assessment of students' ability to use the algorithm.

Materials

- **Labsheet 3.4:** Algorithms for Dividing Fractions (accessibility)

poster paper (optional)

Vocabulary

There are no new glossary terms introduced in this Problem.

Mathematics Background

- Division of Rational Numbers
- Developing a Division Algorithm

At a Glance and Lesson Plan

- At a Glance: Let's Be Rational Problem 3.4
- Lesson Plan: Let's Be Rational Problem 3.4

▼ Launch

Launch Video

This Launch animation provides students with vocabulary support for the word *algorithm*. The video shows a real-world algorithm—the steps needed to properly wash a dog. Just as the students will add details and conditions to their algorithms for dividing fractions, characters in this animation learn the importance of providing detailed steps when developing a dog-washing algorithm. You can show this video instead of using the Connecting to Prior Knowledge section. Visit Teacher Place at mathdashboard.com/cmp3 to see the complete video.

After showing the video, ask students whether the order of the steps can be changed in the Dog Wash Algorithm. Then, have students discuss an mathematical algorithm for a process they are familiar with, such as adding two fractions. Ask what changes they would make to their algorithm so that is also works for mixed numbers.

Connecting to Prior Knowledge

Talk with the class about what an algorithm is in mathematics.

Suggested Questions

- What is an algorithm? (a set of rules for performing a procedure)
- Can someone describe a mathematical algorithm you use? (Sample answer: To add two fractions, you can write each fraction with a common denominator and then add the numerators.)

Record what students say and revise the written algorithm until the class agrees that what is written makes sense. This will help students to understand what is necessary for a complete description. You might ask them to refer back to algorithms that they developed in Problems 3.1–3.3.

Presenting the Challenge

When students understand what an algorithm is, explain that division problems involving fractions and mixed numbers have algorithms too, and that Problem 3.4 is about helping students to develop and understand an algorithm that will work for any division situation involving fractions. Then have them begin work on the Problem.

▼ Explore

Providing for Individual Needs

Make sure students check their solutions and discuss the groups before moving on to the algorithms. Most students will group the problems in the following two groups:

- Group 1: Problems that require little work to solve.

The problems in Group 1 are likely to consist of fractions, or a fraction and a whole number.

- Group 2: Problems that require much work to solve.

The problems in Group 2 are likely to have one or two mixed numbers, which require more steps to solve.

The above grouping is what we want students to recognize; however, students may come up with other groupings. If that occurs, then you may want to ask students to examine the number of steps a problem took to solve as an indicator of problems that require much work.

Going Further

Encourage students who finish early to find another way to sort the cards. Ask them to describe the criteria for each group and supply a new member.

Planning for the Summary

What evidence will you use in the summary to clarify and deepen understanding of the Focus Question?

What will you do if you do not have evidence?

▼ Summarize

Orchestrating the Discussion

Some teachers check students' work on Question A during the Explore phase of the lesson, and then summarize Questions B and C together.

Suggested Questions

Ask questions such as the following:

- Would someone share their grouping of the problems in Question A? (Group 1: parts 1, 2, 3, 6, 7, 8, 9, 12. Group 2: parts 4, 5, 10, 11)

- What about the problems in Group 1 required less work than those problems in Group 2? (Group 1 problems all involved dividing by a proper fraction or a whole number.)

- What is similar about the problems in Group 2? (Group 2 problems mostly involved dividing by a mixed number.)

- What new problems did you write to fit Group 1? (We wrote problems that involved only division by proper fractions or whole numbers, like parts 1, 2, 3, 6, 7, 8, 9, 12.)

Then summarize Question D, the algorithms.

Ask questions such as the following.

- How did you use Group 1 and Group 2 to help you write your algorithm? (Working with Group 1 showed us that for proper fractions and whole numbers, you multiply the dividend by the denominator of the divisor and then divide by the numerator of the divisor. This is the same as multiplying by the reciprocal. You can also think of this as writing the dividend and divisor with common denominators and then dividing the numerator of the dividend by the numerator of the divisor.)

  Students may have other criteria for what easy-to-calculate means. For example, some may group those that have common denominators.

- Which group made it easier to start writing an algorithm? (Using either algorithm was easy for Group 1.)

- Would someone share their group's algorithm? (For fractions and whole numbers, multiply the dividend by the reciprocal of the divisor. For mixed numbers, convert to an improper fraction and then multiply the dividend by the reciprocal of the divisor.)

- What do others think about this group's algorithm? Will it work for all cases? (It works for all cases.)

- How does this algorithm compare to yours? (Students may phrase things differently, but all algorithms are equivalent.)

For students who use the common denominator method, ask the following question:

- Why is it important to have fractions with the same denominators? (To divide fractions, we divide the numerator of the dividend by the numerator of the divisor, but only when the fractions have the same denominator.)

  If your class is ready you may want to show how these two methods are equivalent.

Evaluating whether each algorithm is usable and comparing it with other algorithms will further students' understanding of division involving fractions. As each algorithm is presented, students may not be able to completely understand the algorithm unless they try to use it. As students describe their algorithms, encourage them to use the problems from Questions A to show how their algorithm works. When it seems appropriate, have the class test a group's algorithm as a way to evaluate whether it is useable and helpful.

- Let's try this algorithm on this problem. (Give an appropriate problem, for instance $1\frac{1}{4} \div 2\frac{1}{2}$.)

  Does the algorithm work? (Yes; if you apply the algorithm, you can see that it works.)

- Does the algorithm account for all the things that you have to think about to solve this problem? (Yes; it accounts for dividends and divisors that are any kind of fraction, and for whole numbers, too.)

The class does not have to develop one agreed-upon algorithm, but each student should have at least one algorithm that he or she can explain and use. After the class discussion, you might ask students to take their algorithms home to show their families. Have students report on whether their families understand what the student has written and why the algorithm makes sense.

Reflecting on Student Learning

Use the following questions to assess student understanding at the end of the lesson.

- What evidence do I have that students understand the Focus Question?
  - Where did my students get stuck?
  - What strategies did they use?
  - What breakthroughs did my students have today?
- How will I use this to plan for tomorrow? For the next time I teach this lesson?
- Where will I have the opportunity to reinforce these ideas as I continue through this Unit? The next Unit?

ACE Assignment Guide

- **Applications:** 20–35
- **Connections:** 41–48

▼ Mathematical Reflections

Possible Answers to Mathematical Reflections

1. Division is involved when the question is *How many of this are in that?* or *How much is in one group?*

2. **a.** Many people think about dividing a whole number by a fraction as asking *How many of this are in that?* They think about dividing a fraction by a whole number as asking *How much is in one group?*

   b. Renaming both dividend and divisor with common denominators and then finding the quotient of the numerators works for all cases. Other strategies are variants of this.

3. Think of dividing by a fraction as asking *How many of this are in that?* Then when we make smaller groups (smaller this), we need more of them to make the total (that). For example, if we have $4 \div \frac{1}{2}$, then we are asking how many halves are in 4, and the answer is 8, which is greater than the dividend. That is because $\frac{1}{2}$ is smaller than 4, so $\frac{1}{2}$ fits into 4 more than 4 times. But, if we have $4 \div 4\frac{1}{4}$ then we are asking how many times $4\frac{1}{4}$ fits into 4, and this is not even one time. $4 \div 4\frac{1}{4}$ is the same as $\frac{16}{4} \div \frac{17}{4}$, which is the same as $\frac{16}{17}$. The quotient is less than the dividend this time.

   This reasoning works for whole-number divisors too. $2\frac{1}{2} \div 2$ means making 2 groups out of $2\frac{1}{2}$, and clearly each group will be smaller than $2\frac{1}{2}$.

Possible Answers to Mathematical Practices Reflections

Students may have demonstrated all of the eight Common Core Standards for Mathematical Practice during this Investigation. During the class discussion, have students identify their use of as many different examples of the Mathematical Practices as they can.

One student observation is provided in the Student Edition. Here is another sample student response.

> When we worked on the pizza problem in Problem 3.2, we had to really think about what we were dividing by and what our answer meant. We were trying to find the number of pizzas that can be made if we have 9 blocks of cheese and each pizza takes $\frac{1}{3}$ of a block of cheese. So we were finding how many $\frac{1}{3}$ a block of cheese are in 9 total blocks, or $9 \div \frac{1}{3}$.
>
> Our class came up with mainly two strategies for solving divisions such as $9 \div \frac{1}{3}$. Our group used common denominators to make the fraction pieces the same size so then we could divide the numerators.
>
> $$\frac{27}{3} \div \frac{1}{3} = 27$$
>
> We used what we knew about $\frac{1}{3}$ block of cheese to find out how many pizzas can be made using $\frac{2}{3}$ of a block. Since $\frac{2}{3}$ is twice as big as $\frac{1}{3}$, we used the division problem expression $9 \div \frac{2}{3}$. Since the number we were dividing by was twice as big, that meant that the answer was twice as small, as if we were dividing each problem by 2.
>
> $$\frac{27}{3} \div \frac{2}{3} = 13\frac{1}{2}$$

MP2: Reason abstractly and quantitatively

Notes

3

Dividing With Fractions

So far in *Let's Be Rational,* you have solved problems using addition, subtraction, and multiplication. In Investigation 3, you will solve problems that require division of fractions. As you work on these problems, think about similarities and differences among the problems.

In the number sentence $21 \div 7 = 3$, 21 is the *dividend,* 7 is the *divisor,* and 3 is the result, or *quotient*.

You can use the vocabulary of division problems as placeholders in a division number sentence. The division sentence below shows how these quantities relate to one another.

$$\text{dividend} \div \text{divisor} = \text{quotient}$$

First, you need to understand what division of fractions means. Then you can calculate quotients when the divisor or the dividend, or both, is a fraction.

....

Common Core State Standards

6.NS.A.1 Apply and extend previous understandings of multiplication and division to divide fractions by fractions.

6.EE.A.2b Identify parts of an expression using mathematical terms (sum, term, product, factor, quotient, coefficient); view one or more parts of an expression as a single entity.

Investigation 3 Dividing With Fractions **47**

Notes

When you do the division $12 \div 5$, what does the answer mean?

The answer should tell you how many fives are in 12 wholes. Because a whole number of fives will not fit into 12, you might write

$$12 \div 5 = 2\tfrac{2}{5}$$

Then, what does the fractional part of the answer mean?

The answer means you can make 2 fives and $\tfrac{2}{5}$ of *another* five.

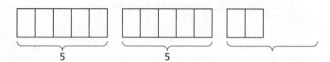

You can check your work by seeing that the related number sentence is true.

$$5 \times 2\tfrac{2}{5} = 12$$

In the division problem above, the divisor and dividend are both whole numbers. In Problem 3.1, you will explore division problems in which the divisor and dividend are both fractions. You will answer questions such as the following.

- How many $\tfrac{1}{4}$'s are in $\tfrac{1}{2}$?
- How can you draw a model to show this?
- How can you write this as a division number sentence?
- What does the answer to this division problem mean?
- What does it mean to divide a fraction by a fraction?

Notes

3.1 Preparing Food
Dividing a Fraction by a Fraction

At Humboldt Middle School football games, the students and teachers run a concession stand to raise money. Mrs. Drake's class is hosting a cookout. The students sell hamburgers to raise money.

Problem 3.1

For each question, do the following.

- Solve the problem.
- Draw a model to help explain your reasoning.
- Write a number sentence showing your calculations.
- Explain what your answer means.

A Mrs. Drake is grilling the hamburgers. Some people like big patties, some medium patties, and some small patties.

1. How many $\frac{1}{8}$-pound patties can she make from $\frac{7}{8}$ of a pound of hamburger?

2. How many $\frac{2}{8}$-pound patties can she make from $\frac{7}{8}$ of a pound of hamburger?

3. A teacher brings $2\frac{3}{4}$ pounds of hamburger to make $\frac{1}{4}$-pound patties. How many patties can he make?

B **1.** Sam has $\frac{3}{4}$ of a can of hot chocolate mix for drinks to keep everyone warm. To make a cup of hot chocolate, Sam adds hot water to one scoop of hot chocolate mix. The scoop holds $\frac{1}{24}$ of a can. How many cups of hot chocolate can Sam make?

2. Tom decided not to use the $\frac{1}{24}$ scoop used by Sam. Instead, he uses a scoop that is $\frac{1}{8}$ of a can of hot chocoloate mix. Tom and Sam each start with the same amount, $\frac{3}{4}$ of a can of hot chocolate mix. Who can make more cups of hot chocolate? Explain.

C Describe a strategy for dividing a fraction by a fraction.

A C E Homework starts on page 55.

Notes

3.2 Into Pieces
Whole Numbers or Mixed Numbers Divided by Fractions

Suppose you ask, "How many $\frac{3}{4}$'s are in 14?" You can write this question as a division expression, $14 \div \frac{3}{4}$. Then you can represent it on a number line. Sam starts to use the number line below, but does not know what to do next. What should Sam do?

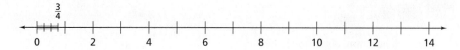

- Can you make a whole number of $\frac{3}{4}$'s out of 14 wholes? If not, what does the fractional part of the answer mean?

- What does it mean to divide a whole number or mixed number by a fraction?

Problem 3.2

For each part of Question A below, do the following.

- Solve the problem.
- Draw a model to help explain your reasoning.
- Write a number sentence that shows your reasoning.

A **1.** Naylah plans to make small cheese pizzas to sell at the school carnival. She has nine blocks of cheese. How many pizzas can she make if each pizza needs the given amount of cheese?

    a. $\frac{1}{3}$ block   **b.** $\frac{1}{4}$ block

    c. $\frac{1}{5}$ block   **d.** $\frac{2}{3}$ block

    e. $\frac{3}{3}$ block   **f.** $\frac{4}{3}$ block

2. The answer to part (d) above is a mixed number. What does the fractional part of the answer mean?

continued on the next page >

Notes _____

_____

_____

Problem **3.2** *continued*

B Use your ideas from Question A to write questions that the following expressions could fit. Then do the calculations. Be sure to label your answers.

1. $12 \div \frac{2}{3}$

2. $12 \div \frac{5}{6}$

3. $12 \div \frac{7}{6}$

4. $12 \div 1\frac{1}{3}$

C **1.** Jasmine has $5\frac{1}{4}$ cups of frosting. She wants to put $\frac{3}{8}$ cup of frosting on each cupcake she makes. About how many cupcakes can she frost?

2. Chris needs $3\frac{1}{2}$ cups of flour. His only clean measuring cup holds $\frac{1}{3}$ cup. How many $\frac{1}{3}$ cups of flour does Chris need?

D Describe a strategy for dividing a whole number or a mixed number by a fraction.

A C E Homework starts on page 55.

Investigation 3   **Dividing With Fractions**   51

Notes _____

3.3 Sharing a Prize
Dividing a Fraction by a Whole Number

At a recent school carnival, teams of students competed in contests. The members of each winning team shared prizes donated by store owners. Sharing the prizes leads to a new kind of division.

- What does it mean to divide a fraction by a whole number?

 Problem 3.3

A Ms. Li gave peanuts as a prize for a relay race. The members of the winning team share the peanuts equally among themselves. What fraction of a pound of peanuts does each team member get in each situation? Use diagrams and number sentences to explain your reasoning.

1. Four students share $\frac{1}{2}$ pound of peanuts.

2. Three students share $\frac{1}{4}$ pound of peanuts.

3. Two students share $\frac{3}{4}$ pound of peanuts.

4. Four students share $1\frac{1}{2}$ pounds of peanuts.

B Find each quotient and explain how you thought about it.

1. $\frac{2}{3} \div 5$

2. $\frac{3}{2} \div 2$

3. $\frac{2}{5} \div 3$

4. $\frac{4}{5} \div 4$

C Write a story problem that can be represented by $\frac{8}{3} \div 4$. Explain why the division makes sense.

D Describe a strategy for dividing a fraction by a whole number.

A C E Homework starts on page 55.

Notes _____

_____

_____

3.4 Examining Algorithms for Dividing Fractions

In Problems 3.1, 3.2, and 3.3, you solved a variety of division problems. In Problem 3.4, you will develop an algorithm to handle all of them. You begin by dividing division problems into categories.

> **?** What is an algorithm you can use to divide any two fractions, including mixed numbers?

Problem 3.4

A For each division expression below, do the following.

- Estimate the quotient.
- Calculate the exact value of the quotient.
- State what the answer to the division expression means.

1. $\frac{1}{3} \div 9$
2. $12 \div \frac{1}{6}$
3. $\frac{5}{6} \div \frac{1}{12}$
4. $5 \div 1\frac{1}{2}$
5. $\frac{1}{2} \div 3\frac{2}{3}$
6. $\frac{3}{4} \div \frac{3}{4}$
7. $5 \div \frac{2}{3}$
8. $\frac{1}{6} \div 12$
9. $3 \div \frac{2}{5}$
10. $3\frac{1}{3} \div \frac{2}{3}$
11. $5\frac{2}{3} \div 1\frac{1}{2}$
12. $\frac{9}{5} \div \frac{1}{2}$

continued on the next page >

Notes _____

Problem 3.4 continued

B **1.** Sort the expressions from Question A into two groups:

- Group 1. Problems that require little work to evaluate.

- Group 2. Problems that require much work to evaluate.

2. Explain why you put each expression into the group you chose.

C Write two new division expressions involving fractions for each of your groups. Explain why each expression goes with one group.

D Write an algorithm for division involving *any* two fractions, including mixed numbers.

E Use your division algorithm to divide.

1. $9 \div \frac{4}{5}$

2. $1\frac{7}{8} \div 3$

3. $1\frac{2}{3} \div \frac{1}{5}$

4. $2\frac{5}{6} \div 1\frac{1}{3}$

F April notices that sometimes a quotient is less than one and sometimes a quotient is greater than one. What is the relationship between the dividend and the divisor in each case?

dividend ÷ divisor = quotient

A C E Homework starts on page 55.

Notes _____

_____

_____

Applications

1. A latte (LAH tay) is the most popular drink at Antonio's Coffee Shop.

Antonio makes only one size of latte, and he uses $\frac{1}{3}$ cup of milk in each drink. How many lattes can Antonio make with the amount of milk in containers (a)–(c)? If there is a remainder, what does it mean?

a. $\frac{7}{9}$ cup

b. $\frac{5}{6}$ cup

c. $3\frac{2}{3}$ cups

2. Write a story problem that can be solved using $1\frac{3}{4} \div \frac{1}{2}$. Explain how the calculation matches your story.

3. The Easy Baking Company makes muffins. They make several sizes, ranging from very small to very large. There are 20 cups of flour in the packages of flour they buy. How many muffins can they make from a package of flour if each muffin takes one of the following amounts of flour?

a. $\frac{1}{4}$ cup

b. $\frac{2}{4}$ cup

c. $\frac{3}{4}$ cup

d. $\frac{1}{10}$ cup

e. $\frac{2}{10}$ cup

f. $\frac{7}{10}$ cup

g. $\frac{1}{7}$ cup

h. $\frac{2}{7}$ cup

i. $\frac{6}{7}$ cup

j. Explain how the answers for $20 \div \frac{1}{7}$, $20 \div \frac{2}{7}$, and $20 \div \frac{6}{7}$ are related. Show why this makes sense.

Notes _____

For Exercises 4–7, find each quotient.

4. $6 \div \frac{3}{5}$ **5.** $5 \div \frac{2}{9}$

6. $3 \div \frac{1}{4}$ **7.** $4 \div \frac{5}{8}$

For Exercises 8–10, find each quotient. Describe any patterns that you see.

8. $5 \div \frac{1}{4}$

9. $5 \div \frac{1}{8}$

10. $5 \div \frac{1}{16}$

For Exercises 11–13, answer the question. Then draw a picture or write a number sentence to show why your answer is correct. If there is a remainder, tell what it means for the given situation.

11. Bill wants to make 22 small pizzas for a party. He has 16 cups of flour. Each pizza crust takes $\frac{3}{4}$ cup of flour. Does he have enough flour?

12. It takes $18\frac{3}{8}$ inches of wood to make a frame for a small photo. Ms. Jones has 3 yards of wood. How many frames can she make?

13. There are 12 rabbits at a pet store. The manager lets Gabriella feed vegetables to the rabbits. She has $5\frac{1}{4}$ ounces of parsley today. She wants to give each rabbit the same amount. How much parsley does each rabbit get?

Notes _____

_____

_____

14. Anoki is in charge of giving prizes to teams at a mathematics competition. With each prize, he also wants to give all the members of the team equal amounts of mints. How much will each team member get if Anoki has the given amounts of mints?

   a. $\frac{1}{2}$ pound of mints for 8 students

   b. $\frac{1}{4}$ pound of mints for 4 students

   c. $\frac{3}{4}$ pound of mints for 3 students

   d. $\frac{4}{5}$ pound of mints for 10 students

   e. $1\frac{1}{2}$ pounds of mints for 2 students

15. Maria uses $5\frac{1}{3}$ gallons of gas to drive to work and back four times.

   a. How many gallons of gas does Maria use in one round trip to work?

   b. Maria's car gets 28 miles to the gallon. How many miles is her round trip to work?

16. Multiple Choice Nana's recipe for applesauce makes $8\frac{1}{2}$ cups. She serves the applesauce equally among her three grandchildren. How many cups of applesauce will each one get?

   A. $\frac{3}{2}$ cups   **B.** $25\frac{1}{2}$ cups

   C. $\frac{9}{6}$ cups   **D.** none of these

STUDENT PAGE

Notes _____

For Exercises 17–19, find each quotient. Draw a picture to prove that each quotient makes sense.

17. $\frac{4}{5} \div 3$

18. $1\frac{2}{3} \div 5$

19. $\frac{5}{3} \div 5$

20. Multiple Choice Which of the following diagrams represents $\frac{1}{3} \div 4$?

A.

B.

C.

D.

21. Multiple Choice Which of the following diagrams represents $4 \div \frac{1}{3}$?

F.

G.

H.

J.

Notes _____

_____

_____

For Exercises 22–25, is each quotient greater than or less than one? Explain your reasoning.

22. $\frac{7}{9} \div \frac{1}{9}$

23. $\frac{2}{3} \div \frac{1}{9}$

24. $\frac{1}{18} \div \frac{1}{9}$

25. $1 \div \frac{1}{9}$

For Exercises 26–34, find the quotient.

26. $\frac{5}{6} \div \frac{1}{3}$ **27.** $\frac{2}{3} \div \frac{1}{9}$ **28.** $1\frac{1}{2} \div \frac{3}{8}$

29. $10 \div \frac{2}{3}$ **30.** $5 \div \frac{3}{4}$ **31.** $\frac{6}{7} \div 4$

32. $\frac{3}{10} \div 2$ **33.** $\frac{2}{5} \div \frac{1}{3}$ **34.** $2\frac{1}{2} \div 1\frac{1}{3}$

35. For Exercises 29 and 31 above, write a story problem to fit the computation.

Connections

For Exercises 36–39, find two equivalent fractions. (For example, $\frac{12}{15}$ and $\frac{24}{30}$ are equivalent fractions.) One fraction should have a numerator greater than the one given. The other fraction should have a numerator less than the one given.

36. $\frac{4}{6}$

37. $\frac{10}{12}$

38. $\frac{12}{9}$

39. $\frac{8}{6}$

Notes

40. Toshi has to work at the car wash for 3 hours. So far, he has worked $1\frac{3}{4}$ hours. How many more hours will it be before he can leave work?

For Exercises 41–44, find each sum or difference.

41. $\frac{9}{10} + \frac{1}{5}$ **42.** $\frac{5}{6} + \frac{7}{8}$

43. $\frac{2}{3} + 1\frac{1}{3}$ **44.** $12\frac{5}{6} - 8\frac{1}{4}$

For Exercises 45–48, find each product.

45. $\frac{2}{7} \times \frac{1}{3}$ **46.** $\frac{3}{4} \times \frac{7}{8}$

47. $1\frac{1}{2} \times \frac{1}{3}$ **48.** $4\frac{2}{3} \times 2\frac{3}{4}$

49. Kendra jogs $2\frac{2}{5}$ km on a trail and then sits down to wait for Louis. Louis has jogged $1\frac{1}{2}$ km on the same trail.

How much farther will Louis have to jog to reach Kendra?

Notes _____

_____

_____

50. The marks on each number line are spaced so that the distance between any two consecutive tick marks is the same. Copy each number line and label the marks.

a.
1.8   2

b.
1   1.1

c.
2.93   2.95

d.
1.99   2.01

e. Explain how you determined what the labels should be.

Use the cartoon below to answer Exercises 51–53.

51. How many slices of the pizza will have olives?

52. How many slices of the pizza will be plain?

53. What fraction of the pizza will have onions and green peppers?

Notes _____

_____

Extensions

54. Dante says there is an easy way to find out how many quarters are in some whole number of dollars. He says you should divide the number of dollars by $\frac{1}{4}$. Vanna says she knows an easier way. You just need to multiply the number of dollars by 4. With whom do you agree? Explain.

Use the table of equivalent measures below to solve Exercises 55–59.

Measurement	Equivalent Measurement
1 cup	16 tablespoons
1 quart	4 cups
1 quart	2 pints
1 gallon	4 quarts
1 tablespoon	3 teaspoons

55. Brian is missing his measuring cup. He needs to measure out $\frac{1}{2}$ cup of vegetable oil. How many tablespoons should he use?

56. To measure out $\frac{1}{2}$ cup of vegetable oil, how many teaspoons does Brian need?

57. What fraction of a quart is $\frac{1}{2}$ cup?

58. What fraction of a gallon is $\frac{1}{2}$ cup?

59. Suppose you need to measure out exactly one gallon of water. The only measuring scoops you have are $\frac{1}{2}$ cup, 1 cup, and 1 pint. Which scoop would you use? How would you make sure you had exactly one gallon?

Notes _____

_____

_____

Mathematical Reflections 3

In this Investigation, you developed strategies for dividing when fractions are involved. You developed algorithms to use for division problems involving fractions or mixed numbers. The following questions will help you summarize what you have learned.

Think about these questions. Discuss your ideas with other students and your teacher. Then write a summary of your findings in your notebook.

1. When solving a problem, **how** do you recognize when division is the operation you need to use?

2. **a. How** is dividing a whole number by a fraction similar to or different from dividing a fraction by a whole number?

   b. Explain your strategy for dividing one fraction by another fraction. Does your strategy also work for divisions where the dividend or divisor is a whole number or a mixed number? Explain.

3. When dividing a whole number by a whole number greater than 1, the quotient is always less than the dividend. For example, $15 \div 3 = 5$, and 5 is less than 15 (the dividend). Use examples to help **explain** the following statement:

   When you divide a fraction by another fraction, your answer might be greater than the dividend or less than the dividend.

Notes

Common Core Mathematical Practices

As you worked on the Problems in this Investigation, you used prior knowledge to make sense of them. You also applied Mathematical Practices to solve the Problems. Think back over your work, the ways you thought about the Problems, and how you used Mathematical Practices.

Hector described his thoughts in the following way:

In Problem 3.4, we solved and sorted all sorts of division problems. Then, we found an algorithm that works for all of them. If you make a mixed number into an improper fraction, you can use the same division algorithm all of the time.

We came up with two algorithms. The first was finding common denominators and then dividing the numerators. The second was multiplying the dividend by the denominator of the divisor. Then divide the result by the numerator of the divisor.

Both algorithms consistently give the correct answer. We looked for patterns. Then we made sure those patterns worked for all division with fractions problems.

Common Core Standards for Mathematical Practice

MP8 Look for and express regularity in repeated reasoning.

• What other Mathematical Practices can you identify in Hector's reasoning?

• Describe a Mathematical Practice that you and your classmates used to solve a different Problem in this Investigation.

Notes _____

_____

_____

Investigation 4

PLANNING

▶ INVESTIGATION
OVERVIEW

GOALS AND
STANDARDS

Wrapping Up the Operations

▼ Investigation Overview

Investigation Description

Investigation 4 concludes *Let's Be Rational*'s exploration of the four arithmetic operations with fractions, first by considering more abstract relationships among the four operations, and second by considering what kinds of contexts lead to each of the operations in order to highlight their structure. Problems 4.1 and 4.2 have students use fact families to express additive and multiplicative relationships among fractional quantities. In doing so, students also work on the ideas of inverse and decomposition, each of which is an important numerical precursor to algebra work. Problem 4.3 presents students with a variety of contextual problems. Students have to sort out for themselves which operations apply in each situation. Being able to recognize which operation is called for in a problem situation strengthens students' understanding of the meaning of each operation.

Investigation Vocabulary

• fact family

Mathematics Background

• Choosing Appropriate Operations
• Multiplication of Rational Numbers
• Developing a Multiplication Algorithm
• Division of Rational Numbers
• Developing a Division Algorithm

Planning Chart

Content	ACE	Pacing	Materials	Resources
Problem 4.1	1–13, 42–43	1 day		**Teaching Aid 4.1** Fact Families for Addition and Subtraction
Problem 4.2	14–22, 29–41, 44–46	1 day		**Teaching Aid 4.2A** Fact Families for Multiplication and Division 1 **Teaching Aid 4.2B** Fact Families for Multiplication and Division 2
Problem 4.3	23–28, 47–56	1 day		
Mathematical Reflections		½ day		
Looking Back		½ day		
Assessment: Self-Assessment		Take Home		
Assessment: Unit Test		1 day		

Goals and Standards

Goals

Fraction Operations Revisit and continue to develop meanings for the four arithmetic operations and skill at using algorithms for each

- Determine when addition, subtraction, multiplication, or division is the appropriate operation to solve a problem

- Develop ways to model sums, differences, products, and quotients with areas, fraction strips, and number lines

- Use knowledge of fractions and equivalence of fractions to develop algorithms for adding, subtracting, multiplying, and dividing fractions

- Write fact families with fractions to show the inverse relationship between addition and subtraction, and between multiplication and division

- Compare and contrast dividing a whole number by a fraction to dividing a fraction by a whole number

- Recognize that when you multiply or divide a fraction, your answer might be less than or more than the numbers you started with

- Solve real-world problems using arithmetic operations on fractions

Variables and Equations Use variables to represent unknown values and equations to represent relationships

- Represent unknown real-world and abstract values with variables

- Write equations (or number sentences) to represent relationships among real-world and abstract values

- Use fact families to solve for unknown values

Mathematical Reflections

Look for evidence of student understanding of the goals for this Investigation in their responses to the questions in *Mathematical Reflections*. The goals addressed by each question are indicated below.

1. How do you decide which operations to use when you are solving a problem?

Goals
- Determine when addition, subtraction, multiplication, or division is the appropriate operation to solve a problem
- Solve real-world problems using arithmetic operations on fractions

2. How is the relationship between addition and subtraction like the relationship between multiplication and division? How is it different?

Goal
- Write fact families with fractions to show the inverse relationship between addition and subtraction, and between multiplication and division

3. In working with fact families, you thought about *decomposing* numbers.

a. What does it mean to decompose a number?

b. How do fact families help you figure out the value for *N* in a sentence such as $N \div 2\frac{1}{2} = 1\frac{1}{4}$?

Goals
- Represent unknown real-world and abstract values with variables
- Write equations (or number sentences) to represent relationships among real-world and abstract values
- Use fact families to solve for unknown values

Standards

Common Core Content Standards

6.EE.A.2 Write, read, and evaluate expressions in which letters stand for numbers. *Problems 1, 2, and 3*

6.EE.A.2a Write expressions that record operations with numbers and with letters standing for numbers. *Problems 1, 2, and 3*

6.EE.A.2b Identify parts of an expression using mathematical terms (sum, term, product, factor, quotient, coefficient); view one or more parts of an expression as a single entity. *Problems 1, 2, and 3*

6.EE.A.2c Evaluate expressions at specific values of their variables. Include expressions that arise from formulas used in real-world problems. Perform arithmetic operations, including those involving whole-number exponents, in the conventional order when there are no parentheses to specify a particular order (Order of Operations). *Problems 1, 2, and 3*

6.EE.B.6 Use variables to represent numbers and write expressions when solving a real-world or mathematical problem; understand that a variable can represent an unknown number, or, depending on the purpose at hand, any number in a specified set. *Problems 1, 2, and 3*

6.EE.B.7 Solve real-world and mathematical problems by writing and solving equations of the form $x + p = q$ and $px = q$ for cases in which p, q and x are all nonnegative rational numbers. *Problems 1, 2, and 3*

Facilitating the Mathematical Practices

Students in *Connected Mathematics* classrooms display evidence of multiple Common Core Standards for Mathematical Practice every day. Here are just a few examples where you might observe students demonstrating the Standards for Mathematical Practice during this Investigation.

Practice 1: **Make sense of problems and persevere in solving them.**

Students are engaged every day in solving problems and, over time, learn to persevere in solving them. To be effective, the problems embody critical concepts and skills and have the potential to engage students in making sense of mathematics. Students build understanding by reflecting, connecting, and communicating. These student-centered problem situations engage students in articulating the "knowns" in a problem situation and determining a logical solution pathway. The student-student and student-teacher dialogues help students to not just make sense of the problems, but also to persevere in finding appropriate strategies to solve them. The suggested questions in the Teacher Guides provide the metacognitive scaffolding to help students monitor and refine their problem-solving strategies.

Practice 2: **Reason abstractly and quantitatively.**

In Problem 4.3, students use quantitative reasoning in deciding which mathematical operation to use in a given situation.

Practice 8: **Use appropriate tools strategically.**

Students use fact families to rewrite equations and solve for variables. In Problem 4.1, they look at patterns of addition and subtraction to discover the relationships of numbers in addition and subtraction problems.

Students identify and record their personal experiences with the Standards for Mathematical Practice during the Mathematical Reflections at the end of the Investigation.

Just the Facts
Fact Families for Addition and Subtraction

▼ Problem Overview

Focus Question How do fact families help you solve equations such as
$\frac{4}{5} - N = \frac{3}{8}$?

Problem Description

In Problem 4.1, students use fact families to solve equations. Fact families involving whole numbers are familiar, and the equivalent rearrangements of whole numbers in a number sentence are intuitive for students.

This is not the case, however, when the sentences involve rational numbers or variables. Students need to develop fluency, based on understanding, in moving between equivalent equations of the form $a + b = c$ and $c - a = b$. Because this is not intuitive for students, a concrete model is offered to illustrate how the addends relate to the sum.

Problem Implementation

Students can work in pairs and then share answers with another pair.

Materials
• **Teaching Aid 4.1:** Addition and Subtraction 1

Vocabulary

• fact family

Mathematics Background

• Choosing Appropriate Operations

At a Glance and Lesson Plan

• At a Glance: Let's Be Rational Problem 4.1
• Lesson Plan: Let's Be Rational Problem 4.1

▼ Launch

Launch Video

You can show this video before Connecting to Prior Knowledge to establish a foundation for fact families with fractions. This entertaining video illustrates the relationships between numbers in a Fact Family set to music. The animation begins with whole numbers to give students a connection to prior knowledge. Characters, representing the numbers 2, 3, and 5, switch positions and change signs to show the four members of this addition-subtraction fact family. Visit Teacher Place at mathdashboard.com/cmp3 to see the complete video.

After showing the video, continue with the Suggested Questions in Connecting to Prior Knowledge.

Connecting to Prior Knowledge

Fact families are used in elementary grades to help students become fluent with number facts. For example, $5 + 2 = 7$, $2 + 5 = 7$, $7 - 2 = 5$, $7 - 5 = 2$ is one family; $5 \times 2 = 10$, $2 \times 5 = 10$, $10 \div 2 = 5$, $10 \div 5 = 2$ is another. Students have also used this idea in solving simple equations, for example, $N + 8 = 10$.

In the first table in the introduction, students see the familiar addition and subtraction fact family for 2, 3, and 5. This is a good place to show the Launch video. It is important that students understand that the sentences are all true because they all represent the same relationship between two addends and a sum.

Suggested Questions

• How are the three additional sentences in a fact family related to the original sentence? (Expect students to say things such as "Subtracting and adding are inverses," or that the operations "undo" each other. Or, "If you subtract one of the addends, you get the other addend.")

• Suppose I asked you to write addition/subtraction sentences with 2,351; 7,223; and 4,872. How do you know which order to put the numbers in? (Expect students to say size is a cue.)

- How do you know which are the addends and which is the sum? (The addends are the quantities that are being combined. The sum is the largest number.)

- How does Ravi's model help you to write number sentences with $25\frac{2}{3}$, N, and 42? (Expect students to talk about "parts, or addends" and the "total, or sum.")

- How do you know that the related sentences in the tables are true? (Expect some students to show that the sentences are true by computing. Push them to explain how the sentences are equivalent to the original sentence; the related sentences in the family are just as true as the original sentence because they express the same relationship between the numbers involved.)

Presenting the Challenge

It is critical that students relate their understanding of the equivalence of these number sentences to the underlying relationship. Memorizing rearrangements is not effective, and relying on the size of the parts (addends and sum) or on computations is not helpful when fractions or symbols are involved.

▼ Explore

Providing for Individual Needs

As you walk around observing students, listen to the ways they justify the position of the numbers and the operations in the sentences they write for Question A. Ask about their methods for finding the value of N in Question B.

Suggested Questions

- In part (1) of Question A, how do you know to write $\frac{5}{10} - N$ and not $N - \frac{5}{10}$?

- In the sentence $\frac{5}{10} - \frac{2}{5} = N$, we can see that $\frac{5}{10}$ is the sum, and $\frac{2}{5}$ and N are the addends. So, the sentence can be rewritten to show that $\frac{5}{10} = \frac{2}{5} + N$, or that subtracting either of the addends from $\frac{5}{10}$ will give the other addend. Thus, $\frac{5}{10} - \frac{2}{5} = N$.

- Suppose you rewrote all the fractions with a common denominator for part (3) of Question B. How does $N - \frac{4}{8} = \frac{3}{8}$ help you find the value of N? ($N - \frac{4}{8} = \frac{3}{8}$ can be rewritten as $N = \frac{4}{8} + \frac{3}{8}$, which is easy to solve.)

- Would it help to rewrite part (2) of Question B as a related sentence first? What would the sentence say? (Yes; $N = \frac{17}{12} - \frac{3}{4}$.)

Going Further

You might ask students who finish early to extend their skills to variations such as the following.

- $\dfrac{N}{8} - \dfrac{1}{8} = \dfrac{3}{8}$
- $2N - \dfrac{4}{8} = \dfrac{3}{8}$
- $\dfrac{N}{4} - \dfrac{1}{2} = \dfrac{3}{8}$

These sentences can be rearranged, using fact families, but a second step is needed to find N. For example, if $\dfrac{N}{4} - \dfrac{1}{2} = \dfrac{3}{8}$, then $\dfrac{N}{4} = \dfrac{3}{8} + \dfrac{1}{2}$, so $\dfrac{N}{4} = \dfrac{7}{8}$. Then equivalent fractions will help to find $2N = 7$, so $N = 3\dfrac{1}{2}$.

Since solutions can be checked by substituting the found value for N, questions like these will keep students thinking. There is no need to ask if they have the right answers.

Planning for the Summary

What evidence will you use in the summary to clarify and deepen understanding of the Focus Question?

What will you do if you do not have evidence?

▼ Summarize

Orchestrating the Discussion

As students finish, you might have them display the answers for Question A and Question B. If errors occur, such as reversing the order of the subtraction, these can be a helpful part of the summary. Some students will rename all fractions with a common denominator in Question B and then find n by inspection. Some will rewrite the sentence first so that n is isolated and then find n. Display these two strategies for Question B side by side to aid in making comparisons.

Suggested Questions

- How do you know that $\dfrac{5}{10} - \dfrac{2}{5} = n$ is the same relationship as $\dfrac{5}{10} - n = \dfrac{2}{5}$ and not $n - \dfrac{5}{10} = \dfrac{2}{5}$ (or whatever the error may be)? (Expect some students to compute n and use this value to show which arrangements are true. Push students to explain how they can justify these rearrangements without first evaluating n. For instance, explain that $\dfrac{5}{10}$ is composed of $\dfrac{2}{5}$ and some other amount. So, if you subtract the $\dfrac{2}{5}$, you will find the rest of the amount needed to make $\dfrac{5}{10}$.)

- Anna rearranged part (3) of Question B as $n = \frac{3}{8} + \frac{1}{2}$ and then found $n = \frac{3}{8} + \frac{4}{8}$. Sara renamed all the fractions with the same denominator and wrote $n - \frac{4}{8} = \frac{3}{8}$. Then she guessed at n. Do these methods give the same answer? How are they related? (Sara's guess will be "What is $\frac{3}{8}$ more than $\frac{4}{8}$?" This is equivalent to the addition in Anna's method.)

Reflecting on Student Learning

Use the following questions to assess student understanding at the end of the lesson.

- What evidence do I have that students understand the Focus Question?
  - Where did my students get stuck?
  - What strategies did they use?
  - What breakthroughs did my students have today?
- How will I use this to plan for tomorrow? For the next time I teach this lesson?
- Where will I have the opportunity to reinforce these ideas as I continue through this Unit? The next Unit?

ACE Assignment Guide

- **Applications:** 1–13
- **Connections:** 42–43

PROBLEM
4.2

Multiplication and Division Fact Families

▼ Problem Overview

> *Focus Question*   How do fact families help you solve equations such as
> $\frac{2}{9} \div N = \frac{2}{3}$?

Problem Description

Students are asked to make fact families for multiplication and division statements and use them to solve equations. This is again familiar to them in the context of multiplication of whole numbers. However, it is much more difficult for students to translate this knowledge into the context of rational numbers than it was for addition and subtraction fact families. This is because when we add whole numbers or positive fractions the sum is always larger than the addends, so there is something concrete about the size comparison to hold on to. In student language, "part of the amount + part of the amount = all of the amount."

This comparison of sizes is not possible for factors and products of fractions. The product of two positive fractions may be smaller than either factor, larger than one factor, or larger than both. This makes the rearrangements of the sentences much harder for students. Students are offered a verbal model to guide them in making rearrangements: (factor 1) × (factor 2) = product. So once the product and factors are identified in the original sentence, these words help to guide rearrangements such as product ÷ (factor 1) = (factor 2).

Problem Implementation

Have students talk with a partner to justify rearrangements of sentences.

Materials

- **Teaching Aid 4.2A:** Fact Families for Multiplication and Division 1
- **Teaching Aid 4.2B:** Fact Families for Multiplication and Division 2

Vocabulary

There are no new glossary terms introduced in this Problem.

Mathematics Background

- Multiplication of Rational Numbers
- Division of Rational Numbers

At a Glance and Lesson Plan

- At a Glance: Let's Be Rational Problem 4.2
- Lesson Plan: Let's Be Rational Problem 4.2

▼ Launch

Connecting to Prior Knowledge

Students are familiar with the concept of fact families of multiplication and division sentences in the domain of whole numbers. As in Problem 4.1, you want them to focus on the relationship between operations (this time multiplication and division) that makes $ab = c$ equivalent to $c \div a = b$.

Trying to memorize rearrangements is not effective, and relying on the size of the numbers, when fractions are involved, is not as helpful a cue as it was with whole numbers. A concrete model will not work for all cases, so a verbal model is offered.

Suggested Questions

- What multiplication sentence relates 53; 11,925; and 225? Can you rearrange this as a division sentence? ($53 \times 225 = 11,925$; $11,925 \div 225 = 53$)

- What multiplication number sentence relates $\frac{1}{2}$, $\frac{3}{4}$, and $\frac{2}{3}$? Why is it harder to figure out how these relate than for whole numbers? ($\frac{1}{2} = \frac{2}{3} \times \frac{3}{4}$. You have to know that when both fraction factors are less than 1 the product will be smaller than either of the factors. If you don't know that, then you spend a lot of time checking different combinations of possible factors before you find one that works.)

- In the true sentence $\frac{1}{2} = \frac{2}{3} \times \frac{3}{4}$, which of the fractions are factors, and which is the product? ($\frac{2}{3}$ and $\frac{3}{4}$ are factors of the product $\frac{1}{2}$.)

- How might you rearrange these factors and product to make a division sentence? ($\frac{1}{2} \div \frac{2}{3} = \frac{3}{4}$)

- Are there other ways to rearrange the original multiplication sentence? ($\frac{1}{2} \div \frac{3}{4} = \frac{2}{3}$ and $\frac{3}{4} \times \frac{2}{3} = \frac{1}{2}$)

- In general, if (factor 1) $\times$ (factor 2) = product, what are some rearrangements of this sentence? (product $\div$ (factor 1) = (factor 2), and so forth)

- How might you rearrange $\frac{2}{3} \times N = \frac{2}{9}$? ($N \times \frac{2}{3} = \frac{2}{9}$, $\frac{2}{9} \div N = \frac{2}{3}$, and $\frac{2}{9} \div \frac{2}{3} = N$.)

Refer students to Example 2 in the table in **Teaching Aid 4.2B: Fact Families for Multiplication and Division 2**.

- Which arrangement is easiest for finding N? ($\frac{2}{9} \div \frac{2}{3} = N$.)

Presting the Challenge

Make sure your students understand that rearranging multiplication and division fact families depends on how multiplication and division are related to each other. Then tell them that they are going to practice writing fact families. They are also going to use this skill to find missing values.

▼ Explore

Providing for Individual Needs

As you walk around listening to your students, ask them to describe their thinking about rearranging the sentences in Question A and Question B. Encourage them to use vocabulary words such as *factor* and *product*. Once the factors have been identified, it is relatively easy to rearrange the sentence. A rearranged sentence can either show factors being multiplied to give a product or show a product being divided by a factor to give another factor.

Suggested Questions

- How can you tell from a sentence such as $\frac{3}{8} \times N = \frac{21}{80}$ which fraction is the product and which is a factor? (The fraction that is a factor is next to the multiplication sign. Factors can appear on both sides of the multiplication sign.)

- How can you tell from a sentence such as $\frac{8}{15} \div N = \frac{2}{3}$ which fraction is the product and which is the factor? (When the sentence is written in this form, the product is before the division sign.)

- Of all the rearrangements of $\frac{8}{15} \div N = \frac{2}{3}$, which is easiest to use to find the answer for N? (the one with N by itself)

Some students will resist doing this rearrangement first, preferring to guess at N, which may help some students make sense of the situation. Also, encourage students to rewrite the equations. They should soon see how straightforward solving becomes once N is isolated. Look for student solutions done both ways so they can be compared in the Summarize.

Planning for the Summary

What evidence will you use in the summary to clarify and deepen understanding of the Focus Question?

What will you do if you do not have evidence?

▼ Summarize

Orchestrating the Discussion

You may want to display student solutions, particularly if common errors, such as mistaking the order of the division, occur. Displaying two different solutions for the same problem helps in making comparisons.

Suggested Questions

- For part (1) of Question B, one student wrote $N = \frac{21}{80} \div \frac{3}{8}$. Another student wrote $N = \frac{3}{8} \div \frac{21}{80}$. Which is correct? (Some students will compute both answers and check which works in the original sentence. Push them to think about which fraction is the product in the original sentence. They do not have to compute the answer for N to know which arrangement is correct.)

- For part (4) of Question B, one student renamed the fractions and wrote $\frac{8}{15} \div N = \frac{10}{15}$. Then she could not guess N. Another student rearranged the sentence first as $\frac{8}{15} \div \frac{2}{3} = N$. Which of these methods can you complete? (The second method is easier, because N appears by itself.)

Check for Understanding

Have students make up a true fraction multiplication sentence and a true fraction division sentence. Then have them replace one of the values with N in each sentence. Finally, have students exchange the two sentences with variables with their partners and find the value of N in each sentence.

Reflecting on Student Learning

Use the following questions to assess student understanding at the end of the lesson.

- What evidence do I have that students understand the Focus Question?
  - Where did my students get stuck?
  - What strategies did they use?
  - What breakthroughs did my students have today?
- How will I use this to plan for tomorrow? For the next time I teach this lesson?
- Where will I have the opportunity to reinforce these ideas as I continue through this Unit? The next Unit?

ACE Assignment Guide

- **Applications:** 14–22
- **Connections:** 29–41, 44–46

▼ Problem Overview

> *Focus Question* How do you know when a particular operation is called for to solve a problem? How do you represent the problem with a number sentence?

Problem Description

Problem 4.3 consolidates all the students' work in *Let's Be Rational*. Students now have strategies for all four operations, and they can relate these operations to each other in a way that permits solving simple equations. All that remains is to continue interpreting real situations in order to recognize which operation is needed to solve a problem.

Problem 4.3 gives practice in the computational skills acquired in *Let's Be Rational* and in the number sense needed to apply those operations appropriately. The Distributive Property appears in some examples, a reminder that this property applies to fractions as well as to whole numbers.

Problem Implementation

Have students think individually about which operation is called for in each problem and write their number sentences. Then have them share their ideas with a partner or a small group.

Vocabulary

There are no new glossary terms introduced in this Problem.

Mathematics Background

- Choosing Appropriate Operations
- Multiplication of Rational Numbers
- Division of Rational Numbers

At a Glance and Lesson Plan

- At a Glance: Let's Be Rational Problem 4.3
- Lesson Plan: Let's Be Rational Problem 4.3

▼ Launch

Launch Video

You may want to show this video before Connecting to Prior Knowledge to help start the discussion on when to use certain operations. This Launch video shows a detective working through a problem situation. The detective is given certain information and has to figure out which operation he should use in order to solve a mystery. You can use this video to model how students might reason through a problem in order to decide upon an operation. Visit Teacher Place at mathdashboard.com/cmp3 to see the complete video.

After showing the video, ask which operation should be used to solve the situation in the video. Then continue with Connecting to Prior Knowledge.

Connecting to Prior Knowledge

The questions in the introduction are all about whole numbers, so students will be familiar with the relationships that signal different operations.

Before reading the questions in the Student Edition, you can show the Launch video. Give students time to look at each question and then ask the following.

Suggested Questions

- How do you know when a situation calls for addition? For subtraction? For multiplication? For division? (Addition means increasing by an amount, and subtraction means decreasing by an amount. Multiplication is about adding a number of equal size groups. Division means sharing or grouping.)

- What number sentences would describe these situations? ($389 - 29 = n$, $15 + 10 = n$, $360 \div 30 = n$, and $30 \times 50 = n$)

- How might you rearrange these number sentences to keep the same relationships among the quantities? (Each number sentence can be made into three equivalent number sentences that are members of its fact family.)

Presenting the Challenge

Tell your students that they now know how to do all four operations with fractions, and they know how to rearrange number sentences to make them easier to solve for N. All that is left to do is to decide which operation is called for to solve a problem.

▼ Explore

Providing for Individual Needs

If you observe a student struggling to decide on the appropriate operation, you might suggest changing the numbers into easy whole numbers, or trying a drawing. When students are sharing their ideas, push them to clarify their explanations of how they know which operation is needed. If you see different correct solutions (Question G lends itself to two solutions) you can display them in the Summarize.

Suggested Questions

- Would replacing fractions with whole numbers help you see which operation makes sense? (Yes; whole numbers are easier to think about.)

- Would a drawing help you see which operation to use? (Yes; it's easier to think about something you can see.)

- In Question H, what does $1\frac{5}{8} + N$ mean? What does $3N$ mean? What does $10 \div 1\frac{5}{8}$ mean? ($1\frac{5}{8} + N$ is the number of yards of fabric grandmother needs for each child. $3N$ is the number of yards for the three extra items. $10 \div 1\frac{5}{8}$ is the number of jackets she could make from 10 yards of fabric, which is not something she needs to know.)

Going Further

Find the answer to the grandmother's problem in Question H. How much fabric does she have for each one of the extra items?

Planning for the Summary

What evidence will you use in the summary to clarify and deepen understanding of the Focus Question?

What will you do if you do not have evidence?

Summarize

Orchestrating the Discussion

Display student solutions where there are different correct solutions to compare, for example in Question G. Most students will use efficient algorithms to compute in Question A, but a few may have drawn diagrams to clarify which algorithm to choose. Sharing these diagrams will be helpful. If there is a difference of opinion about Question H, have students justify their answers.

Suggested Questions

- Anna thought $10 \div 1\frac{5}{8} = N$ in Question H would give the amount of fabric for each extra item. What does $10 \div 1\frac{5}{8}$ mean in terms of this problem? Is this the same as N? (How many jackets you can cut from 10 yards of material. N does not represent this.)

- Sara thought that $3 \times 1\frac{5}{8} + N = 10$ in Question H would give the amount of fabric for each item. If you rearrange this sentence you get $N = 10 - 3 \times 1\frac{5}{8}$. What would $10 - 3 \times 1\frac{5}{8}$ mean in terms of this problem? (It would give what is left after the three jackets are cut from 10 yards, which is not what N represents.)

Finally, have students share ideas about how they recognized which operations are called for in a problem.

Reflecting on Student Learning

Use the following questions to assess student understanding at the end of the lesson.

- What evidence do I have that students understand the Focus Question?
  - Where did my students get stuck?
  - What strategies did they use?
  - What breakthroughs did my students have today?
- How will I use this to plan for tomorrow? For the next time I teach this lesson?
- Where will I have the opportunity to reinforce these ideas as I continue through this Unit? The next Unit?

ACE Assignment Guide

- **Applications:** 23–28
- **Extensions:** 47–56

▼ Mathematical Reflections

Possible Answers to Mathematical Reflections

1. Addition and subtraction relate to joining and separating parts and wholes. They are also useful for thinking about comparisons when you want to know how many more than another one quantity is. Multiplication and division relate to grouping, and are useful for thinking about comparisons when you want to how many times more than another one quantity is.

2. If you know an addition sentence, you can find two related subtraction sentences in the same fact family. Similarly if you know a multiplication sentence, you can find two related division sentences in the same fact family. Subtraction helps solve addition equations such as $5 + n = 12$, while division helps solve multiplication equations such as $5 \times n = 12$.

One difference is that you cannot divide by zero, so the multiplication equation $5 \times 0 = 0$ is missing one division fact; there is no solution to $0 \div 0$.

3. a. Decomposing means to take apart. You can decompose using multiplication: $15 = 3 \times 5$, or you can decompose using addition: $15 = 10 + 5$. Each of these ways of decomposing is useful for different purposes.

b. Fact families are related sentences that are all true because they all show the same relationship between parts of a quantity. The two parts of a quantity might be addends, $a + b = N$, or they might be factors, $xy = N$. Rearrangements of these sentences will be equally true, for example $N - a = b$ and $N \div x = y$. In the example given, $N \div 2\frac{1}{2} = 1\frac{1}{4}$, so $2\frac{1}{2}$ and $1\frac{1}{4}$ are factors of N. One of the related sentences is $N = 2\frac{1}{2} \times 1\frac{1}{4} = 3\frac{1}{8}$.

Possible Answers to Mathematical Practices Reflections

Students may have demonstrated all of the eight Common Core Standards for Mathematical Practice during this Investigation. During the class discussion, have students identify their use of as many different examples of the Mathematical Practices as they can.

One student observation is provided in the Student Edition. Here is another sample student response.

In Problem 4.1, we looked at patterns of addition and subtraction in the fact families to see the relationship between the numbers in addition and subtractions problems. Then we used these relationships to rewrite equations that had variables in them to find the value of the variable.

MP8: Look for and express regularity in repeated reasoning

Wrapping Up the Operations

4.1 Just the Facts
Fact Families for Addition and Subtraction

In Investigation 1, you wrote addition and subtraction sentences to show calculations you did. For each addition sentence you write, there are related number sentences that show the same information. These sets of number sentences form a related set of facts called a *fact family*.

- How could you write a number sentence showing a relationship among 7, 2, and 9?

- Is there more than one correct number sentence?

Below are two fact families. The family on the left has all values included. The family on the right has a missing value.

	Example 1	Example 2
Addition Sentence	$2 + 3 = 5$	$2 + n = 5$
Related Number Sentences	$3 + 2 = 5$ $5 - 3 = 2$ $5 - 2 = 3$	$n + 2 = 5$ $5 - n = 2$ $5 - 2 = n$

- How are the three additional sentences related to the original sentence?

Common Core State Standards

6.EE.A.2 Write, read, and evaluate expressions in which letters stand for numbers.

6.EE.B.6 Use variables to represent numbers and write expressions when solving a real-world or mathematical problem; understand that a variable can represent an unknown number . . .

6.EE.B.7 Solve real-world and mathematical problems by writing and solving equations of the form $x + p = q$ and $px = q$ for cases in which p, q and x are all nonnegative rational numbers.

Investigation 4   **Wrapping Up the Operations**   65

Notes _____

_____

_____

You can also create fact families with fractions.

- What number sentences can you write showing a relationship among $\frac{1}{2}$, $\frac{1}{4}$, and $\frac{3}{4}$?

Ravi says that when he is thinking about fact families, he thinks about a picture like a section in Tupelo Township. The parts of the large rectangle represent the *addends*. The entire large rectangle represents the total acreage, or the *sum*.

- The total area of the rectangle below is 42 acres. What number sentence does this model represent?

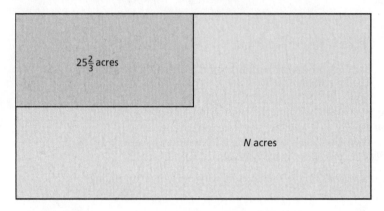

- What are some other ways of writing the relationship between $25\frac{2}{3}$, N, and 42 acres?

The model shows that any sum can be broken down, *or decomposed*, into two (or more) parts. The parts are the addends. In Ravi's model, the total acreage, the sum, is 42 acres. The parts, N acres and $25\frac{2}{3}$ acres, are the addends.

Notes _____

_____

_____

Below are two fact families expressing relationships among fractions.

	Example 1	Example 2
Addition Sentence	$\frac{3}{4} + \frac{1}{8} = \frac{7}{8}$	$\frac{6}{8} + N = \frac{7}{8}$
Related Number Sentences	$\frac{1}{8} + \frac{3}{4} = \frac{7}{8}$	$N + \frac{6}{8} = \frac{7}{8}$
	$\frac{7}{8} - \frac{3}{4} = \frac{1}{8}$	$\frac{7}{8} - \frac{6}{8} = N$
	$\frac{7}{8} - \frac{1}{8} = \frac{3}{4}$	$\frac{7}{8} - N = \frac{6}{8}$

- How are these fact families different from each other?

- How do you know that the three related sentences below the top row are true?

In Problem 4.1 you will create fact families and use them to find unknown numbers.

Problem 4.1

A For each number sentence, write a complete fact family and find the value of N.

1. $\frac{5}{10} - \frac{2}{5} = N$

2. $3\frac{3}{5} + 1\frac{2}{3} = N$

3. Describe the relationship between addition and subtraction. Use the fact families in parts (1) and (2) as examples.

B For each number sentence, find the value of N.

1. $N + 1\frac{2}{3} = 5\frac{5}{6}$

2. $\frac{3}{4} + N = \frac{17}{12}$

3. $N - \frac{1}{2} = \frac{3}{8}$

4. How can fact families help you find the value of N in parts (1)–(3)?

A C E Homework starts on page 73.

Notes

4.2 Multiplication and Division Fact Families

In Problem 4.1 you wrote fact families made up of related addition and subtraction sentences. You can also use fact families to show relationships between multiplication and division.

	Example 1	Example 2
Multiplication Sentence	$4 \times 5 = 20$	$17 \times N = 51$
Related Number Sentences	$5 \times 4 = 20$ $20 \div 5 = 4$ $20 \div 4 = 5$	$N \times 17 = 51$ $51 \div N = 17$ $51 \div 17 = N$

In Problem 4.1, you saw Ravi's rectangular model for adding area. For multiplication, Ravi uses words instead of a model to help him decide on the correct rearrangements. Any multiplication sentence, whether involving fractions or whole numbers, can be written in the form below.

$$(\text{factor 1}) \times (\text{factor 2}) = \text{product}$$

- How might you rearrange the sentence above but still keep the same relationship between factor 1, factor 2, and the product?

- How might you rearrange the sentence $\frac{2}{3} \times N = \frac{1}{2}$ to complete the following table?

	Example 1	Example 2
Multiplication Sentence	$\frac{1}{2} \times \frac{1}{3} = \frac{1}{6}$	$\frac{2}{3} \times N = \frac{1}{2}$
Related Number Sentences	$\frac{1}{3} \times \frac{1}{2} = \frac{1}{6}$ $\frac{1}{6} \div \frac{1}{3} = \frac{1}{2}$ $\frac{1}{6} \div \frac{1}{2} = \frac{1}{3}$	

- In Example 2 in the table above, which rearrangement is most helpful for finding the value of N?

Notes _____

_____

_____

Problem 4.2

Now it is your turn to write fact families.

A Write a complete fact family for each of the following sentences.

1. $\frac{2}{3} \times \frac{1}{5} = \frac{2}{15}$
2. $\frac{3}{4} \times \frac{5}{8} = \frac{15}{32}$
3. $\frac{9}{40} \div \frac{3}{5} = \frac{3}{8}$
4. $\frac{4}{15} \div \frac{2}{5} = \frac{2}{3}$

B Write a complete fact family for each of the following equations. Use your fact family to find the value of N.

1. $\frac{3}{8} \times N = \frac{21}{80}$
2. $\frac{2}{3} \times N = \frac{10}{15}$
3. $1 \div N = \frac{2}{3}$
4. $\frac{8}{15} \div N = \frac{2}{3}$

C Marla says she can use the idea of *decomposing* a product to find the unknown factor, N, in $15 = 2 \times N$. She rearranges this multiplication sentence as the division sentence $15 \div 2 = N$. Does Marla's strategy work? Explain why or why not.

D Below are sets of three numbers. Some of these sets can be related using addition and subtraction. Some can be related using multiplication and division. For each set, identify what the relation is. Then write a complete fact family.

1. $\frac{3}{5}, \frac{1}{3}, \frac{14}{15}$
2. $\frac{3}{4}, \frac{4}{3}, 1$
3. $1\frac{1}{2}, 2\frac{2}{3}, 4\frac{1}{6}$
4. $\frac{3}{2}, 3, \frac{9}{2}$

A C E Homework starts on page 73.

STUDENT PAGE

Notes

4.3 Becoming an Operations Sleuth

In *Let's Be Rational* you have revisited and deepened your skills with the operations addition, subtraction, multiplication, and division. In the real world, problems do not come with labels saying *add, subtract, multiply,* or *divide*. You need to use your mathematics knowledge to identify which operation will be helpful to solve a problem.

Think about the operations you would use in the following situations.

The sixth-grade class is taking a field trip to the state capital. There are 389 students in the sixth grade, but 29 did not get the permission slip signed by their parents. The principal needs to know how many sixth-grade students have permission to go on the field trip.

A varsity softball team has 15 players. The junior varsity team has 10 players. The fan club is buying the teams new uniforms. The fan club wants to know how many uniforms they need to buy.

There are 360 students going on a field trip. Each school bus carries 30 students. The school office needs to know how many buses to send.

The school auditorium has 30 rows of 50 seats each. You want to find out how many seats are in the auditorium.

- Which situations require you to add? Which require you to subtract?
- Which require you to multiply? Which require you to divide?
- How do you know?

In Problem 4.3 you will examine situations that require computations with fractions. In each case your first task is to determine what operations will help you solve the problem.

Notes _____

_____

_____

Problem 4.3

For each of the Questions below, do the following.

- Decide which operation you need to find an answer. Explain how you identified the operation.

- When you use more than one operation, explain the order in which you use them.

- Write the number sentence(s) you use.

- Find the answer.

A Sammy the turtle can walk $\frac{1}{8}$ of a mile in an hour. How many hours will it take him to walk $1\frac{1}{4}$ miles?

B Jimarcus plans to build a fence $5\frac{1}{3}$ yards long at the back of his garden. How many $\frac{2}{3}$-yard sections of fence will he need?

C Sasha bought $3\frac{1}{2}$ pints of blueberries to make jelly. She ate $\frac{3}{4}$ of a pint of berries on her way home. How many pints of berries does she have left to make jelly?

D Judi uses $2\frac{3}{4}$ pounds of potatoes every week. How many pounds of potatoes does she use in $3\frac{1}{2}$ weeks?

continued on the next page >

Investigation 4 **Wrapping Up the Operations**   71

Notes

Problem 4.3 *continued*

E At a bake sale, Leslie sold $2\frac{1}{2}$ dozen sweet rolls. Christie sold sweet rolls but did not keep track of what she sold. She started with 5 dozen sweet rolls and had $1\frac{2}{3}$ dozen left at the end of the sale. Who sold more sweet rolls? How many more did she sell?

F Raymar ate $\frac{1}{4}$ of a pan of brownies. His brother Kalen ate $\frac{1}{4}$ of the rest of the pan of brownies. What part of the whole pan did Kalen eat?

G Mrs. Larnell is making snack packs for a class picnic. She puts $\frac{1}{4}$ pound of apples, $\frac{1}{8}$ pound of nut mix, and $\frac{1}{16}$ pound of chocolate in each student's pack. There are 24 students in the class. What is the total weight of the snack packs? Is there more than one way to solve this problem?

H A grandmother is making clothes for her three granddaughters. She will make a jacket and one other item for each granddaughter. The three other items will be exactly the same. A jacket takes $1\frac{5}{8}$ yards of fabric. She has ten yards of material in all. She is trying to figure out how much fabric she has for each of the three extra items.

Let N represent the fabric needed for one extra item. Explain why each of the sentences below does or does not describe the situation. (More than one sentence may apply.)

1. $3\left(1\frac{5}{8} + N\right) = 10$ **2.** $10 - 4\frac{7}{8} = 3N$

3. $3 \times 1\frac{5}{8} + N = 10$ **4.** $10 \div 1\frac{5}{8} = N$

A C E Homework starts on page 73.

Notes _____

_____

_____

 ## Applications

For each of Exercises 1–4, write a complete fact family.

1. $\frac{1}{16} + \frac{1}{12} = N$

2. $\frac{5}{4} - \frac{4}{5} = N$

3. $N - 1\frac{1}{3} = 2\frac{2}{3}$

4. $N + \frac{4}{3} = \frac{1}{3}$

For Exercises 5–10, find the value for N that makes each number sentence true.

5. $\frac{2}{3} + \frac{3}{4} = N$

6. $\frac{3}{4} + N = \frac{4}{5}$

7. $N - \frac{3}{5} = \frac{1}{4}$

8. $\frac{2}{2} - \frac{2}{4} = N$

9. $\frac{3}{8} - N = \frac{1}{4}$

10. $\frac{3}{4} + N = \frac{5}{8}$

11. Find the value for m that makes this number sentence true:
$\frac{1}{2} + \frac{9}{10} + m = 2$.

12. Find values for m and n that make this number sentence true:
$\frac{1}{2} + \frac{9}{10} + m + n = 2$.

13. Find the value for m that makes this number sentence true:
$\frac{1}{2} + \frac{9}{10} = 2 - m$.

For Exercises 14 and 15, write a complete multiplication and division fact family for the operation given.

14. $\frac{2}{3} \times \frac{5}{7} = \frac{10}{21}$

15. $\frac{3}{4} \div 1\frac{1}{2} = \frac{1}{2}$

Notes _____

Solve Exercises 16–21.

16. $N \times \frac{1}{5} = \frac{2}{15}$

17. $N \div \frac{1}{5} = \frac{2}{3}$

18. $\frac{1}{2} \times N = \frac{1}{3}$

19. $\frac{1}{5} \div N = \frac{1}{3}$

20. $1\frac{3}{4} \div N = \frac{1}{4}$

21. $2\frac{2}{3} \div N = 8$

22. Find the value for m that makes each number sentence true.

a. $\frac{2}{3} \times \frac{4}{5} \times m = \frac{1}{3}$

b. $\frac{4}{5} \times \frac{2}{3} \times m = \frac{1}{3}$

c. $\frac{2}{3} \times \frac{4}{5} = \frac{1}{3} \div m$

23. Gregory is building a pen for his new puppy. He needs the pen to be $9\frac{1}{2}$ feet by $6\frac{3}{4}$ feet. How many feet of fencing does he need?

24. Sam goes to the market to buy hamburger for a cookout. He buys $3\frac{3}{4}$ pounds of hamburger. How many $\frac{1}{4}$-pound patties can he make?

25. **a.** Kalisha made two dozen large buns. She ate $\frac{1}{2}$ of a bun and gave her mother and father one each. How many buns does she have left?

b. She is going to cut the remaining buns into thirds for a party. How many $\frac{1}{3}$-size buns will she have?

26. Eun Mi raked $\frac{1}{3}$ of her mother's lawn. Her brother, Yeping, raked $\frac{1}{3}$ of the rest of the lawn. What part of the whole lawn still needs raking?

27. Monday through Friday a grocery store buys $\frac{2}{3}$ bushel of apples per day from a local grower. Saturday the grocer buys $1\frac{1}{3}$ bushels of apples. If the grocer buys apples for four weeks, how many bushels of apples does he buy?

28. Kalin walks at a steady rate of $3\frac{2}{3}$ miles per hour. The beach is $4\frac{1}{4}$ miles from his home. How long will it take Kalin to walk from his home to the beach and back to his home?

Notes _____

_____

_____

Connections

29. **a.** Find the value for N that makes this number sentence true:
$$\left(\tfrac{1}{4} + \tfrac{1}{3}\right)N = \tfrac{1}{2}.$$

   b. Find the value for N that makes this number sentence true:
$$\tfrac{1}{4} + \tfrac{1}{3}N = \tfrac{1}{2}.$$

   c. Why are the correct answers for part (a) and part (b) different from each other?

For Exercises 30–38, find each missing number.

30. $2 \times \blacksquare = 1$

31. $\tfrac{1}{2} \times \blacksquare = 1$

32. $3 \times \blacksquare = 1$

33. $\tfrac{1}{3} \times \blacksquare = 1$

34. $\blacksquare \times \tfrac{2}{3} = 1$

35. $\tfrac{3}{4} \times \blacksquare = 1$

36. $\blacksquare \times \tfrac{5}{2} = 1$

37. $1\tfrac{1}{4} \times \blacksquare = 1$

38. $\tfrac{7}{12} \times \blacksquare = 1$

For Exercises 39–41, find the missing numbers in each pair of number sentences. What is the relationship between each pair of numbers?

39. $3 \div \blacksquare = 9$

    $3 \times \blacksquare = 9$

40. $3 \div \blacksquare = 12$

    $3 \times \blacksquare = 12$

41. $2\tfrac{1}{2} \div \blacksquare = 5$

    $2\tfrac{1}{2} \times \blacksquare = 5$

For Exercises 42–43, estimate which sum or difference is greater. Then compute the answers to compare with your estimates. Show your work.

42. $\tfrac{1}{8} + \tfrac{5}{6}$ or $\tfrac{1}{6} + \tfrac{5}{8}$

43. $\tfrac{5}{6} - \tfrac{1}{8}$ or $\tfrac{5}{8} - \tfrac{1}{6}$

44. Find the value for N that makes this number sentence true:
$$3 \times \left(N + \tfrac{1}{3}\right) = 2$$

45. Find the value for N that makes this number sentence true:
$$\left(N + \tfrac{1}{2}\right) \times 1\tfrac{1}{2} = 2\tfrac{1}{4}$$

46. In the number sentence below, find values for m and n that make the sum exactly 3.
$$\tfrac{5}{8} + \tfrac{1}{4} + \tfrac{2}{3} + m + n = 3$$

Investigation 4   Wrapping Up the Operations   **75**

Notes _____

Extensions

For Exercises 47–50, find the value of N that makes each number sentence true.

47. $\frac{1}{2} + N = \frac{1}{2}$

48. $\frac{1}{2} - N = \frac{1}{2}$

49. $\frac{1}{2} \times N = \frac{1}{2}$

50. $\frac{1}{2} \div N = \frac{1}{2}$

51. Mathematicians call the number 0 the *additive identity*. They call the number 1 the *multiplicative identity*. Based on your work in Exercises 47–50, what do you think *identity* means?

For Exercises 52–55, find the value of N that makes each number sentence true.

52. $\frac{1}{2} + N = 0$

53. $\frac{2}{3} + N = 0$

54. $\frac{1}{2} \times N = 1$

55. $\frac{2}{3} \times N = 1$

56. Mathematicians have a special name for each value of N you found in Exercises 52–55. Each N is the additive or multiplicative *inverse* of the number you started with.

- An *additive inverse* is the number you add to another number to get 0.

- A *multiplicative inverse* is the number you multiply by another number to get 1.

    a. Does every number have an additive inverse?

    b. Does every number have a multiplicative inverse?

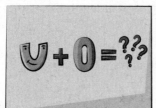
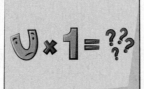

Notes _____

_____

_____

Mathematical Reflections 4

In this Investigation, you explored relationships among addition, subtraction, multiplication and division. The following questions will help you summarize what you have learned.

Think about these questions. Discuss your ideas with other students and your teacher. Then write a summary of your findings in your notebook.

1. **How** do you decide which operation to use when you are solving a problem?

2. **How** is the relationship between addition and subtraction like the relationship between multiplication and division? **How** is it different?

3. While working with fact families, you thought about *decomposing* numbers.

   a. **What** does it mean to decompose a number?

   b. **How** do fact families help you figure out the value for *N* in a sentence such as $N \div 2\frac{1}{2} = 1\frac{1}{4}$?

Notes _____

_____

_____

Common Core Mathematical Practices

As you worked on the Problems in this Investigation, you used prior knowledge to make sense of them. You also applied Mathematical Practices to solve the Problems. Think back over your work, the ways you thought about the Problems, and how you used Mathematical Practices.

Tori described her thoughts in the following way:

In Problem 4.3, we had to figure out whether to add, subtract, multiply, or divide. Sometimes we used a combination of operations. We had to read each problem really carefully.

Sometimes we drew a picture to represent what the problem was asking. This helped us figure out which operation to use. For example, if the problem called for combining quantities, we used addition.

This was a good way to end because in real life, you don't get told which operation to use. You need to figure it out.

Common Core Standards for Mathematical Practice
MP2 Reason abstractly and quantitatively.

- What other Mathematical Practices can you identify in Tori's reasoning?

- Describe a Mathematical Practice that you and your classmates used to solve a different Problem in this Investigation.

Notes _____

_____

_____

During this Unit, you developed strategies for estimating and computing with fractions and mixed numbers. You learned how to determine which situations call for which operations when working with fractions and mixed numbers. You developed algorithms for adding, subtracting, multiplying, and dividing fractions. You learned how to solve problems with fractions. Use what you have learned to solve the following examples.

Use Your Understanding: Fraction Operations

1. The Scoop Shop sells many types of nuts. Lily asks for this mix:
   - $\frac{1}{2}$ pound peanuts
   - $\frac{1}{6}$ pound hazelnuts
   - $\frac{1}{3}$ pound almonds
   - $\frac{3}{4}$ pound cashews
   - $\frac{1}{4}$ pound pecans

   a. Mixed nuts cost $5.00 per pound. What is Lily's bill?

   b. What fraction of the mix does each type of nut represent?

   c. Diego does not like cashews, so he asks for Lily's mix without the cashews. What is Diego's bill?

   d. Taisha is making small bowls of nuts for a party. Each bowl can hold $\frac{1}{4}$ cup of nuts. Taisha has $3\frac{3}{8}$ cups of nuts. How many full bowls can she make?

Notes

2. Shaquille likes dried fruit. He wants a mix of peaches, cherries, pineapple chunks, and apple rings. The following chart shows how much The Scoop Shop has of each fruit. It also shows how much of each fruit Shaquille buys.

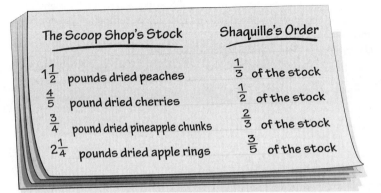

The Scoop Shop's Stock

$1\frac{1}{2}$ pounds dried peaches

$\frac{4}{5}$ pound dried cherries

$\frac{3}{4}$ pound dried pineapple chunks

$2\frac{1}{4}$ pounds dried apple rings

Shaquille's Order

$\frac{1}{3}$ of the stock

$\frac{1}{2}$ of the stock

$\frac{2}{3}$ of the stock

$\frac{3}{5}$ of the stock

a. How many pounds of dried fruit does Shaquille buy?

b. Dried fruit costs $6.00 per pound. What is Shaquille's bill?

Explain Your Reasoning

When you solve a problem or make a decision, it is important to be able to support each step of your reasoning.

3. What operations did you use to calculate Lily's bill?

4. How did you find the fraction of Lily's mix that each type of nut represented?

5. Jacob says that $4 \div \frac{1}{3} = 12$ and $4 \div \frac{2}{3} = 6$. Why is the answer in the second number sentence half of the answer in the first number sentence?

6. Use the following problems to show the steps involved in the algorithms for each operation on fractions. Be prepared to explain your reasoning.

   a. $\frac{5}{6} + \frac{1}{4}$ **b.** $\frac{3}{4} - \frac{2}{3}$ **c.** $\frac{2}{5} \times \frac{3}{8}$ **d.** $\frac{3}{8} \div \frac{3}{4}$

Notes

A   **algorithm** A set of rules for performing a procedure. Mathematicians invent algorithms that are useful in many kinds of situations. Some examples of algorithms are the rules for long division or the rules for adding two fractions.

To add two fractions, first change them to equivalent fractions with the same denominator. Then add the numerators and put the sum over the common denominator.

algoritmo Un conjunto de reglas para realizar un procedimiento. Los matemáticos inventan algoritmos que son útiles en muchos tipos de situaciones. Algunos ejemplos de algoritmos son las reglas para una división larga o las reglas para sumar dos fracciones. El siguiente es un algoritmo escrito por un estudiante de un grado intermedio.

Para sumar dos fracciones, primero transfórmalas en fracciones equivalentes con el mismo denominador. Luego suma los numeradores y coloca la suma sobre el denominador común.

B   **benchmark** A reference number that can be used to estimate the size of other numbers. For work with fractions, 0, $\frac{1}{2}$, and 1 are good benchmarks. We often estimate fractions or decimals with benchmarks because it is easier to do arithmetic with them, and estimates often give enough accuracy for the situation. For example, many fractions and decimals—such as $\frac{37}{50}$, $\frac{5}{8}$, 0.43, and 0.55—can be thought of as being close to $\frac{1}{2}$. You might say $\frac{5}{8}$ is between $\frac{1}{2}$ and 1 but closer to $\frac{1}{2}$, so you can estimate $\frac{5}{8}$ to be about $\frac{1}{2}$. We also use benchmarks to help compare fractions and decimals. For example, we could say that $\frac{5}{8}$ is greater than 0.43 because $\frac{5}{8}$ is greater than $\frac{1}{2}$ and 0.43 is less than $\frac{1}{2}$.

punto de referencia Un número "bueno" que se puede usar para estimar el tamaño de otros números. Para trabajar con fracciones, 0, $\frac{1}{2}$ y 1 son buenos puntos de referencia. Por lo general estimamos fracciones o decimales con puntos de referencia porque nos resulta más fácil hacer cálculos aritméticos con ellos, y las estimaciones suelen ser bastante exactas para la situación. Por ejemplo, muchas fracciones y decimales, como por ejemplo $\frac{37}{50}$, $\frac{5}{8}$, 0.43 y 0.55, se pueden considerar como cercanos a $\frac{1}{2}$. Se podría decir que $\frac{5}{8}$ está entre $\frac{1}{2}$ y 1, pero más cerca de $\frac{1}{2}$, por lo que se puede estimar que $\frac{5}{8}$ es alrededor de $\frac{1}{2}$. También usamos puntos de referencia para ayudarnos a comparar fracciones. Por ejemplo, podríamos decir que $\frac{5}{8}$ es mayor que 0.43, porque $\frac{5}{8}$ es mayor que $\frac{1}{2}$ y 0.43 es menor que $\frac{1}{2}$.

Notes

E **equivalent fractions** Fractions that are equal in value, but may have different numerators and denominators. For example, $\frac{2}{3}$ and $\frac{14}{21}$ are equivalent fractions. The shaded part of this rectangle represents both $\frac{2}{3}$ and $\frac{14}{21}$.

fracciones equivalentes Fracciones de igual valor, que pueden tener diferentes numeradores y denominadores. Por ejemplo, $\frac{2}{3}$ y $\frac{14}{21}$ son fracciones equivalentes. La parte sombreada de este rectángulo representa tanto $\frac{2}{3}$ como $\frac{14}{21}$.

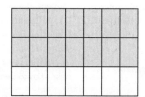

explain Academic Vocabulary To give facts and details that make an idea easier to understand. Explaining can involve a written summary supported by a diagram, chart, table, or a combination of these.

related terms *analyze, clarify, describe, justify, tell*

Sample Explain why the answer to $12 \div \frac{3}{4}$ is equal to one third of the answer to $12 \div \frac{1}{4}$.

Because $\frac{3}{4} = 3 \times \frac{1}{4}$, it takes three $\frac{1}{4}$s to make every $\frac{3}{4}$. There are forty-eight $\frac{1}{4}$s in 12, but there are only sixteen $\frac{3}{4}$s in 12.

explicar Vocabulario académico Dar datos y detalles que hacen que una idea sea más fácil de comprender. Explicar puede incluir un resumen escrito apoyado por un diagrama, una gráfica, una tabla o una combinación de éstos.

términos relacionados *analizar, aclarar, describir, justificar, decir*

Ejemplo Explica por qué el resultado de $12 \div \frac{3}{4}$ es igual a un tercio del resultado de $12 \div \frac{1}{4}$.

Porque $\frac{3}{4} = 3 \times \frac{1}{4}$, se requieren tres $\frac{1}{4}$ para formar cada $\frac{3}{4}$. Hay cuarenta y ocho $\frac{1}{4}$ en 12, pero sólo hay dieciséis $\frac{3}{4}$ en 12.

Notes _____

_____

_____

F   **fact family** A set of related addition–subtraction sentences or multiplication–division sentences. For example, the set of numbers, 3, 5, and 15, is part of this multiplication–division fact family:

$$3 \times 5 = 15 \qquad\qquad 5 \times 3 = 15$$
$$15 \div 5 = 3 \qquad\qquad 15 \div 3 = 5$$

If you have one fact from a family, you can use the addition–subtraction or multiplication–division relationship to write the three related facts that are also part of the family. For example, with $2 + 3 = 5$, you can use the relationship between addition and subtraction to write the related number sentences $3 + 2 = 5$, $5 - 3 = 2$, and $5 - 2 = 3$.

familia de operaciones Conjunto de oraciones relacionadas de suma y resta o de multiplicación y división. Por ejemplo, los números 3, 5 y 15, son parte de esta familia de operaciones de multiplicación y división:

$$3 \times 5 = 15 \qquad\qquad 5 \times 3 = 15$$
$$15 \div 5 = 3 \qquad\qquad 15 \div 3 = 5$$

Si conoces una operación de una familia de operaciones, puedes usar la relación entre la suma y la resta, y entre la multiplicación y la división, para escribir las otras tres operaciones relacionadas que son parte de esa familia. Por ejemplo, con $2 + 3 = 5$, puedes usar la relación entre la suma y la resta para escribir las oraciones numéricas relacionadas $3 + 2 = 5$, $5 - 3 = 2$ y $5 - 2 = 3$.

M   **model** *Academic Vocabulary* To represent a situation using pictures, diagrams, number sentences, or experiments.

related terms *represent, demonstrate*

Sample Yolanda has one half of an apple pie. She eats one third of the half of a pie. Model this situation using a number sentence or a picture.

I can write one third as $\frac{1}{3}$ and one half as $\frac{1}{2}$, so one third of one half can be written as $\frac{1}{3} \times \frac{1}{2}$. Because $\frac{1}{3} \times \frac{1}{2} = \frac{1}{6}$, she eats $\frac{1}{6}$ of the entire pie.

I can also fold a whole fraction strip into halves, then fold each half into thirds.

$\frac{1}{2}$			$\frac{1}{2}$		
$\frac{1}{6}$	$\frac{1}{6}$	$\frac{1}{6}$	$\frac{1}{6}$	$\frac{1}{6}$	$\frac{1}{6}$

Yolanda eats $\frac{1}{6}$ of the entire pie.

demostrar *Vocabulario académico* Representar una situación con dibujos, diagramas, oraciones numéricas o experimentos.

término relacionado *representar*

Ejemplo Yolanda tiene la mitad de una tarta de manzana. Se come un tercio de la mitad de la tarta. Demuestra esta situación con una oración numérica o un dibujo.

Puedo escribir un tercio como $\frac{1}{3}$ y la mitad como $\frac{1}{2}$, así que un tercio de una mitad puede escribirse como $\frac{1}{3} \times \frac{1}{2}$.

Debido a que $\frac{1}{3} \times \frac{1}{2} = \frac{1}{6}$, ella se come $\frac{1}{6}$ de la tarta entera.

También puedo doblar una tira de fracciones por el medio para obtener mitades y doblar cada mitad en tres tercios.

$\frac{1}{2}$			$\frac{1}{2}$		
$\frac{1}{6}$	$\frac{1}{6}$	$\frac{1}{6}$	$\frac{1}{6}$	$\frac{1}{6}$	$\frac{1}{6}$

Yolanda se come $\frac{1}{6}$ de la tarta entera.

Notes

N **number sentence** A mathematical statement that gives the relationship between two expressions that are composed of numbers and operation signs. For example, $3 + 2 = 5$ and $6 \times 2 > 10$ are number sentences; $3 + 2$, 5, 6×2, and 10 are expressions.

oración numérica Enunciado matemático que describe la relación entre dos expresiones compuestas por números y signos de operaciones. Por ejemplo, $3 + 2 = 5$ y $6 \times 2 > 10$ son oraciones numéricas; $3 + 2$, 5, 6×2 y 10 son expresiones.

O **overestimate** To make an estimate that is slightly greater than the actual value.

estimación por exceso Una estimación que es un poco mayor que el valor real.

R **reason** Academic Vocabulary To think through using facts and information.

related terms *think, examine, logic*

Sample To find the number of $\frac{1}{2}$-cup servings in 6 cups, Jenni says it is necessary to multiply 6 by $\frac{1}{2}$. Zach says that 6 must be divided by $\frac{1}{2}$ to find the number of servings. Do you agree with Jenni or Zach? Explain how you reasoned.

I agree with Zach because you want to know how many halves there are in 6. This question is answered by division: $6 \div \dfrac{1}{2} = 12$. Multiplying 6 by $\dfrac{1}{2}$ separates it into 2 equal parts of 3 each. That is not what is asked for in the question.

razonar Vocabulario académico Pensar algo con cuidado usando operaciones e información.

términos relacionados *pensar, examinar, lógico*

Ejemplo Para hallar el número de porciones de $\frac{1}{2}$ taza que hay en 6 tazas, Jenni dice que se debe multiplicar 6 por $\frac{1}{2}$. Zach dice que hay que dividir 6 por $\frac{1}{2}$ para hallar el número de porciones. ¿Estás de acuerdo con Jenni o con Zach? Explica tu razonamiento.

Estoy de acuerdo con Zach porque se desea saber cuántas mitades hay en 6. Esta pregunta se responde usando la división: $6 \div \dfrac{1}{2} = 12$. Multiplicar 6 por $\dfrac{1}{2}$ lo separa en 2 partes iguales de 3 cada una. Esto no es lo que se pide en la pregunta.

Notes _____

_____

_____

recall Academic Vocabulary To remember a fact quickly.

related terms *remember, recognize*

Sample Mateo wants to add 0.3 to $\frac{1}{2}$. What fact can you recall about $\frac{1}{2}$ or 0.3 that will help him find the sum? Explain.

> I recall that $\frac{1}{2}$ is equivalent to the decimal 0.5. When both numbers are in decimal form, they can be added easily. Mateo can add 0.5 + 0.3 to get 0.8.
>
> I also recall that 0.3 is the same as $\frac{3}{10}$ and $\frac{1}{2}$ is equivalent to $\frac{5}{10}$. Mateo can add $\frac{3}{10} + \frac{5}{10}$ to get $\frac{8}{10}$ which is the same as 0.8.

recordar Vocabulario académico Acordarse de una operación rápidamente.

términus relacionados *acordarse, reconocer*

Ejemplo Mateo quiere sumar 0.3 y $\frac{1}{2}$. ¿Qué operación con $\frac{1}{2}$ ó 0.3 puedes recordar para ayudarlo a hallar la suma? Explica tu respuesta.

> Recuerdo que $\frac{1}{2}$ es equivalente al número decimal 0.5. Cuando ambos números están en forma decimal, pueden sumarse con facilidad. Mateo puede sumar 0.5 + 0.3 para obtener 0.8.
>
> También recuerdo que 0.3 igual $\frac{3}{10}$ y $\frac{1}{2}$ es equivalente a $\frac{5}{10}$. Mateo puede sumar $\frac{3}{10} + \frac{5}{10}$ para obtener $\frac{8}{10}$, que es igual a 0.8.

---

reciprocal A factor by which you multiply a given number so that their product is 1. For example, $\frac{3}{5}$ is the reciprocal of $\frac{5}{3}$, and $\frac{5}{3}$ is the reciprocal of $\frac{3}{5}$ because $\frac{3}{5} \times \frac{5}{3} = 1$. Note that the reciprocal of $1\frac{2}{3}$ is $\frac{3}{5}$ because $1\frac{2}{3} \times \frac{3}{5} = 1$.

recíproco Un factor por el cual multiplicas un dado de manera que su producto sea 1. Por ejemplo, $\frac{3}{5}$ es el recíproco de $\frac{5}{3}$, y $\frac{5}{3}$ es el recíproco de $\frac{3}{5}$, porque $\frac{3}{5} \times \frac{5}{3} = 1$. Observa que el recíproco de $1\frac{2}{3}$ es $\frac{3}{5}$, porque $1\frac{2}{3} \times \frac{3}{5} = 1$.

U **underestimate** To make an estimate that is slightly less than the actual value.

estimación por defecto Una estimación que es un poco menor que el valor real.

Notes _____

END MATTER

STUDENT PAGE

Index

Notes _____

_____

_____

Index

Notes

END MATTER

STUDENT PAGE

Acknowledgments

Cover Design

Three Communication Design, Chicago

Photographs

Photo locators denoted as follows: Top (T), Center (C), Bottom (B), Left (L), Right (R), Background (Bkgd)

002 Serguei Liachenko/Fotolia; **003** Christy Thompson/Shutterstock; **013** Gigra/ Fotolia; **040** Serguei Liachenko/Fotolia; **061** ©2001 Hilary B. Price/King Features Syndicate; **074** Photoexpert117/Fotolia.

Notes _____

_____

_____

1.1 Getting Close: Estimating Sums

Focus Question What are some strategies for estimating the sums of fractions?

Launch

Display Teaching Aid 1.1A: Estimating Sums of Fractions and ask:

- *Is the sum of $\frac{1}{2} + \frac{5}{8}$ between 0 and 1 or between 1 and 2?*
- *Is the sum closer to 1 or closer to 2?*

Read through the directions for playing the Getting Close game, and make sure that students understand how to play. Have each group play the game several times before they answer the Questions.

Explore

As you listen to groups share their strategies, take note of interesting strategies to share in the Summarize.

Summarize

Before discussing the strategies students used for estimating sums, you may want to ask the students about other elements of the game.

- *What kinds of sums were easy to estimate?*
- *Were there any sums that were difficult to estimate? What made them difficult?*
- *What did you do when one game card was a fraction and the other was a decimal?*
- *For the game cards $\frac{4}{9}$ and $1\frac{1}{3}$, is the actual sum exactly 2, less than 2, or greater than 2? How do you know?*
- *Suppose two fractions, each less than $\frac{1}{2}$, are added. What can you tell me about the actual sum?*
- *What are some strategies you found useful in the game?*

Conclude the discussion by asking students to share their strategies for estimating sums of fractions and decimals.

Key Vocabulary
- benchmark

Materials

Labsheets
- 1.1A: Getting Close Fraction Game Cards
- 1.1B: Getting Close Decimal Game Cards
- 1.1C: Getting Close Number Squares

Teaching Aids
- 1.1A: Estimating Sums of Fractions
- 1.1B: Student Strategies for Estimation
- 1.1C: Benchmarks of Sums – Classroom Dialogue Model
- fraction strips
- calculators

Answers to Problem 1.1

A. 1. The two greatest numbers of the game cards will have the greatest sum, so $\frac{1}{2} + \frac{5}{8}$ will have the greatest sum. The sum is close to 2 since $\frac{9}{10}$ and $\frac{5}{6}$ are both close to 1.

2. The two least numbers of the game cards will have the least sum, so $\frac{1}{2} + \frac{2}{3}$ will have the least sum. The sum is close to 1 since $\frac{2}{3}$ is only $\frac{1}{3}$ away from 1, and $\frac{1}{3}$ is close to $\frac{1}{2}$.

B. 1. The two greatest numbers of the game cards will have the greatest sum, so $0.9 + 0.75$ will have the greatest sum. $0.9 + 0.75 = 1.65$, which is close to 2.

2. The two least numbers of the game cards will have the least sum, so $0.125 + 0.25$ will have the least sum. $0.125 + 0.25 = 0.375$, which is close to 0.

C. 1. The two greatest numbers of the game cards will have the greatest sum, so $\frac{3}{4} + 0.33$ will have the greatest sum. The sum is close to 1 since $\frac{3}{4}$ is just $\frac{1}{4}$ or 0.25, away from 1, and 0.33 is close to 0.25. The least two numbers of the game cards will have the least sum, so $\frac{1}{5} + 0.25$ will have the least sum. The sum is close to 0 since $\frac{1}{5}$ is equivalent to 0.2 and $0.25 + 0.2 = 0.45$.

2. If you are trying to find a sum for a decimal number and a fraction, you can either rewrite the decimal number as a fraction or rewrite the fraction as a decimal number. This will make it easier for you to use estimation strategies.

D. 1. This sum is a bit less than 1. $\frac{2}{3} + \frac{1}{3} = 1$ and $\frac{1}{5} < \frac{1}{3}$.

2. This sum is exactly 6. The whole number parts add to 5. The fractional parts add to 1.

3. This is approximately 2. $\frac{3}{4}$ is less than 1. $\frac{4}{3}$ is greater than 1. Together, they make a sum approximately 2. **Note:** Some students may say that $\frac{3}{4}$ is $\frac{1}{4}$ less than 1 and $\frac{3}{4}$ is $\frac{1}{3}$ greater than 1 and thus conclude that the sum is a bit more than 2.

1.2 Estimating Sums and Differences

> *Focus Question* How do you know if your estimate is an underestimate or an overestimate? What information does an underestimate or overestimate tell you?

Launch

Explain to students that they are going to practice estimating answers for realistic problems.

- *Name some situations where you might want to overestimate.*
- *Name some situations where you might want to underestimate.*

Read through Question A with the students to be sure they understand what they are expected to do during the Problem.

Explore

Students may struggle with deciding if they should overestimate or underestimate. You might suggest that they first estimate, and then decide if they correctly overestimated or underestimated.

- *How do you know if you have too much (an overestimate) or too little (an underestimate)?*

When students have completed most of the Questions and seem ready to discuss them, move to the Summarize.

Key Vocabulary
- overestimate
- underestimate

Materials

Accessibility Labsheet
- 1ACE: Exercise 22

Summarize

Begin by having students share their estimates for Question A. Have them describe why they think it is an underestimate or an overestimate.

For Question D, have students share their estimates. For Question E, students must underestimate because there is a limit on how much gas the tank will hold.

Close the Summarize by generalizing and describing overestimates and underestimates. Revisit student examples of situations in which an underestimate is needed and some in which an overestimate is needed.

Answers to Problem 1.2

A. She should buy the 14-inch length. The whole number parts of these lengths add to 13 inches. The fractional parts add to a bit more than $\frac{1}{2}$ an inch. This leaves a bit less than $\frac{1}{2}$ an inch of extra wood. This is an overestimate. Mrs. Edwards should be sure to buy at least the amount that she needs so that she doesn't run out of wood and need to go back to the store. Overestimating ensures that Mrs. Edwards will have enough.

B. He should buy 4 yards of material. There are two whole yards needed. Considering the fractional lengths, $\frac{3}{4} + \frac{1}{3} > 1$, he needs more than 3 yards total. 4 yards is an overestimate. Mr. Cheng needs to buy a whole-number length of material. 3 yards would be too little material while 4 yards is too much. However, Mr. Cheng should buy too much material so that he does not need to get more material later.

C. Mr. Aleman plans to spend too much money. The sum is close to 1 since $\frac{1}{2} + \frac{1}{4} + \frac{1}{4} = 1$ and $\frac{1}{3}$ is close to $\frac{1}{4}$. However, since $\frac{1}{3} > \frac{1}{4}$, the sum of these fractions is greater than one and greater than the amount the troop has to spend. The troop cannot spend more money than it has. Since Mr. Aleman is making a budget, he should overestimate the amount that he has. He is able to spend less then the money the troop has so that he can have leftover money, but he cannot spend more money than the troop has.

D. **1.** Jasmine needs to pick about one additional quart. She needs $\frac{1}{2} + \frac{1}{3}$ more quarts of berries, which is more than $\frac{1}{2}$ of a quart but less than 1 additional quart. She should pick 1 additional quart because $\frac{1}{2} + \frac{1}{3}$ is closer to 1 than to $\frac{1}{2}$. Also, Jasmine should overestimate the additional quarts of berries she needs to pick. If she picks too few, she won't be able to make her jam. So, Jasmine should pick more than enough berries.

2. This sum is exactly 6. The whole number parts add to 5. The fractional parts add to 1.

3. This is approximately 2. $\frac{3}{4}$ is less than 1. $\frac{4}{3}$ is greater than 1. Together, they make a sum approximately 2. **Note:** Some students may say that $\frac{3}{4}$ is $\frac{1}{4}$ less than 1 and $\frac{4}{3}$ is $\frac{1}{3}$ greater than 1 and thus conclude that the sum is a bit more than 2.

E. Assuming Priya's estimate for what she has added to the tank from the gas canister is accurate, she needs to buy $5 - 2\frac{1}{4}$ gallons. She has to be sure that what she asks for will fit in the gas tank so she should underestimate and ask for $2\frac{1}{2}$ gallons.

Let's Be Rational   **At a Glance**

At a Glance   Problem 1.3   Pacing 1 Day

1.3 Land Sections: Adding and Subtracting Fractions

> *Focus Question*   What are some strategies for adding and subtracting fractions?

Launch

Display Labsheet 1.3: Land Sections. Pose questions such as the following:

- *About how much land does Foley own?*
- *About how much land does Burg own?*
- *What would be a reasonable estimate for Burg + Foley's land?*
- *What does "write a number sentence" in Question B mean?*

Explore

Be sure to ask students how they chose the operation for their number sentence. It is important that students know which operations apply to which situations.

Summarize

Select groups to show their work and discuss the strategy they used to name the pieces. After a group has presented their strategy, ask the class questions like the following:

- *What do others think about this group's strategy? Does it seem reasonable?*
- *Did anyone have a different answer or use a different strategy?*

Continue to emphasize equivalence when discussing the number sentences that students wrote.

After a group has presented its strategy, ask questions like the following:

- *What equation represented your solution?*
- *How does this solution compare to Group B's solution? Are the two equations equivalent? How do you know?*

Key Vocabulary

- number sentence

Materials

Labsheet
- 1.3: Land Sections

Accessibility Labsheet
- 1ACE: Exercise 27

Teaching Aids
- 1.3A: Land Divided Into 64ths
- 1.3B: Question C - Classroom Dialogue Model
- colored pencils or markers

Answers to Problem 1.3

A. Section 18: Bouck: $\frac{1}{16}$; Fitz: $\frac{5}{32}$; Fuentes: $\frac{1}{16}$; Gardella: $\frac{3}{16}$; Krebs: $\frac{1}{32}$; Lapp: $\frac{1}{4}$; Stewart: $\frac{5}{32}$; Wong: $\frac{3}{32}$ Section 19: Burg: $\frac{3}{16}$; Foley: $\frac{5}{16}$; Theule: $\frac{3}{16}$; Walker: $\frac{5}{16}$

B. **1.** They would own $\frac{7}{32}$ of a section.
$(\frac{5}{32} + \frac{1}{16} = \frac{5}{32} + \frac{2}{32} = \frac{7}{32})$

2. $\frac{5}{16} + \frac{3}{16} = \frac{8}{16} = \frac{1}{2}$. They own $\frac{1}{2}$ a section (Foley + Burg = their combined land.)

3. $\frac{1}{4} - \frac{3}{32} = \frac{8}{32} - \frac{3}{32} = \frac{5}{32}$ of a section. (Lapp − Wong = difference)

C. **1.** Answers will vary. Possible answers include: All of the owners in Section 18 plus Foley and Burg
$(\frac{1}{4} + \frac{3}{16} + \frac{5}{32} + \frac{1}{16} + \frac{1}{32} + \frac{3}{32} + \frac{1}{16} + \frac{5}{32} + \frac{5}{16} + \frac{3}{16})$.

2. Answers will vary. Possible answers include: All of the owners except for Lapp would have $1\frac{3}{4}$ of a section combined.
$(2 - \frac{1}{4} = 1\frac{3}{4})$

D. **1.** Section 18: Bouck: 40 acres; Fitz: 100 acres; Fuentes: 40 acres; Gardella: 120 acres; Krebs: 20 acres; Lapp: 160 acres; Stewart: 100 acres; Wong: 60 acres

Section 19: Burg: 120 acres; Foley: 200 acres; Theule: 120 acres; Walker: 200 acres

2. 540 acres: Foley + Walker + Burg + Krebs
200 acres + 200 acres + 20 acres + 20 acres = 540 acres
Or, $(\frac{5}{16} + \frac{5}{16} + \frac{3}{16} + \frac{1}{32})$ of 640 acres = $\frac{27}{32}$ of 640 acres = 540 acres

Theule's part of the section is still in private hands. This is 120 acres, or $\frac{3}{16}$ of a section.
Or, 1−(Foley + Walker + Burg), which is $1 - (\frac{5}{16} + \frac{5}{16} + \frac{3}{16}) = 1 - \frac{13}{16} = \frac{3}{16}$

E. **1.** Students might say that in this number sentence the "1" represents the sum of Foley's, Burg's, Walker's and Theule's land; the "$\frac{1}{4}$" represents Lapp's land, "$\frac{3}{16}$" represents Gardella's land and "$\frac{1}{16}$" represents Fuente's land.

2. They might reason that this is $1\frac{1}{2}$ sections by visually identifying the areas. They should check that their visual identification is exactly $1\frac{1}{2}$ sections. One way to do this is to rename all the parts with the same denominator, which gives:
$1 + \frac{4}{16} + \frac{3}{16} + \frac{1}{16} = 1 + \frac{8}{16} = 1\frac{1}{2}$

At a Glance

Problem 1.4 Pacing $1\frac{1}{2}$ Days

1.4 Visiting the Spice Shop: Adding and Subtracting Mixed Numbers

Focus Question What are some strategies for adding and subtracting mixed numbers?

Launch

You may want to introduce the Problem with a statement such as this:

In this Problem, we will still use estimation to predict and check our answers. The focus of this Problem, however, is to develop strategies for finding exact answers to problems involving fractions.

Explore

Look for different strategies that the students use as they work.

- *What denominator did you use in the Spice Parisienne recipe?*
- *Why is this a good choice?*

For Question B, part (2), be sure that students share their strategies with each other during the Pair-Share portion of the Explore.

Summarize

Have students share their answers for Questions A–D. Ask:

- *What are some strategies you have found useful when combining or adding quantities of spices?*

When students are comfortable with addition of mixed numbers, shift the focus to subtraction.

Use Question F to explicitly summarize strategies. The explanations in Teaching Aid 1.4B: Student Algorithms represent some students' explanations.

Key Vocabulary
- algorithm

Materials

Accessibility Labsheets
- 1.4: Recipe Cards
- 1ACE: Exercises 31, 32, 37, 38

Teaching Aids
- 1.4A: Student Strategies
- 1.4B: Student Algorithms

- Check Up 1
- containers of spices of different weights

(A)(C)(E)
Assignment Guide for Problem 1.4

Applications: 30–50 | Connections: 58–61, 71
Extensions: 77

Answers to Problem 1.4

A. 1. She buys less than 4 ounces. The whole number parts add to 3 ounces. The fractional parts add to less than 1 ounce.

2. One recipe of Garam Masala weighs about 2 ounces more than one recipe of Betty's Cake Spices. The whole numbers in the Garam Masala total 10. The fractional parts can be added as follows: $\frac{1}{2} + \frac{1}{2} = 1$, $\frac{1}{3} + \frac{2}{3} = 1$ and $\frac{2}{3} + \frac{3}{4} > 1$, for a total weight a bit more than 13 ounces. The whole numbers in Betty's Cake Spices total 9 ounces. The fractional parts can be put together: $\frac{1}{2} + \frac{5}{8} \approx 1$ and $\frac{1}{4} + \frac{5}{8} \approx 1$. So the total is about 11 ounces.

B. 1. Betty buys about 11 ounces of spice.

Students may estimate that $9 + \frac{17}{8}$ is a little more than $9 + 2$, so the answer should be a little more than 11.

For an exact answer:

$1\frac{1}{8} + 2\frac{1}{2} + 2\frac{5}{8} + \frac{5}{8} =$

$1\frac{1}{8} + 2\frac{4}{8} + 2\frac{5}{8} + \frac{5}{8} = 5\frac{15}{8} = 6\frac{7}{8}$

Then, they will add the $4\frac{1}{4}$ ounces of cinnamon:

$4\frac{1}{4} + 6\frac{7}{8} = 4\frac{2}{8} + 6\frac{7}{8} = 10\frac{9}{8} = 11\frac{1}{8}$

2. $6\frac{7}{8}$ ounces since

$11\frac{1}{8} - 4\frac{1}{4} = 10\frac{9}{8} - 4\frac{2}{8} = 6\frac{7}{8}$

or

$1\frac{1}{8} + 2\frac{1}{2} + 2\frac{5}{8} + \frac{5}{8} =$

$1\frac{1}{8} + 2\frac{4}{8} + 2\frac{5}{8} + \frac{5}{8} = 5\frac{15}{8} = 6\frac{7}{8}$

Addition represents combining the weights of the spices used (not including the cinnamon). Subtraction represents removing the weight of the cinnamon from the total weight of the mixture. Students may have trouble subtracting with regrouping. The class may need to discuss this renaming and the meaning of the improper fraction $\frac{9}{8}$.

C. The Garam Masala should weigh $13\frac{5}{12}$ ounces. This is $2\frac{1}{2}$ ounces more than Ms. Garza had at home, so she must have forgotten the cumin. Number sentences will vary. Possible answers include addition $(\frac{2}{3} + \frac{1}{3} + 6\frac{1}{2} + \frac{2}{3} + 2\frac{3}{4} = 10\frac{11}{12}$, where the measure of $2\frac{1}{2}$ ounces of cumin is missing) or subtraction $(13\frac{5}{12} - 10\frac{11}{12} = 2\frac{6}{12} = 2\frac{1}{2})$.

D. $29\frac{1}{4}$ ounces $(32 - 2\frac{3}{4} = 29\frac{1}{4})$; two pounds of pepper would equal 32 ounces since there are 16 ounces in a pound.

E. Answers will vary. Different groups should post their answers. Possible answers:

1. Carrie needed $3\frac{1}{6}$ ounces of cinnamon, but the spice shop only had $1\frac{3}{4}$ ounces of cinnamon. How many more ounces does Carrie need? $(N = 1\frac{5}{12})$

2. Alex had some oregano in his spice cabinet and then bought $\frac{3}{4}$ ounces more oregano. He now has $1\frac{1}{2}$ ounces of oregano. How much did he have to start with? $(N = \frac{3}{4})$

3. Kimberly had $2\frac{2}{3}$ ounces of black pepper. Her cat knocked the container over and spilled a bunch onto the floor. Now Kimberly has $1\frac{1}{4}$ ounces of black pepper left. How much did her cat spill? $(N = 1\frac{5}{12})$

F. 1. Answers will vary. Possible answers include: When adding, combine whole numbers first, and then use benchmarks such as $\frac{1}{2}, \frac{1}{4}, \frac{3}{4}$, and 1 to estimate the sums of the fractional parts. When subtracting, use the same ideas, but be prepared to subtract a larger fraction from a smaller one. This will require you to change the whole-number part of the difference.

2. Answers will vary. The algorithms should discuss the need for common denominators. Also, the algorithms should mention the regrouping that happens when the sum of two fractions is greater than 1, or when a larger fractional part is subtracted from a smaller one.

Possible answers include: When adding mixed numbers, combine whole numbers first, then add the fractional parts. When adding the fractional parts, look for denominators that go together well, such as thirds and sixths, or eighths and halves. When necessary, find equivalent fractions so that the fractions you are adding have the same denominator. Then add the numerators, keeping the denominators the same. You may have to regroup if the fractional part of the sum is an improper fraction. When subtracting, use these ideas also, but be prepared to subtract a larger fraction from a smaller one. You will need to change the whole number part of the difference in that case.

2.1 How Much of the Pan Have We Sold?
Finding Parts of Parts

Focus Question How does an area model relate to multiplying fractions?

Launch

Engage students in thinking about area models by discussing Paulo and Shania's brownie booth problem.

- *As you work on this Problem, think about how large or small the answer should be when you are finding a part of a part. Questions A, B, and C ask you to draw models. First, you should show how the brownie pan might look before a customer buys some brownies. It is not full. Then, you need to mark the part of the brownie pan that shows how much the customer buys.*

Explore

As you circulate, ask students what it means to find a fraction of something, such as $\frac{1}{2}$ of $\frac{3}{4}$.

- *How does your drawing help someone see the part of the whole pan that is bought?*

- *What could you do in your drawing to make this clearer?*

For Questions A and B, notice how students transition from finding a fraction of a fraction to finding a fraction of $12. Ask them to compare these strategies.

Summarize

For Questions A–C, have groups share their solutions and strategies. Focus the conversation on taking a "part of a part."

It is helpful to write the number sentence next to the models. By doing this, students typically notice that you can multiply the numerators and denominators to find the numerator and denominator of the product. If students raise this idea, push them to explain why it works.

- *Why does multiplying the numerators and multiplying the denominators work?*

After the discussion, consider having a student display his or her work, or show Teaching Aid 2.1: $\frac{1}{2}$ of $\frac{2}{3}$. This may help students to visualize what was discussed.

Materials

Accessibility Labsheet
- 2.1A: Brownie Pans

Labsheet
- 2.1B: Extra Brownie Pan Problems

Teaching Aid
- 2.1: $\frac{1}{2}$ of $\frac{2}{3}$
- poster paper
- colored pencils

Answers to Problem 2.1

A. 1.

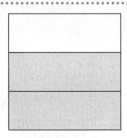

2. Answers will vary. Possible answers include:

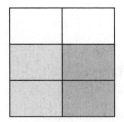 or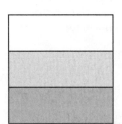

3. He buys $\frac{2}{6}$ or $\frac{1}{3}$ of a pan of brownies: $\frac{1}{2}$ of $\frac{2}{3} = \frac{1}{3}$. He pays $4.00 because $\frac{1}{3}$ of $12 = 4$.

B. 1.

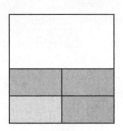

2.

 or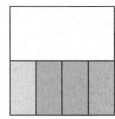

She bought $\frac{3}{8}$ of a pan: $\frac{3}{4}$ of $\frac{1}{2} = \frac{3}{8}$. She pays $4.50 because $\frac{3}{8}$ of $12 = \$4\frac{1}{2}$

C. 1. $\frac{1}{3}$ of $\frac{1}{4} = \frac{1}{12}$
(Figure 1)

2. $\frac{1}{4}$ of $\frac{1}{3} = \frac{1}{12}$
(Figure 2)

Figure 1

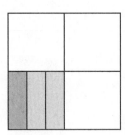 or 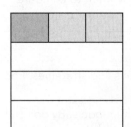 or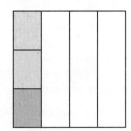

Figure 2

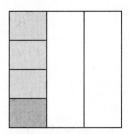 or 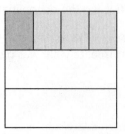 or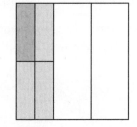

3. $\frac{1}{3}$ of $\frac{3}{4} = \frac{3}{12}$ or $\frac{1}{4}$
(Figure 3)

4. $\frac{3}{4}$ of $\frac{2}{5} = \frac{6}{20}$ or $\frac{3}{10}$

D. 1. $\frac{3}{5}$ of $\frac{1}{2} = \frac{3}{10}$

2. $\frac{1}{4}$ of $\frac{3}{4} = \frac{3}{16}$

3. $\frac{3}{5}$ of $\frac{2}{4} = \frac{6}{20}$

4. $\frac{2}{3}$ of $\frac{4}{6} = \frac{8}{18}$

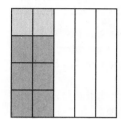 or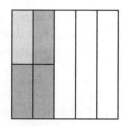

Figure 3

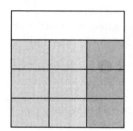 or 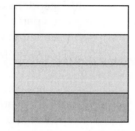 or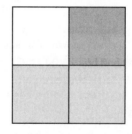

E. 1. a.

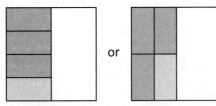

or

b.

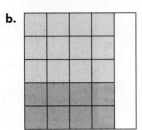

2. In each case, you multiply the denominators of the two fractions to get the denominator of the answer. You see this pattern translates when you start your model with two pieces (each a $\frac{1}{2}$), and then repartition these two pieces so that each $\frac{1}{2}$ has 4 pieces. Each piece is then called $\frac{1}{8}$ because there are 2×4, or 8 pieces in all. (Similarly, for the second example, each $\frac{1}{5}$ is partitioned into five pieces making 5×5, or 25 pieces in all.)

3. In each case, you multiply the numerators of the two fractions to get the numerator of the answer. You see this pattern when you start your model with one out of two pieces ($\frac{1}{2}$) shaded. Then, you further shade 3 out of 4 pieces ($\frac{3}{4}$). The overlap of those two shaded pieces (3×1 pieces, or 3 pieces) shows the numerator of the answer. (Similarly, for the second example, four out of the five pieces (4×2) are initially shaded, then two out of a further partition into fifths ($\frac{2}{5}$) are shaded. The overlap is then 4×2, or 8 pieces shaded.)

4. Note: At this time, students may not understand the difference between finding a part of a part when the parts represent more than, less than, or exactly 1. At this time, this limited understanding is acceptable.

Sample answer: Paulo is correct, as long as both parts are fractions less than 1. The first fraction you draw is subdivided, and only a part of that first fraction is the resulting product. You can also look at this geometrically: the part of the pan that is double-shaded (the product) is contained inside each part representing the original fractions. It can never be bigger than either of the original fractions.

2.2 Modeling Multiplication Situations

> *Focus Question* What strategies can you use to multiply all combinations of factors including whole numbers, fractions, and mixed numbers?

Launch

Tell students that they will work with multiplication problems that use fractions, whole numbers, and mixed numbers.

- *Do you think the fraction multiplication strategies you used in Problem 2.1 will work for all kinds of fractions?*

Explore

Look for various models for students to present in the Summarize. When they present, ensure that groups write number sentences for the problems. They should explain how these number sentences relate to their diagrams.

Materials

Accessibility Labsheet
- 2ACE: Exercise 33

- poster paper

Summarize

After a solution is presented, ask questions like the following:

- *Do you agree with this answer and the reasoning supporting it? Explain.*
- *Does the exact answer seem reasonable given the estimate?*
- *Does anyone have a different way to think about the problem?*

After a context for a number sentence is presented, ask:

- *How does the context match the number sentence?*
- *Do you agree with this answer and the reasoning? Explain.*
- *Does anyone have a different context to relate to this number sentence?*

A C E

Assignment Guide for Problem 2.2

Applications: 3–12
Connections: 30–38, 54–55

Answers to Problem 2.2

A. 1. Estimates will vary. Possible estimate: 10 ounces

Diagrams will vary. For a possible diagram, see Teaching Aid 2.2: Display of Problem Answers.

$\frac{2}{3} \times \frac{4}{5} = \frac{8}{15}$ or $\frac{2}{3}$ of $16 = 10\frac{2}{3}$

2. Estimates will vary. Possible estimate: a bit less than 1 pound

Diagrams will vary. For a possible diagram, see Teaching Aid 2.2: Display of Problem Answers.

$2\frac{1}{2} \times \frac{1}{3} = \frac{5}{6}$ or $2\frac{1}{2}$ of $\frac{1}{3} = \frac{5}{6}$

3. Estimates will vary. Possible estimate: between 20 and 25 acres

Diagrams will vary. For a possible diagram, see Teaching Aid 2.2: Display of Problem Answers.

$2\frac{1}{2} \times 10\frac{1}{2} = 24\frac{1}{2}$ or $2\frac{1}{3}$ of $10\frac{1}{2} = 24\frac{1}{2}$

B. Answers will vary. Possible answers include:

1. Suzie went to the hardware store and bought a rod that was a yard long. At home, she used $\frac{5}{6}$ of the rod. How long was the amount of the rod she used? $\left(\frac{5}{6}\text{ of a yard long}\right)$.

2. Gretchen bought $\frac{3}{7}$ of a 2-pound package of oranges. How much did her purchase weigh? ($\frac{6}{7}$ of a pound)

3. Michael tried to run a race. The race was nine laps around a track that measured $\frac{1}{3}$ of a mile. Michael completed only half of the race. How far did Michael run? ($1\frac{1}{2}$ miles)

4. Ten pounds of peanut butter was split evenly among 7 jars. Bowen ate $\frac{9}{10}$ of the peanut butter in one jar. How much peanut butter did Bowen eat? ($1\frac{2}{7}$ pounds of peanut butter)

C. Answers will vary. Possible answer:

Jacinta is not correct. The product will always be less than either of the factors if the factors are both proper fractions (as in the Brownie Pan problems). The product will be more than one or both of the factors if at least one of the factors is greater than 1.

D. Most students will be able to express their strategies without drawings. These students will likely be working with one of the strategies that are made explicit in Problem 2.3. Both strategies can be linked directly to the drawings they have done.

One strategy is to use the Distributive Property in order to compute with easier numbers. For example,

$2\frac{1}{3} \times 1\frac{1}{2} = 2 \times 1\frac{1}{2} + \frac{1}{3} \times 1\frac{1}{2} =$

$2 \times 1 + 2 \times 1\frac{1}{2} + \frac{1}{3} \times 1 + \frac{1}{3} \times \frac{1}{2} =$

$(2 \times 1) + \left(2 \times \frac{1}{2}\right) + \left(\frac{1}{3} \times 1\right) + \left(\frac{1}{3} \times \frac{1}{2}\right) =$

$2 + 1 + \frac{1}{3} + \frac{1}{6} = 3\frac{1}{2}$

To view a model of this strategy, view Teaching Aid 2.2: Display of Problem Answers.

Another strategy is to turn all mixed-number or whole-number factors into improper fractions.

For example, $2\frac{1}{3} \times 1\frac{1}{2} = \frac{7}{3} \times \frac{3}{2} = \frac{21}{6} = 3\frac{3}{6} = 3\frac{1}{2}$

To view a model of this strategy, view Teaching Aid 2.2: Display of Problem Answers.

2.3 Changing Forms: Multiplication with Mixed Numbers

> *Focus Question* How can you use number properties and equivalent fractions to multiply rational numbers?

Launch

Display Teaching Aid 2.3A: Takoda's and Yuri's Strategies. Read through Question A and pose the following questions.

- *What do you think about Takoda's strategy? Is his problem equivalent to the original problem?*
- *What is the product of $\frac{8}{3} \times \frac{1}{2}$?*
- *What do you think of Yuri's strategy? Is his problem equivalent to the original problem?*

Explore

For Question A, part (3), discuss with the students in each group which strategy, Takoda's or Yuri's, they find more efficient. Ask them to identify why they think the strategy they chose is more efficient.

Summarize

Have each group present their estimation and computation work for a part of Question B. Then, ask questions such as those below.

- *What is a reasonable estimate for $2\frac{1}{2} \times 1\frac{1}{6}$?*
- *How did you come up with a little more than $2\frac{1}{2}$?*
- *Would the estimate of $2\frac{1}{2}$ be an underestimate or an overestimate?*
- *Did anyone estimate a different way?*
- *How did you multiply $2\frac{1}{2} \times 1\frac{1}{6}$?*
- *Did anyone use a different strategy?*
- *Did anyone make a diagram of this problem that they can share?*
- *Can the equivalent fractions strategy and the Distributive Property strategy be considered algorithms?*

Key Vocabulary
- reciprocal

Materials

Teaching Aids
- 2.3A: Takoda's and Yuri's Strategies
- 2.3B: Student Model of Problem 2.3
- 2.3C: Diagrams for Question B, part (3)
- Partner Quiz

Answers to Problem 2.3

A. 1. A reasonable estimate for $\frac{1}{2} \times 2\frac{2}{3}$ would be between $\frac{1}{2}$ of 2 and $\frac{1}{2}$ of 3, but closer to $\frac{1}{2}$ of 3. So, between 1 and $1\frac{1}{2}$, but closer to $1\frac{1}{2}$.

2. a. Both strategies are correct. Students' explanations of why they both work will vary widely. At a minimum, both strategies give the same answers to any problems we use them on. Students can also verify that these strategies give the same answer as drawing methods for this example.

Depending on what the Summarize of Problem 2.2 included, some or most students will be able to map these strategies onto drawings representing the products.

b. At some point, each strategy makes use of the algorithm discovered in Problem 2.1 for multiplying a proper fraction by a proper fraction: $\frac{a}{b} \times \frac{c}{d} = \frac{ac}{bd}$. The strategies are different because one strategy involves addition and more steps; the other strategy just uses multiplication and fewer steps.

3. Yuri's strategy:
$$1\frac{1}{3} \times \frac{4}{5} = \frac{4}{5} + \left(\frac{1}{3} \times \frac{4}{5}\right) =$$
$$\frac{4}{5} + \frac{4}{15} = \frac{12}{15} + \frac{4}{15} = \frac{16}{15} = 1\frac{1}{15}$$
Takoda's strategy:
$$1\frac{1}{3} \times \frac{4}{5} = \frac{4}{5} + \left(\frac{1}{3} \times \frac{4}{5}\right) = \frac{16}{15} = 1\frac{1}{15}$$
In the figure below, the rectangles within the top squares can be consolidated to give the resulting squares at the bottom.

(Figure 1)

Figure 1

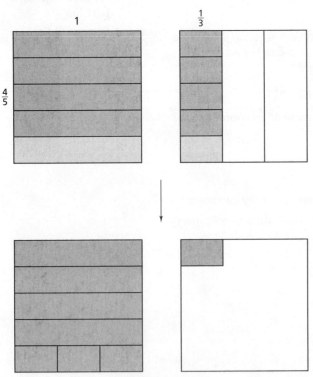

Consolidated

B. **1.** $3\frac{4}{5}$ is nearly 4, while $4 \times \frac{1}{4} = 1$. Therefore $3\frac{4}{5} \times \frac{1}{4}$ is a bit less than 1.

$3\frac{4}{5} \times \frac{1}{4} = \frac{19}{5}$ or

$3\frac{4}{5} \times \frac{1}{4} = 3 \times \frac{1}{4} + \frac{4}{5} \times \frac{1}{4} =$

$\frac{3}{4} + \frac{4}{20} = \frac{15}{20} + \frac{4}{20} = \frac{19}{20}$

2. This product is greater than 8 because and $\frac{3}{4} > \frac{1}{2}$ and $\frac{1}{2}$ of $16 = 8$.

$\frac{3}{4} \times 16 = \frac{3}{4} \times \frac{16}{1} = \frac{48}{4} = 12$

3. This product is between $2\frac{1}{2}$ and 3. This is because 2 groups of $1\frac{1}{6}$ would be almost $2\frac{1}{2}$; another half of a group should make the total almost 3.

$2\frac{1}{2} \times 1\frac{1}{6} = \frac{5}{2} \times \frac{7}{6} = \frac{35}{12} = 2\frac{11}{12}$

or

$2\frac{1}{2} \times 1\frac{1}{6} = (2 \times 1\frac{1}{6}) + (\frac{1}{2} \times 1\frac{1}{6}) =$

$(2 \times 1) + (2 \times \frac{1}{6}) + (\frac{1}{2} \times 1) + (\frac{1}{2} \times \frac{1}{6}) =$

$2 + \frac{2}{6} + \frac{1}{2} + \frac{1}{12} = 2 + \frac{4}{12} + \frac{6}{12} + \frac{1}{12} = 2\frac{11}{12}$

4. This product is about 5. This is because 1 group of $3\frac{6}{7}$ is almost 4, and another $\frac{1}{3}$ of a group is a bit more than 1, totaling about 5.

$1\frac{1}{3} \times 3\frac{6}{7} = \frac{4}{3} \times \frac{27}{7} = \frac{108}{21} = 5\frac{3}{21} = 5\frac{1}{7}$

or

$1\frac{1}{3} \times 3\frac{6}{7} = (1 \times 3\frac{6}{7}) + (\frac{1}{3} \times 3\frac{6}{7}) =$

$(1 \times 3) + (1 \times \frac{6}{7}) + (\frac{1}{3} \times 3) + (\frac{1}{3} \times \frac{6}{7}) =$

$3 + \frac{6}{7} + \frac{3}{3} + \frac{6}{21} = 3 + \frac{18}{21} + 1 + \frac{6}{21} = 5\frac{3}{21} = 5\frac{1}{7}$

5. This product is a little more than $1 \times 2\frac{1}{4}$, but not as much as $2 \times 2\frac{1}{4}$ or $4\frac{1}{2}$. It is closer to $2\frac{1}{4}$. A good estimate might be 3.

$1\frac{1}{5} \times 2\frac{1}{4} = \frac{6}{5} \times \frac{9}{4} = \frac{54}{20} = 2\frac{14}{20} = 2\frac{7}{10}$

or

$1\frac{1}{5} \times 2\frac{1}{4} = (1 \times 2\frac{1}{4}) + (\frac{1}{5} \times 2\frac{1}{4}) =$

$(1 \times 2) + (1 \times \frac{1}{4}) + (\frac{1}{5} \times 2) + (\frac{1}{5} \times \frac{1}{4}) =$

$2 + \frac{1}{4} + \frac{2}{5} + \frac{1}{20} = 2 + \frac{5}{20} + \frac{8}{20} + \frac{1}{20} =$

$2\frac{14}{20} = 2\frac{7}{10}$

6. This product is around 54 because 12×4 is 48. $\frac{4}{9}$ is close to $\frac{1}{2}$ and $\frac{1}{2}$ of 12 is 6. So, a good estimate would be $48 + 6$, or 54.

$12 \times 4\frac{4}{9} = \frac{12}{1} \times \frac{40}{9} = \frac{480}{9} = 53\frac{3}{9} = 53\frac{1}{3}$

or

$12 \times 4\frac{4}{9} = (12 \times 4) + (12 \times \frac{4}{9}) =$

$48 + (\frac{12}{1} \times \frac{4}{9}) = 48 + \frac{48}{9} =$

$48 + 5\frac{3}{9} = 53\frac{1}{3}$

C. 1. $4 \times \frac{1}{3}$ is already more than $4\frac{1}{6}$, so $4\frac{1}{2} \times 1\frac{1}{3}$ will be even greater. This is a common error when trying to apply the Distributive Property. Referring back to Yuri's strategy, we can see than 4×1 is part of the answer, and $\frac{1}{2} \times \frac{1}{3}$ is part of the answer. However, there are other parts of the answer: $4 \times \frac{1}{3}$ and $\frac{1}{2} \times 1$. So $4\frac{1}{6}$ is definitely not big enough. For the diagram below, the purple portion represents 4×1, the blue portion represents $\frac{1}{2} \times 1$, the orange portion represents $4 \times \frac{1}{3}$, and the green portion represents $\frac{1}{2} \times \frac{1}{3}$.

(Figure 2)

2. Lisa thought only about $4 \times 1 + \frac{1}{2} \times \frac{1}{3}$. Yuri is trying to give Lisa another step in between the problem and the final answer. If Lisa uses the Distributive Property once more, she can take what Yuri writes and come up with a fully expanded expression:

$$4 \times 1\frac{1}{3} + \frac{1}{2} \times 1\frac{1}{3} =$$
$$(4 \times 1) + \left(4 \times \frac{1}{3}\right) + \left(\frac{1}{2} \times 1\right) + \left(\frac{1}{2} \times \frac{1}{3}\right)$$

D. To multiply two fractions, you multiply the numerator by the numerator and the denominator by the denominator, and then simplify the result. If the problem involves mixed numbers or whole numbers, you can either use the Distributive Property to multiply (as Yuri did), or you can convert the mixed numbers to improper fractions (as Takoda did).

Figure 2

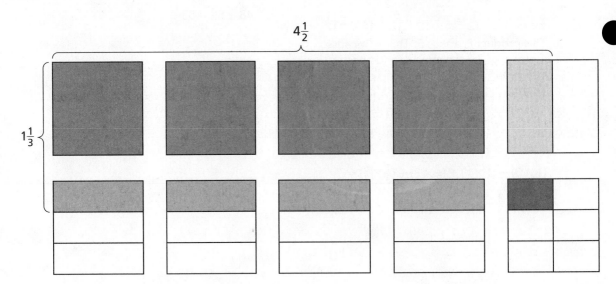

Let's Be Rational **At a Glance**

3.1 Preparing Food: Dividing a Fraction by a Fraction

> **Focus Question** What does it mean to divide a fraction by a fraction? What strategies help you divide a fraction by a fraction?

Launch

Problem 3.1 involves fractions. Students use what they know about whole-number computation and about fractions to answer these questions.

- How would you write a division number sentence for "How many $\frac{1}{4}$'s are in $\frac{1}{2}$?"
- How can you draw a model to show this?
- How does the diagram help you think about finding the quotient for $\frac{1}{2} \div \frac{1}{4}$?

Materials

Teaching Aids
- 3.1A: Dividing With Fractions
- 3.1B: Student Strategies

Explore

Circulate as the class works, paying attention to how students are thinking about the problems and where they are having difficulty.

- What do you know and what are you trying to find?
- What kind of diagram will help?
- Is there a shortcut for doing this problem that makes sense to you?

Summarize

Begin the Summarize by asking students if the hamburger and chocolate problems are grouping or sharing problems.

- Are these sharing or grouping problems?
- Which was harder, Question A or Question B? Explain.
- Did your strategies change for Question B?

Answers to Problem 3.1

A. **1.** You can make 7 hamburger patties.

$$\frac{7}{8} \div \frac{1}{8} = 7$$

(Figure 1)

2. You can make 312 hamburger patties.

$$\frac{7}{8} \div \frac{2}{8} = 3\frac{1}{2}$$

(Figure 2)

3. You can make 11 patties.

$$2\frac{3}{4} \div \frac{1}{4} = \frac{11}{4} \div \frac{1}{4} = 11$$

B. **1.** $\frac{3}{4} = \frac{18}{24}$, so he can make 18 cups of hot chocolate.

2. If each cup takes more of the mix, then there will be fewer cups from a can. The $\frac{1}{8}$ scoop is larger than the $\frac{1}{24}$ scoop, so the number of cups of chocolate that Tom makes will be less than what Sam makes. Some students may compute the number of cups of chocolate that Tom makes and compare them to the number of cups Sam makes.

C. Answers will vary. Many students will rely on drawings as above. Some will start to rename the dividend and divisor so they have the same denominator. For $\frac{2}{3} \div \frac{1}{4}$, the common denominator is 12, and the question becomes, how many times does $\frac{3}{12}$ go into $\frac{8}{12}$? The answer is the same as $8 \div 3$, or $2\frac{2}{3}$ times.

Figure 1

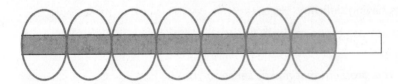

Figure 2

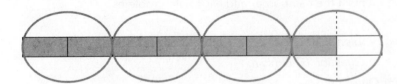

3.2 Into Pieces: Whole Numbers or Mixed Numbers Divided by Fractions

> **Focus Question** What does it mean to divide a whole number or mixed number by a fraction? What strategies help you divide a whole number or mixed number by a fraction?

Launch

Use the introduction to Problem 3.2 in the Student Edition to introduce situations with whole numbers divided by fractions.

- *How would you write a division sentence for "How many $\frac{3}{4}$'s are in 14?"*

- *You are going to work on situations such as this in Problem 3.2. Before you start, what is a reasonable estimate for how many times $\frac{3}{4}$ will go into 14? Remember that you know that $14 \div 1 = 14$.*

- *How can you use a number line to represent $14 \div \frac{3}{4}$? How does this help you find the quotient?*

Materials

Accessibility Labsheet
- 3ACE: Exercise 6
- poster paper

Explore

Encourage students to write number sentences that represent their pictures and reflect how they solved the problems. Ask whether the problems are about sharing something equally or about how many groups or things of a certain kind can be made.

Summarize

As you move through the Summarize for Question A, compare both approaches and compare the equations for unit fractions and those for non-unit fractions. Question B provides a place for students to use the approaches developed in Question A and for you to informally assess students' progress.

In Question D, discuss student strategies. Some students may see that dividing by a fraction is the same as multiplying by its reciprocal. Others may feel more comfortable with saying that you multiply the dividend by the denominator of the divisor and then divide the product by the numerator of the divisor. Still others may prefer to make common denominators and then divide the numerators.

Ask students to justify their answers and share any drawings they did to make sense of the problem.

Answers to Problem 3.2

A. 1. a. $9 \div \frac{1}{3} = \frac{27}{3} = 27$ (27 pizzas)
(Figure 1)

b. $\frac{36}{4} \div \frac{1}{4} = 36$ (36 pizzas)

c. 45 pizzas

d. $\frac{27}{3} \div \frac{2}{3} = 36 \div 2 = 13\frac{1}{2}$ $\left(13\frac{1}{2}\text{ pizzas}\right)$
(Figure 2)

e. $9 \div 1 = 9$ (9 pizzas)

f. $\frac{27}{3} \div \frac{4}{3} = 27 \div 4 = 6\frac{3}{4}$ $\left(6\frac{3}{4}\text{ pizzas}\right)$

2. The fractional part of the answer to Question A, part (1.d) refers to $\frac{1}{2}$ of a pizza $\left(\text{not }\frac{1}{2}\text{ of a block of cheese}\right)$.

B. Answers will vary.

1. If Ali has 12 blocks of cheese to make pizzas, and each pizza requires $\frac{2}{3}$ of a block of cheese, how many pizzas can he make?

$12 \div \frac{2}{3} = \frac{36}{3} \div \frac{2}{3} = 18$ (18 pizzas)

2. If Regina has 12 blocks of cheese to make pizzas, and each pizza requires $\frac{5}{6}$ of a block of cheese, how many pizzas can she make?

$12 \div \frac{5}{6} = \frac{72}{6} \div \frac{5}{6} = 14\frac{2}{5}$ $\left(14\frac{2}{5}\text{ pizzas}\right)$

3. If Kate has 12 blocks of cheese to make pizzas, and each pizza requires $\frac{7}{6}$ of a block of cheese, how many pizzas can she make?

$12 \div \frac{7}{6} = \frac{72}{6} \div \frac{7}{6} = 10\frac{2}{7}$ $\left(10\frac{2}{7}\text{ pizzas}\right)$

4. If Kate has 12 blocks of cheese to make pizzas, and each pizza requires $1\frac{1}{3}$ blocks of cheese, how many pizzas can she make?

$12 \div 1\frac{1}{3} = \frac{36}{3} \div \frac{4}{3} = 9$ (9 pizzas)

C. 1. $5\frac{1}{4} \div \frac{3}{8} = \frac{42}{8} \div \frac{3}{8} = 42 \div 3 = 14.$
She can frost 14 cupcakes.

2. $3\frac{1}{2} \div \frac{2}{3} = \frac{21}{6} \div \frac{4}{6} = \frac{21}{4} = 5\frac{1}{4}.$
He should fill his measuring cup $5\frac{1}{4}$ times.

Figure 1

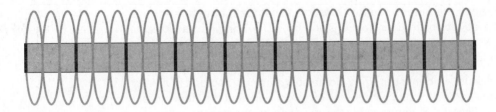

Figure 2

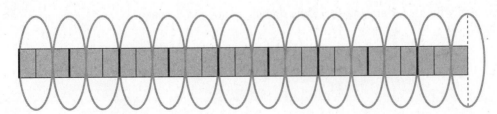

D. Answers will vary. Some students will still be drawing, but many will have developed a renaming strategy, that is renaming both fractions with the same denominator and then dividing the numerators. Some will have noticed that when dividing a whole number by a unit fraction the result is the same as multiplying the whole number by the denominator of the unit fraction, for example, $9 \div \frac{1}{4} = 36$. A few may have noticed that when dividing a whole number by a proper fraction the result is the same as multiplying the whole number by the denominator and dividing by the numerator, for example, $9 \div \frac{2}{3} = 9 \times 3 \div 2 = 13\frac{1}{2}$. In both cases students should be pushed to explain, with reference to drawings, why these apparent shortcuts work. When the division problem involves mixed numbers, the mixed numbers can be written in equivalent form as improper fractions, and then similar strategies may be used.

Figure 3

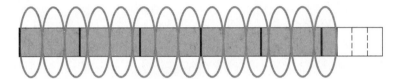

3.3   Sharing a Prize: Dividing a Fraction by a Whole Number

Focus Question   What does it mean to divide a fraction by a whole number? What strategies help you divide a fraction by a whole number?

Launch

Read Question A with your students and remind them of things such as the following.

Materials

• Sample Student Work 3.3

• Drawing a diagram is often very helpful.

• Label your answer so that you know that the number you get is telling you about the situation.

Suggested Questions

• *What are the numbers (quantities) given in the Problem?*

• *What do you need to find?*

• *What does the answer tell you?*

Explore

As students work, walk around and ask questions to make sure that they notice the types of problems that make up Question A.

• *Are these grouping or sharing problems?*

• *Do you see a pattern that would give you a short way of finding the answer?*

Summarize

Review Question A with the students. Call on students to illustrate how they did the divisions called for in Question A.

• *Who can give me an answer for Question A, part (1), and explain why you think you are correct?*

Look for opportunities to express students' ideas as number sentences. Ask questions such as the following:

• *Is $\frac{2}{5} \div 3$ equivalent to $\frac{2}{5} \times \frac{1}{3}$?*

• *Is $\frac{2}{5} \div 3$ equivalent to $\frac{2}{5} \times \frac{15}{5}$?*

Have students present their solutions and models for Question C. Use Question D to summarize an algorithm for dividing any fraction by any whole number.

Assignment Guide for Problem 3.3

Applications: 14–20 | Connections: 49–53
Extensions: 55–59

Answers to Problem 3.3

A. 1. Each student gets $\frac{1}{8}$ of a pound of peanuts. A picture provides a useful explanation.
(Figure 1)

2. Each student gets $\frac{1}{12}$ of a pound of peanuts.

3. Each student gets $\frac{3}{8}$ of a pound of peanuts.
Note: Some students may express this as $1\frac{\frac{1}{2}}{4}$ based on their work in *Comparing Bits and Pieces*.

4. Each student gets $\frac{3}{8}$ of a pound of peanuts.

B. 1. $\frac{2}{15}$; this could be thought of as $\frac{2}{3}$ pound of peanuts shared among 5 people, or $\frac{2}{3}$ of a brownie pan divided into 5 pieces.

2. $\frac{3}{4}$; this could be thought of as $\frac{3}{2}$, or $1\frac{1}{2}$, pounds of peanuts shared between 2 people. This also could be thought of $\frac{3}{2}$, or $1\frac{1}{2}$, brownie pans divided into 2 equal shares.

3. $\frac{2}{15}$; this could be thought of as $\frac{2}{5}$ of a pound of peanuts shared among 3 people. This also could be thought of as $\frac{2}{5}$ of a brownie pan divided into 3 pieces.

4. $\frac{4}{20}$, or $\frac{1}{5}$; some students may notice that $\frac{4}{5}$ pound shared among 4 people gives $\frac{1}{5}$ each.

C. A relay race is $\frac{8}{3}$ miles long. A team has 4 runners in the race. How far does each runner run? Each runner will run $\frac{8}{3} \div 4 = \frac{2}{3}$ mile. Some students may apply a renaming strategy and get $\frac{8}{3} \div \frac{12}{3} = \frac{8}{12} = \frac{2}{3}$.

D. Answers will vary. Students may say that they multiplied the denominator of the dividend by the whole number divisor. Be sure to connect this strategy to multiplying by the reciprocal of the divisor.

Figure 1

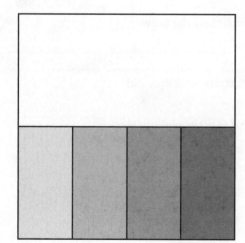

3.4 Examining Algorithms for Dividing Fractions

> *Focus Question* What is an efficient algorithm for division problems involving fractions and mixed numbers?

Launch

Talk with the class about what an algorithm is in mathematics.

When students understand what an algorithm is, explain that division problems involving fractions and mixed numbers have algorithms too.

Explore

Make sure students check their solutions and discuss the groups before moving on to the algorithms. Most students will group the problems in the following two groups:

Group 1: Problems that require little work to solve.

Group 2: Problems that require much work to solve.

Summarize

Ask questions such as the following:

- *Would someone share their grouping of the problems in Question A?*
- *What about the problems in Group 1 required less work than those problems in Group 2?*
- *What is similar about the problems in Group 2?*
- *What new problems did you write to fit Group 1?*

Then summarize Question D, the algorithms. Ask questions such as the following.

- *How did you use Group 1 and Group 2 to help you write your algorithm?*
- *Which group made it easier to start writing an algorithm?*
- *Would someone share their group's algorithm?*
- *What do others think about this group's algorithm? Will it work for all cases?*
- *How does this algorithm compare to yours?*

Evaluating whether each algorithm is usable and comparing it with other algorithms will further students' understanding of division involving fractions.

Materials

Accessibility Labsheet
- 3.4: Algorithms for Dividing Fractions
- poster paper

AT A GLANCE 3

Answers to Problem 3.4

A. *Estimation strategies* Students typically use common benchmarks, such as $\frac{1}{2}$, 1, and $\frac{1}{4}$ to estimate the size of the answer. For instance, consider part (10). Students may estimate the dividend as close to 3 and the divisor as between $\frac{1}{2}$ and 1, so the quotient will be between 6 and 3. For part (12), the problem may be estimated to be about 2 divided by $\frac{1}{2}$, which indicates the answer will be about 4.

Interpretations of what the division problem means Students typically interpret problems in which a fraction or mixed number is divided by a whole number as a sharing problem. For instance, students may interpret problem (1) as $\frac{1}{3}$ divided further into 9 pieces to share. When the dividend is a fraction or mixed number, students often interpret this as a grouping problem. For instance, for part (9) students may interpret this as "How many $\frac{2}{5}$'s are in 3?" Or for part (11), they may say it represents "How many $1\frac{1}{2}$'s are in $5\frac{2}{3}$?"

1. $\frac{1}{27}$ **2.** 72   **3.** 10

4. $\frac{10}{3}$ **5.** $\frac{3}{22}$ **6.** 1

7. $\frac{15}{2} = 7\frac{1}{2}$ **8.** $\frac{1}{72}$ **9.** $\frac{15}{2} = 7\frac{1}{2}$

10. $\frac{10}{2} = 5$ **11.** $\frac{34}{9} = 3\frac{7}{9}$ **12.** $\frac{18}{5} = 3\frac{3}{5}$

B. Answers will vary. Possible answers include:

  1. Group 1: 1, 2, 3, 6, 7, 8, 9, and 12; Group 2: 4, 5, 10, and 11

  2. For many students, the problems in Group 1 are likely to consist of fractions, or a fraction and a whole number. The problems in Group 2 are likely to have one or two mixed numbers, which require more steps to solve.

C. For Group 1, an example might be $\frac{5}{12} \div \frac{2}{3}$. For Group 2, an example may be $\frac{33}{4} \div \frac{12}{5}$.

D. Common Denominator Method: Find common denominators to get the same size fractional pieces, and then divide the numerators.

Multiply the dividend by the denominator of the divisor and then divide by the numerator of the divisor.

Multiply the dividend by the reciprocal of the divisor.

E. **1.** $\frac{45}{4}$ or $11\frac{1}{4}$

  2. $\frac{15}{24}$ or $\frac{5}{8}$

  3. $\frac{25}{3}$ or $8\frac{1}{3}$

  4. $\frac{17}{8}$ or $2\frac{1}{8}$

F. In *Let's Be Rational*, consider the magnitude of numbers, or positive numbers when generalizing these statements. When the quotient is between zero and one, the dividend is smaller than the divisor. When the quotient is greater than one, the dividend is larger than the divisor.

4.1 Just the Facts: Fact Families for Addition and Subtraction

> **Focus Question** How do fact families help you solve equations such as $\frac{4}{5} - N = \frac{3}{8}$?

Launch

It is important that students understand that the sentences are all true because they all represent the same relationship between two addends and a sum.

- *How are the three additional sentences in a fact family related to the original sentence?*

- *Suppose I asked you to write addition/subtraction sentences with 2,351; 7,223; and 4,872. How do you know which order to put the numbers in?*

- *How do you know which are the addends and which is the sum?*

It is critical that students relate their understanding of the equivalence of these number sentences to the underlying relationship.

Key Vocabulary

- fact family

Materials

Teaching Aid

- 4.1: Fact Families for Addition and Subtraction

Explore

As you walk around observing students, listen to the ways they justify the position of the numbers and the operations in the sentences they.

- *In part (1) of Question A, how do you know to write $\frac{5}{10} - N$ and not $N - \frac{5}{10}$?*

- *Suppose you rewrote all the fractions with a common denominator for part (3) of Question B. How does $N - \frac{4}{8} = \frac{3}{8}$ help you find the value of N?*

Summarize

As students finish, you might have them display the answers for Question A and Question B.

- *Anna rearranged part (3) of Question B as $n = \frac{3}{8} + \frac{1}{2}$ and then found $n = \frac{3}{8} + \frac{4}{8}$. Sara renamed all the fractions with the same denominator and wrote $n - \frac{4}{8} = \frac{3}{8}$. Then she guessed at n. Do these methods give the same answer? How are they related?*

Answers to Problem 4.1

A. 1. $N = \frac{1}{10}$

$\frac{5}{10} - \frac{2}{5} = N$

$\frac{5}{10} - N = \frac{2}{5}$

$\frac{2}{5} + N = \frac{5}{10}$

$N + \frac{2}{5} = \frac{5}{10}$

2. $N = 5\frac{4}{15}$

$3\frac{3}{5} + 1\frac{4}{15} = N$

$1\frac{2}{3} + 3\frac{3}{5} = N$

$N - 1\frac{2}{3} = 3\frac{3}{5}$

$N - 3\frac{3}{5} = 1\frac{2}{3}$

3. Students' ways of expressing these relationships will vary greatly. Addition and subtraction are inverses, or they undo each other. In a number sentence such as $N + \frac{2}{5} = \frac{5}{10}$, you are adding an unknown number to $\frac{2}{5}$ to get $\frac{5}{10}$. In order to figure out what that number is, you can subtract $\frac{2}{5}$ from $\frac{5}{10}$, getting back to the original starting value.

B. 1. $N = 5\frac{5}{6} - 1\frac{2}{3}$, so $N = 4\frac{1}{6}$

2. $N = \frac{17}{12} - \frac{3}{4}$, so $N = \frac{8}{12}$ or $\frac{2}{3}$

3. $N = \frac{3}{8} + \frac{1}{2}$, so $N = \frac{7}{8}$

4. Using fact families, you can find a fact in the family that expresses *n* as the sum or difference of the two known numbers.

4.2   Multiplication and Division Fact Families

> **Focus Question** How do fact families help you solve equations such as $\frac{2}{9} \div N = \frac{2}{3}$?

Launch

You want students to focus on the relationship between operations that makes $ab = c$ equivalent to $c \div a = b$.

- What multiplication sentence relates 53; 11,925; and 225? Can you rearrange this as a division sentence?
- What multiplication number sentence relates $\frac{1}{2}$, $\frac{3}{4}$, and $\frac{2}{3}$? Why is it harder to figure out how these relate than for whole numbers?
- How might you rearrange $\frac{2}{3} \times N = \frac{2}{9}$?

Make sure your students understand that rearranging multiplication and division fact families depends on how multiplication and division are related to each other.

> **Materials**
>
> **Teaching Aids**
> - 4.2A: Fact Families for Multiplication and Division 1
> - 4.2B: Fact Families for Multiplication and Division 2

Explore

Encourage students to use vocabulary words such as *factor* and *product*.

- How can you tell from a sentence such as $\frac{3}{8} \times N = \frac{21}{80}$ which fraction is the product and which is a factor?
- Of all the rearrangements of $\frac{8}{15} \div N = \frac{2}{3}$, which is easiest to use to find the answer for N?

Summarize

You may want to display student solutions, particularly if common errors, such as mistaking the order of the division, occur.

Have students make up a true fraction multiplication sentence and a true fraction division sentence. Then have them replace one of the values with N in each sentence. Finally, have students exchange the two sentences with variables with their partners and find the value of N in each sentence.

AT A GLANCE 4

Answers to Problem 4.2

A. 1. $\frac{2}{3} \times \frac{1}{5} = \frac{2}{15}$

$\frac{1}{5} \times \frac{2}{3} = \frac{2}{15}$

$\frac{2}{15} \div \frac{2}{3} = \frac{1}{5}$

$\frac{2}{15} \div \frac{1}{5} = \frac{2}{3}$

2. $\frac{3}{4} \times \frac{5}{8} = \frac{15}{32}$

$\frac{5}{8} \times \frac{3}{4} = \frac{15}{32}$

$\frac{15}{32} \div \frac{5}{8} = \frac{3}{4}$

$\frac{15}{32} \div \frac{3}{4} = \frac{5}{8}$

3. $\frac{3}{5} \times \frac{3}{8} = \frac{9}{40}$

$\frac{3}{8} \times \frac{3}{5} = \frac{9}{40}$

$\frac{9}{40} \div \frac{3}{8} = \frac{3}{5}$

$\frac{9}{40} \div \frac{3}{5} = \frac{3}{8}$

4. $\frac{2}{5} \times \frac{2}{3} = \frac{4}{15}$

$\frac{2}{3} \times \frac{2}{5} = \frac{4}{15}$

$\frac{4}{15} \div \frac{2}{5} = \frac{2}{3}$

$\frac{4}{15} \div \frac{2}{3} = \frac{2}{5}$

$\frac{3}{8} \times N = \frac{21}{80}$

B. 1. $\frac{3}{8} \times N = \frac{21}{80}$

$N \times \frac{3}{8} = \frac{21}{80}$

$\frac{21}{80} \div \frac{3}{8} = N$

$\frac{21}{80} \div N = \frac{3}{8}$ so, $N = \frac{7}{10}$.

2. $\frac{2}{3} \times N = \frac{10}{15}$

$N \times \frac{2}{3} = \frac{10}{15}$

$\frac{10}{15} \div \frac{2}{3} = N$

$\frac{10}{15} \div N = \frac{2}{3}$ so, $N = \frac{5}{5} = 1$.

3. $1 \div N = \frac{2}{3}$

$1 \div \frac{2}{3} = N$

$N \times \frac{2}{3} = 1$

$\frac{2}{3} \times N = 1$ so, $N = \frac{3}{2}$.

4. $\frac{8}{15} \div N = \frac{2}{3}$

$\frac{8}{15} \div \frac{2}{3} = N$

$N \times \frac{2}{3} = \frac{8}{15}$

$\frac{2}{3} \times N = \frac{8}{15}$ so, $N = \frac{4}{5}$.

C. Marla is thinking of the relationship between the factors, 2 and N, and the product, 15. Any rearrangement that keeps the same relationship will be as true as the original sentence. So the rearrangement she has chosen is true, and it gives the value of N that makes the original sentence true.

D. 1. $\frac{3}{5} + \frac{1}{3} = \frac{14}{15}$

$\frac{1}{3} + \frac{3}{5} = \frac{14}{15}$

$\frac{14}{15} - \frac{3}{5} = \frac{1}{3}$

$\frac{14}{15} - \frac{1}{3} = \frac{3}{5}$

2. $\frac{3}{4} \times \frac{4}{3} = 1$

$\frac{4}{3} \times \frac{3}{4} = 1$

$1 \div \frac{3}{4} = \frac{4}{3}$

$1 \div \frac{4}{3} = \frac{3}{4}$

3. $1\frac{1}{2} + 2\frac{2}{3} = 4\frac{1}{6}$

$2\frac{2}{3} + 1\frac{1}{2} = 4\frac{1}{6}$

$4\frac{1}{6} - 1\frac{1}{2} = 2\frac{2}{3}$

$4\frac{1}{6} - 2\frac{2}{3} = 1\frac{1}{2}$

4. $\frac{3}{2} \times 3 = \frac{9}{2}$

$3 \times \frac{3}{2} = \frac{9}{2}$

$\frac{9}{2} \div \frac{3}{2} = 3$

$\frac{9}{2} \div 3 = \frac{3}{2}$

4.3 Becoming an Operations Sleuth

> *Focus Question* How do you know when a particular operation is called for to solve a problem? How do you represent the problem with a number sentence?

Launch

The questions in the introduction are all about whole numbers.

- *How do you know when a situation calls for addition? For subtraction? For multiplication? For division?*

Tell your students that they now know how to do all four operations with fractions, and they know how to rearrange number sentences to make them easier to solve for N. All that is left to do is to decide which operation is called for to solve a problem.

Explore

When students are sharing their ideas, push them to clarify their explanations of how they know which operation is needed.

- *Would replacing fractions with whole numbers help you see which operation makes sense?*
- *Would a drawing help you see which operation to use?*

Summarize

Display student solutions where there are different correct solutions to compare.

- *Anna thought $10 \div 1\frac{5}{8} = N$ in Question H would give the amount of fabric for each extra item. What does $10 \div 1\frac{5}{8}$ mean in terms of this problem? Is this the same as N*
- *Sara thought that $3 \times 1\frac{5}{8} + N = 10$ in Question H would give the amount of fabric for each item. If you rearrange this sentence you get $N = 10 - 3 \times 1\frac{5}{8}$. What would $10 - 3 \times 1\frac{5}{8}$ mean in terms of this problem?*

Finally, have students share ideas about how they recognized which operations are called for in a problem.

Answers to Problem 4.3

A. This is a division problem. You need to know how many eighths are in $1\frac{1}{4}$. $1\frac{1}{4} \div \frac{1}{8} = 10$. Sammy will take 10 hours to walk 114 miles.

B. This is a division problem. You need to know how many groups of $\frac{2}{3}$ are in $5\frac{1}{3}$. $5\frac{1}{3} \div \frac{2}{3} = 8$. Kalisha will need 8 sections of fence.

C. This is a subtraction problem. $3\frac{1}{2} - \frac{3}{4} = 2\frac{3}{4}$. Sasha has $2\frac{3}{4}$ pints of blueberries left over.

D. This is a multiplication problem. You need to know how much is the result of $3\frac{1}{3}$ groups with $2\frac{3}{4}$ in each group. $3\frac{1}{3} \times 2\frac{3}{4} = 9\frac{5}{8}$.

E. There are two subtraction problems here. The first is to determine how many sweet rolls Christie sold. $5 - 1\frac{2}{3} = 3\frac{1}{3}$. The second is to determine how many more sweet rolls Christie sold than Leslie did. $3\frac{1}{3} - 2\frac{1}{2} = \frac{5}{6}$. Christie sold $\frac{5}{6}$ dozen sweet rolls more than Leslie did. (Multiplying $\frac{5}{6} \times 12 = 10$ tells you Christie sold 10 more sweet rolls than Leslie did.)

F. First you need to subtract to find the amount remaining after Raymar ate his share of brownies. $1 - \frac{1}{4} = \frac{3}{4}$. Then you need to multiply because Kalen ate part of what was left. $\frac{1}{4} \times \frac{3}{4} = \frac{3}{16}$.

G. This question involves addition and multiplication. You can use these operations in different orders. First you can add to get the total weight of each snack pack, and then you can multiply by the number of students. Or you can multiply each item's weight by the number of students, and add to get the total weight of all the packs.
$$\left(\frac{1}{4} + \frac{1}{8} + \frac{1}{16}\right)24 = \left(\frac{7}{16}\right)24 = \frac{168}{16}$$
which is $10\frac{1}{2}$ pounds.

Or, you can write
$$24\left(\frac{1}{4}\right) + 24\left(\frac{1}{8}\right) + 24\left(\frac{1}{16}\right) = 6 + 3 + 1\frac{1}{2}$$
which is also $10\frac{1}{2}$ pounds.

H. This question involves addition and multiplication. You can use these in different orders. You can add the material for two items for each granddaughter and then multiply by three. Or you can multiply the material for each item by three and then add to get total.

3 (jacket + extra) = 10
$$3\left(1\frac{5}{8} + N\right) = 10$$
Or you can write $3\left(1\frac{5}{8}\right) + 3N = 10$ which is the same as $4\frac{7}{8} + 3N = 10$. Comparing these two statements to the choices, you see that choice (1) is correct. Choice (2) is also correct, because it is a rearrangement of the second strategy. Choices (3) and (4) are incorrect.

At a Glance

Pacing ☐ Day

Mathematical Goals

_____

_____

_____

Launch

_____

_____

_____

_____

Explore

_____

_____

_____

_____

Summarize

_____

_____

_____

_____

Notes

Applications

1. 1; Possible explanation: $\frac{9}{9}$ is 1, so $\frac{10}{9}$ is more than 1.

2. $\frac{1}{2}$; Possible explanation: Since $\frac{8}{16} = \frac{1}{2}$, $\frac{9}{16}$ is close to $\frac{1}{2}$.

3. 1; Possible explanation: $\frac{5}{6}$ is only $\frac{1}{6}$ less than 1 whole.

4. $\frac{1}{2}$; Possible explanation: $\frac{1}{2}$ of 100 is 50, so $\frac{48}{100}$ is closer to $\frac{1}{2}$.

5. $\frac{1}{2}$; Possible explanation: $\frac{1}{2}$ is 0.50 and $\frac{3}{4}$ is 0.75, so 0.67 is close to $\frac{1}{2}$.

6. 0; Possible explanation: 0.0009999 is a very small amount. It does not have any tenths in it, and $\frac{1}{2}$ is equivalent to 5 tenths.

7. 1; Possible explanation: $\frac{7}{8}$ is a little less than 1 and $\frac{4}{9}$ is a little less than $\frac{1}{2}$. Together, a little less than 1 and a little less than $\frac{1}{2}$ is a little less than $1\frac{1}{2}$ or closer to 1 than to 2.

8. 2; Possible explanation: $1\frac{3}{4}$ is closest to 2, and $\frac{1}{8}$ is a small number that will make the sum closer to, but not greater than, 2.

9. 3; Possible explanation: $1\frac{1}{3}$ is a little more than 1.3. 1.3 and 1.3 is 2.6, which is greater than $2\frac{1}{2}$, and closest to 3.

10. 0; Possible explanation: It would take two $\frac{1}{4}$'s to equal exactly $\frac{1}{2}$. Since $\frac{1}{8}$ is less than $\frac{1}{4}$, $\frac{1}{4}$ and $\frac{1}{8}$ is less than $\frac{1}{2}$ and closer to 0.

11. 2; three tenths and eight tenths have a sum greater than 1, so the total sum here is greater than 2.

12. 2; $1\frac{4}{10}$ is equivalent to 1.4 which, when added to 0.375, is 1.775, which is close to 2.

13. 0.5; Possible explanation: $\frac{3}{5}$ is a bit more than half, and $\frac{1}{10}$ is a small fraction, not big enough to push $\frac{3}{5}$ close to 1.

14. 0.5; Possible explanation: $\frac{1}{4}$ is exactly in the middle of 0 and $\frac{1}{2}$. $\frac{1}{10}$ is a small fraction so the sum is closer to $\frac{1}{2}$, but not greater than $\frac{1}{2}$.

15. 0; Possible explanation: $\frac{1}{4} = \frac{2}{8}$. Also, $\frac{1}{4}$ is exactly halfway between 0 and $\frac{1}{2}$. $\frac{1}{9} < \frac{1}{8}$, so $\frac{1}{9} + \frac{1}{8} < \frac{1}{4}$. Therefore the sum is closer to 0 than to $\frac{1}{2}$.

16. **a.** This is incorrect. $\frac{1}{8} < \frac{1}{4}$, so the sum here is less than $\frac{3}{4}$.

    b. Correct. Each fraction is equal to $\frac{1}{2}$, so the sum is 1.

    c. Correct. $\frac{5}{6} > \frac{3}{4}$, so the sum of $\frac{5}{12}$ and $\frac{5}{6}$ is also greater.

    d. Correct. $\frac{5}{10} = \frac{1}{2}$ and $\frac{3}{8} > \frac{1}{4}$, so the sum is greater than $\frac{3}{4}$.

17. Possible answer: $\frac{1}{4}$ and $\frac{1}{7}$

18. Possible answer: $\frac{3}{8}$ and $\frac{4}{9}$

19. Possible answer: $\frac{5}{8}$ and $\frac{1}{2}$

20. Possible answer: $\frac{5}{8}$ and $\frac{7}{8}$

21. **a.** The greatest possible sum is $1.05 + \frac{9}{10}$.

    b. The least possible sum is $\frac{1}{4} + \frac{3}{5}$.

22. **a.** No; In the price list, the whole numbers add up to 9: $2 + 1 + 1 + 1 + 3 + 1 = 9$. The cheese is $1.95, which brings the total to $9.95. There's clearly enough in the cost of other items to put the total over $10. (The exact cost of the groceries is $12.42.)

    b. Possible answers: Milk, cheese, avocado ($4.92); eggs, cheese, honey, bread ($4.91)

    c. cereal, honey, and avocado ($4.94)

23. $\frac{5}{8}$ is closest to $\frac{1}{2}$. Possible explanation: $\frac{4}{8} = \frac{1}{2}$. The other $\frac{1}{8}$ makes $\frac{5}{8}$ just a little more than $\frac{1}{2}$, but not close to $\frac{8}{8}$, or 1 whole.

24. Soo has enough molding. $\frac{7}{8}$ is $\frac{1}{8}$ less than 1 whole and $\frac{8}{7}$ is $\frac{7}{7}$ more than 1 whole or $1\frac{1}{7}$. Since $\frac{1}{7} > \frac{1}{8}$, when the $\frac{1}{7}$ is added to the $\frac{7}{8}$ it will be greater than 1 yard, and the total will be greater than 2 yards.

25. He had about 8 quarts.

26. No; If you add $\frac{3}{4}$ to $1\frac{3}{4}$, you will get $2\frac{1}{2}$. But $\frac{5}{8}$ is a little less than $\frac{3}{4}$, so there is not enough.

27. **a.** Marigolds: $\frac{3}{20}$; Lantana: $\frac{1}{20}$; Impatiens: $\frac{3}{10}$; Petunias: $\frac{1}{10}$; Lilies: $\frac{1}{5}$; Begonias: $\frac{1}{20}$; Tulips: $\frac{1}{20}$; Daisies: $\frac{1}{20}$; Irises: $\frac{1}{20}$

b. $\frac{4}{20} - \frac{1}{20} = \frac{3}{20}$

c. $\frac{4}{20} + \frac{1}{20} + \frac{1}{20} = \frac{6}{20}$, or $\frac{3}{10}$

d. Incorrect. Possible explanation: The number sentence for the situation is $\frac{3}{20} - \frac{1}{20} = \frac{1}{10} + \frac{1}{20}$. If you work out the subtraction problem on the left of the equal sign and the addition problem on the right, the answers are not the same.

e. Possible combinations that total $\frac{3}{10}$, the fraction planted with impatiens:

Marigolds + Petunias + Lantana: $\frac{3}{20} + \frac{1}{10} + \frac{1}{20} = \frac{3}{20} + \frac{2}{20} + \frac{1}{20} = \frac{6}{20} = \frac{3}{10}$

Lilies + Petunias: $\frac{4}{20} + \frac{2}{20} = \frac{6}{20}$, or $\frac{3}{10}$

Marigolds + Begonias + Tulips + Daisies: $\frac{3}{20} + \frac{1}{20} + \frac{1}{20} + \frac{1}{20} = \frac{6}{20}$, or $\frac{3}{10}$

28. **a.** $\frac{1}{8} + \frac{1}{16} = \frac{3}{16}$ of the page is used for ads.

b. $1 - \frac{3}{16} = \frac{13}{16}$ of the page remains.

29. $\frac{3}{4}$ (three $\frac{1}{4}$-page ads, or $3 \times \frac{1}{4}$) plus $\frac{4}{8}$ (four $\frac{1}{8}$-page ads, or $4 \times \frac{1}{8}$) plus $\frac{10}{16}$ (ten $\frac{1}{16}$-page ads, or $10 \times \frac{1}{16}$) $= 1\frac{7}{8}$ pages.

30. $2\frac{3}{4} - 1\frac{5}{8} = 1\frac{5}{8}$ pages

31. $\frac{1}{9} + \frac{1}{18} = \frac{3}{18} = \frac{1}{6}$ of the lasagna is eaten, leaving $\frac{5}{6}$ of the lasagna uneaten.

32. $\frac{3}{4} + \frac{1}{8} = \frac{6}{8} + \frac{1}{8} = \frac{7}{8}$ of a small bag of chips

33. $2\frac{11}{15}$

34. $7\frac{3}{8}$

35. $8\frac{5}{6}$

36. $6\frac{2}{12}$ or $6\frac{1}{6}$

37. $\frac{3}{4} + \frac{4}{5}$ is greater: $\frac{2}{3} + \frac{5}{6} = \frac{4}{6} + \frac{5}{6} = \frac{9}{6} = 1\frac{1}{2} = 1\frac{10}{20}$; $\frac{3}{4} + \frac{4}{5} = \frac{15}{20} + \frac{16}{20} = 1\frac{11}{20}$

38. $\frac{7}{6} - \frac{2}{3}$ is greater: $\frac{7}{6} - \frac{2}{3} = \frac{7}{6} - \frac{4}{6} = \frac{3}{6} = \frac{1}{2} = \frac{5}{10}$; $\frac{3}{5} - \frac{5}{10} = \frac{6}{10} - \frac{5}{10} = \frac{1}{10}$

39. $2\frac{5}{6} + 1\frac{1}{3} = 4\frac{1}{6}$

40. $15\frac{5}{8} + 10\frac{5}{6} = 26\frac{11}{4}$

41. $4\frac{4}{9} + 2\frac{1}{5} = 6\frac{29}{45}$

42. $6\frac{1}{4} - 2\frac{5}{6} = 3\frac{5}{12}$

43. $3\frac{1}{2} - 1\frac{4}{5} = 1\frac{7}{10}$

44. $8\frac{2}{3} - 6\frac{5}{7} = 1\frac{20}{21}$

45. $\frac{3}{4}$

46. $\frac{3}{6}$ or $\frac{1}{2}$

47. $\frac{3}{8}$

48. $\frac{3}{10}$

49. $\frac{3}{12}$

50. $\frac{3}{14}$

In all of the problems, you add unit fraction where one fraction is half the size of the other. The fraction in each part with the lesser denominator is twice the value of the unit fraction with the greater denominator. You can think of the unit fraction with the lesser denominator as two unit fractions with the greater denominator. This gives a sum with a 3 in the numerator over the greater denominator.

51. No. If $\frac{14}{16}$ of all the pizza were eaten, this would be less than one whole pizza. If there are eight sections in each pizza, then people are eating eighths. And all together they ate $\frac{14}{8}$ or $1\frac{6}{8}$ pizzas.

Connections

52. Divide the rectangle into thirds. Each third of the rectangle represents 50% of the original whole. So, 100% is represented by the blue area.

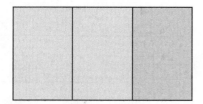

53. 15 beans. There are 9 beans shown in the picture representing three fifths. So each fifth must contain 3 beans. Since the whole is five fifths, there must be 15 beans on the counter.

54. a. $\frac{1}{2}$ is 0.5 and 50%

$\frac{1}{3}$ is about 0.33 and 33%

$\frac{1}{4}$ is 0.25 and 25%

$\frac{2}{3}$ is about 0.66 or 66% (Some students will argue for 0.67 and 67%, if the convention of rounding up is used.)

$\frac{3}{4}$ is 0.75 and 75%

$\frac{1}{6}$ is about 0.16 and 16% (Some students will argue for 0.17 and 17%, if the convention of rounding up is used.)

$\frac{1}{5}$ is 0.2 or 20%

$\frac{1}{8}$ is 0.125 or 12.5%

b. (See Figure 1.)

55. D

56. a and d

a. This set of fractions can be renamed as hundredths because each denominator 2, 4, and 5, are factors of 100.

b. This set of fractions cannot be renamed as hundredths. The denominator 10 is a factor of 100, but 11 and 12 are not.

c. This set of fractions cannot be renamed as hundredths. The denominators 6 and 8 are not factors of 100.

d. This set of fractions can be renamed as hundredths because all the denominators, 5, 10, and 20, are factors of 100.

57. a. The least possible sum is $1\frac{1}{4}$. This is the sum of the least numbers in each of these intervals.

b. The greatest possible sum is $2\frac{1}{2}$. That is the sum of the greatest number in each of these intervals.

58. $N = 2$

59. $N = 3$

60. $N = 8$

61. $N = 24$

Figure 1

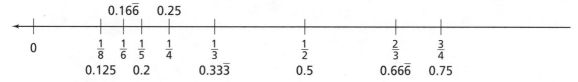

62. $\frac{2}{6} = \frac{4}{12}$

63. $\frac{8}{12} = \frac{2}{3} = \frac{4}{6}$

64. $\frac{3}{9} = \frac{2}{6} = \frac{6}{18}$

65. $18.156 < 18.17$

66. $4.0074 > 4.0008$

67. G

68. Answers will vary. Possible answers include: Foley, Burg, Walker, Theule, and Lapp.
$\frac{5}{16} + \frac{3}{16} + \frac{5}{16} + \frac{3}{16} + \frac{1}{4} = 1\frac{1}{4}$

69. a. $1\frac{1}{3}$ of a whole; 3 squares $= \frac{1}{13}$ of a whole; 9 squares $= 1$ whole; so 12 squares $= 1\frac{1}{3}$ of a whole.

   b. $\frac{7}{9}$ of a whole; 3 squares $= \frac{1}{3}$ or $\frac{3}{9}$ of a whole; 9 squares $= \frac{3}{3}$ or $\frac{9}{9}$ of a whole; so 7 squares $= \frac{7}{9}$ of a whole.

70. a. Note: The purple shaded region represents 1. The green shaded region represents the $\frac{1}{3}$ portion of $1\frac{1}{3}$. The blue shaded region represents $\frac{1}{6}$.

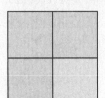 Or,

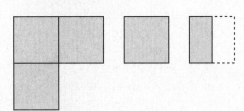

b. Note: The Xs indicate the regions subtracted. The purple and green shaded regions each represent 1. The blue shaded region represents $\frac{2}{3}$. The remaining portion is $\frac{4}{3}$.

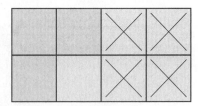

Or,

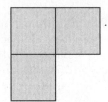 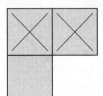 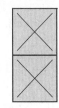

71. a. Since $\frac{70}{150} = \frac{7}{15}$ and $\frac{30}{150} = \frac{2}{10}$, the sum of these two numbers is the same no matter which forms we use.

   b. Answers will vary. Possible answers include: $\frac{14}{30} + \frac{4}{20}$ and $\frac{14}{30} + \frac{6}{30}$.

   c. Any problem with common denominators should be easy to solve. This includes Maribel's problem as well as this one: $\frac{14}{30} + \frac{6}{30}$.

Extensions

72. Answers will vary. Possible answers include:
$\frac{2}{5}$

73. Answers will vary. Possible answers include:
$\frac{2}{7}$

74. It is always possible to find a fraction between any two fractions on the number line. One way to know this is that we can rewrite each given fraction as an equivalent fraction, using common denominators, and then choose a new fraction with a numerator between the two new numerators. For example, given $\frac{1}{3}$ and $\frac{1}{2}$ we can rewrite as $\frac{4}{12}$ and $\frac{6}{12}$, and then we know $\frac{5}{12}$ is between these.

Another method would be to take the number that is halfway between the two fractions, which is the average of the two fractions. For example, to find the fraction between $\frac{3}{4}$ and $\frac{4}{5}$ we can take the average.
$$\frac{1}{2}\left(\frac{3}{4} + \frac{4}{5}\right) = \frac{1}{2}\left(\frac{15}{20} + \frac{16}{20}\right) = \frac{1}{2} \times \frac{31}{20} = \frac{31}{40}$$
Now $\frac{3}{4} = \frac{30}{40} < \frac{31}{40} < \frac{32}{40} = \frac{4}{5}$,
so $\frac{31}{40}$ is between $\frac{3}{4}$ and $\frac{4}{5}$.

75. a. $\frac{1}{32}$ page costs \$5, $\frac{1}{16}$ page costs \$10, $\frac{1}{8}$ page costs \$20, $\frac{1}{4}$ page costs \$40, $\frac{1}{2}$ page costs \$80, 1 full page costs \$160.

b. $40 \times 3 + 20 \times 4 + 10 \times 1 = \$210$

c. Yes. $\frac{2}{8}$ page costs \$40 and $\frac{4}{16}$ page costs \$40, for a total of \$80.

d. Answers will vary. Possible answers include: Any combination adding up to $\frac{1}{2}$ page. This includes two $\frac{1}{4}$-page ads, or one $\frac{1}{4}$-page ad and two $\frac{1}{8}$-page ads.

76. a. 2 acres; 16 people can clear twice as much in the same amount of time.

b. $\frac{1}{4}$ acre; one fourth of the people can clear one fourth as much in the same amount of time.

c. 24 people; three times as many people are needed to clear three times the area in the same amount of time.

d. 48 people; twice as many people are needed to complete part (c) in half of the time.

77. a. Answers will vary. Possible answers include: $\frac{1}{3} - \frac{1}{4} = \frac{1}{12}$.

b. Answers will vary. Possible answers include: $\frac{1}{5} - \frac{1}{6} = \frac{1}{30}$.

Applications

1. a.

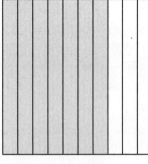

b. $\frac{14}{50}$ or $\frac{7}{25}$

2. a. $\frac{2}{3}$ of $\frac{3}{4}$ (Figure 1)

$\frac{3}{4}$ of $\frac{2}{3}$ (Figure 2)

b. They are equal.

c. These expressions are equal. Another way to say this is that multiplication is commutative.

Figure 1

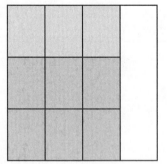   or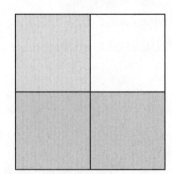

Figure 2

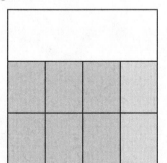   or   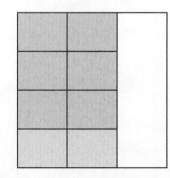   or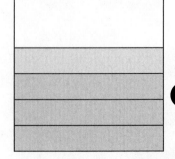

3. a. (Figure 3)

   b. $\frac{2}{3} \times \frac{4}{5} = \frac{8}{15}$ or $\frac{2}{3}$ of $\frac{4}{5} = \frac{8}{15}$

4. a. $\frac{1}{6}$

   b. $\frac{1}{8}$

   c. $\frac{1}{3}$

   d. $\frac{3}{8}$

5. a. Less. You are finding a fraction of 1.

   b. Less. You are finding part of a fraction.

   c. Less. You are finding part of $\frac{2}{3}$.

   d. Less. You can think of this as $\frac{2}{3} \times \frac{3}{4}$. In this case, you are finding part of $\frac{3}{4}$.

6. Possible answer: $\frac{1}{2} \times 2 = 1$

7. Possible answer: $\frac{1}{3} \times 2 = \frac{2}{3}$

8. Possible answer: $\frac{1}{4} \times 10 = 2\frac{1}{2}$

9. Possible answer: $\frac{1}{3} \times 2 = \frac{2}{3}$

10. a. 9 cups of pretzels, 8 cups of popcorn, 4 cups of peanuts, and 3 cups of chocolate chips

   b. $11\frac{1}{4}$ cups of pretzels, 10 cups of popcorn, 5 cups of peanuts, and $3\frac{3}{4}$ cups of chocolate chips

11. a. $\frac{1}{2}$

   b. $\frac{2}{3}$ of $\frac{3}{4} = \frac{1}{2}$ or $\frac{2}{3} \times \frac{3}{4} = \frac{1}{2}$

12. $15\frac{3}{4}$ pounds

13. a. Answers will vary. Possible answer: Approximately 6, because $8\frac{5}{6}$ is near 9. The exact answer is $5\frac{8}{9}$.

   b. Answers will vary. Possible answer: Approximately 10 since $14\frac{1}{2}$ is near 15. The exact answer is $9\frac{2}{3}$.

   c. Answers will vary. Possible answer: Approximately $1\frac{1}{2}$ because $2 \times \frac{2}{3}$ is less than $1\frac{1}{2}$, and adding half of $\frac{2}{3}$ (i.e, $\frac{1}{3}$) should give a result a bit bigger than $1\frac{1}{2}$. The exact answer is $1\frac{2}{3}$.

14. a. 18 caramel squares

   b. $2\frac{3}{4} \times \frac{3}{4} = \frac{6}{4} = 1\frac{1}{2}$

15. $12 \times \frac{11}{3} = 136$

16. $53\frac{1}{2}$

17. a. 6

   b. 12

   c. 30

   d. 30

   e. Possible answers: Each product is a multiple of 6; as the numerator increases, so does the product.

18. $4\frac{3}{8}$ cups

19. $\frac{5}{9}$

20. $\frac{1}{4}$

21. $7\frac{14}{27}$

22. $2\frac{14}{25}$

23. $28\frac{2}{3}$

ACE ANSWERS 2

Figure 3

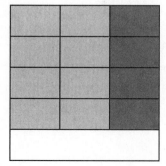 or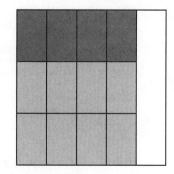

Copyright © Pearson Education, Inc., or its affiliates. All Rights Reserved.

ACE Answers 271

24. $\frac{9}{14}$

25. $1\frac{13}{20}$

26. $2\frac{5}{8}$

27. $1\frac{9}{11}$

Connections

28. $\frac{11}{60}$, or about $\frac{1}{6}$

29. $\frac{17}{30}$, or about $\frac{1}{2}$

30. Yes. If Roshaun started with more than twice as much money as Lea, then $\frac{1}{4}$ of Roshaun's money would be more than $\frac{1}{2}$ of Lea's money.

31. $\frac{7}{16}$ of a yard

32. Aran gets $\frac{1}{2}$ of the pretzels. Jon gets $\frac{1}{3}$ of the pretzels. Kiona gets $\frac{1}{6}$ of the pretzels.

33. $\frac{2}{5}$ of the class wants to go to Navy Pier.

34. **a.** $\frac{3}{5}$ of the class consists of girls with brown hair.

b. Answers will vary. Possible answers: 20 students. The number of students needs to be divisible by both 4 and 5 (so that $\frac{3}{4}$ and $\frac{3}{5}$ both represent whole numbers of people). Any multiple of 20 is possible.

35. **a.** $30 \times \frac{1}{4} + 6 \times \frac{3}{8} + \frac{7}{16} = 10\frac{3}{16}$ inches

b. No. We can know this by finding the exact sum of $8 \times \frac{3}{8} + 8 \times \frac{7}{16} = 6\frac{1}{2}$, or by estimating. One estimation strategy: There are 16 beads altogether; each bead is shorter than an inch, so the whole collection is less than 16 inches.

36. C

37. F

38. B

39. $\frac{2}{9}$

40. $2\frac{1}{2}$

41. $\frac{5}{9}$

42. $\frac{1}{4}$

43. **a.** 60 minutes

b. 30 minutes

c. 30 minutes

d. 6 minutes

e. 75 minutes

f. $3\frac{1}{10}$ or 3.1 hours

44. $1\frac{1}{8}$ cups of flour

$\frac{1}{2}$ teaspoon of baking soda

$\frac{1}{2}$ teaspoon of salt

$\frac{1}{2}$ cup of butter

$\frac{3}{8}$ cup of sugar

$\frac{1}{2}$ teaspoon of vanilla extract

1 large egg

$1\frac{1}{6}$ cups of chocolate morsels

$\frac{1}{3}$ cup of chopped nuts

45. $\frac{3}{4}$ cup of firmly packed brown sugar

$\frac{1}{3}$ cup of shortening

$\frac{1}{2}$ tablespoon of water

$\frac{1}{2}$ teaspoon of vanilla extract

1 large egg

$\frac{3}{4}$ cup of flour

$\frac{1}{6}$ cup of cocoa powder

$\frac{1}{4}$ teaspoon of salt

$\frac{1}{8}$ teaspoon of baking soda

1 cup of chocolate chips

46. Answers will vary on all parts. Possible answers are given for each part.

   a. The product will be greater than, but closer to, 1. The exact answer is $1\frac{9}{20}$.

   b. The product will be greater than, but closer to, 4. The exact answer is $4\frac{7}{20}$.

   c. The product will be greater than, but closer to, 1. The exact answer is $1\frac{3}{7}$.

   d. The product will be between 9 and 10. Estimating whether this product is closer to 9 or to 10 is challenging. The exact product is $9\frac{23}{48}$, which is only slightly closer to 9 than it is to 10.

   e. See solutions to a—d.

47. $6\frac{1}{2}$

48. $7\frac{1}{10}$

49. $6\frac{19}{30}$

50. $2\frac{23}{24}$

51. $2\frac{9}{10}$

52. $4\frac{1}{15}$

53. B

54. **a.** $1\frac{1}{5}$; Fala probably assembled five fifths to make one whole and had one fifth left over.

   b. Jorell probably multiplied numerators and denominators to get $\frac{6}{5}$.

   c. Hiroshi probably got the decimal answer 1.2.

55. F

Extensions

56. $\frac{1}{4}$

57. $\frac{5}{24}$

ACE ANSWERS 2

Applications

1. **1.** **a.** 2 lattes with $\frac{1}{9}$ of a cup of milk left over. This $\frac{1}{9}$ cup of milk is enough to make $\frac{1}{3}$ of a latte.

b. 2 lattes with $\frac{1}{6}$ of a cup of milk left over. This $\frac{1}{6}$ cup of milk is enough to make $\frac{1}{2}$ of a latte.

c. exactly 11 lattes

2. Answers will vary. You have $1\frac{3}{4}$ pounds of cheese. One batch of macaroni and cheese requires $\frac{1}{2}$ pound of cheese. How many batches can you make?

Finding *how many* $\frac{1}{2}$'s are in $1\frac{3}{4}$ is a division problem. You can make $3\frac{1}{2}$ batches.

3. **a.** 80

b. 40

c. $26\frac{2}{3}$

d. 200

e. 100

f. $28\frac{4}{7}$

g. 140

h. 70

i. $23\frac{1}{3}$

j. $20 \div \frac{2}{7}$ is half as large as $20 \div \frac{1}{7}$. This makes sense because the groups of $\frac{2}{7}$ are twice as large, so there are half as many of them in the total of 20. Similarly, $20 \div \frac{6}{7}$ is $\frac{1}{6}$ the size of $20 \div \frac{1}{7}$.

4. 10

5. $22\frac{1}{2}$

6. 12

7. $6\frac{2}{5}$

8. 20

9. 40

10. 80

11. No, he does not have quite enough flour.
$16 \div \frac{3}{4} = 21\frac{1}{3} < 22$

12. She can make five frames: $108 \div 18\frac{3}{8}$ $=5\frac{129}{147}$. An easier computation for many people may be to estimate and then check the solution. $108 \div 18 = 6$, so 5 is a reasonable guess for $108 \div 18\frac{3}{8}$. Checking by multiplication, $5 \times 18\frac{3}{8} = 91\frac{7}{8}$. This is less than 108, but the remainder is not enough to make an additional frame.

13. Each rabbit gets $\frac{21}{48}$ of an ounce of parsley (or a tiny bit less than half an ounce).
$5\frac{1}{4} \div 12 = \frac{21}{48}$

14. a. $\frac{1}{16}$ pound

  b. $\frac{1}{16}$ pound

  c. $\frac{3}{12}$ pound, or $\frac{1}{4}$ pound

  d. $\frac{2}{25}$ pound

  e. $\frac{3}{4}$ pound

15. a. $1\frac{1}{3}$ gallons

  b. $28 \times \frac{4}{3} = \frac{112}{3} = 37\frac{1}{3}$ miles

16. D

17. $\frac{4}{15}$; possible diagram: this diagram is made by renaming $\frac{4}{5}$ as $\frac{12}{15}$. Since there are 12 fifteenths, you can divide by 3, or group the fifteenths into 3 groups. Each of the three groups will have 4 fifteenths in it. (Figure 1)

18. $\frac{1}{3}$; this diagram shows 5 thirds. Since you are dividing by 5, you can make 5 groups. Each group will have $\frac{1}{3}$ in it. (Figure 2)

19. $\frac{1}{3}$; this problem is equivalent to Exercise 18, so the diagram is the same as Figure 2.

20. C

21. F

22. Greater than 1. $\frac{7}{9}$ is greater than $\frac{1}{9}$, so there are multiple groups of $\frac{1}{9}$ in $\frac{7}{9}$.

23. Greater than 1. $\frac{2}{3}$ is greater than $\frac{1}{9}$, so there are multiple groups of $\frac{1}{9}$ in $\frac{2}{3}$.

24. Less than 1. $\frac{1}{18}$ is less than $\frac{1}{9}$, so there is not even one whole group of $\frac{1}{9}$ in $\frac{1}{18}$.

25. Greater than 1. 1 is greater than $\frac{1}{9}$, so there are multiple groups of $\frac{1}{9}$ in 1.

26. $2\frac{1}{2}$

27. 6

28. 4

29. 15

30. $6\frac{2}{3}$

31. $\frac{3}{14}$

32. $\frac{3}{20}$

33. $1\frac{1}{5}$

34. $1\frac{7}{8}$

35. Answers will vary.

Exercise 29: You have 10 feet of string. You are making bracelets that require $\frac{2}{3}$ of a foot per bracelet. How many bracelets can you make?

Exercise 31: You have $\frac{6}{7}$ of a pound of powdered sugar that you need to split equally among four large pancakes. How much powdered sugar goes on each pancake?

Figure 1

| $\frac{1}{15}$ | $\frac{1}{15}$ | $\frac{1}{15}$ | $\frac{1}{15}$ | $\frac{1}{15}$ | $\frac{1}{15}$ |
| $\frac{1}{15}$ | $\frac{1}{15}$ | $\frac{1}{15}$ | $\frac{1}{15}$ | $\frac{1}{15}$ | $\frac{1}{15}$ |

Figure 2

1 2 3 4 5

Connections

Answers will vary for 36–39.

36. $\frac{2}{3}$ and $\frac{8}{12}$

37. $\frac{5}{6}$ and $\frac{20}{24}$

38. $\frac{4}{3}$ and $\frac{24}{18}$

39. $\frac{4}{3}$ and $\frac{16}{12}$

40. $1\frac{1}{4}$ hours

41. $1\frac{1}{10}$

42. $1\frac{17}{24}$

43. 2

44. $4\frac{7}{12}$

45. $\frac{2}{21}$

46. $\frac{21}{32}$

47. $\frac{1}{2}$

48. $12\frac{5}{6}$

49. $\frac{9}{10}$ of a mile

50. **a.** (Figure 3)

    b. (Figure 4)

    c. (Figure 5)

    d. (Figure 6)

    e. Answers will vary. Possible answer: To find the difference between two consecutive marks, take the difference between the two end points. Then divide by 4 because there are four equal divisions between the two endpoints. Then add that amount to the left endpoint to find the value for the first mark. Add that same value to that answer, and then add that amount once more to the next answer.

51. 3

52. 1

53. $\frac{1}{2}$

Extensions

54. Both are correct. Some students may think of this as a division situation, while others may think of it as a multiplication situation, so student thinking may match one or the other of these more closely. But both are correct.

55. 8

56. 24

57. $\frac{1}{8}$

58. $\frac{1}{32}$

59. Any of these will work. Possible answer: I would use 1 pint and fill it 8 times.

Figure 3

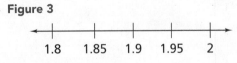

Figure 4

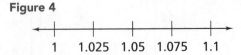

Figure 5

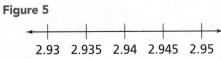

Figure 6

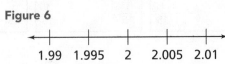

Applications

1. $\frac{1}{16} + \frac{1}{12} = N$

$\frac{1}{12} + \frac{1}{16} = N$

$N - \frac{1}{16} = \frac{1}{12}$

$N - \frac{1}{12} = \frac{1}{16}$

2. $\frac{5}{4} - \frac{4}{5} = N$

$\frac{5}{4} - N = \frac{4}{5}$

$N + \frac{4}{5} = \frac{5}{4}$

$\frac{4}{5} + N = \frac{5}{4}$

3. $N - 1\frac{1}{3} = 2\frac{2}{3}$

$N - 2\frac{2}{3} = 1\frac{1}{3}$

$1\frac{1}{3} + 2\frac{2}{3} = N$

$2\frac{2}{3} + 1\frac{1}{3} = N$

4. $N + \frac{4}{3} = \frac{1}{3}$

$\frac{4}{3} + N = \frac{1}{3}$

$\frac{1}{3} - \frac{4}{3} = N$

$\frac{1}{3} - N = \frac{4}{3}$

5. $1\frac{5}{12}$

6. $\frac{1}{20}$

7. $\frac{17}{20}$

8. $\frac{1}{2}$

9. $\frac{1}{8}$

10. $-\frac{1}{8}$

11. $m = \frac{6}{10}$

12. Answers will vary: $m = \frac{3}{10}$, $n = \frac{3}{10}$, or any choices of m and n with $m + n = \frac{3}{5}$, will solve the problem.

13. $m = \frac{6}{10}$

14. $\frac{2}{3} \times \frac{5}{7} = \frac{10}{21}$

$\frac{5}{7} \times \frac{2}{3} = \frac{10}{21}$

$\frac{10}{21} \div \frac{5}{7} = \frac{2}{3}$

$\frac{10}{21} \div \frac{2}{3} = \frac{5}{7}$

15. $\frac{3}{4} \div 1\frac{1}{2} = \frac{1}{2}$

$\frac{3}{4} \div \frac{1}{2} = 1\frac{1}{2}$

$\frac{1}{2} \times 1\frac{1}{2} = \frac{3}{4}$

$1\frac{1}{2} \times \frac{1}{2} = \frac{3}{4}$

16. $N = \frac{2}{3}$

17. $N = \frac{2}{15}$

18. $N = \frac{2}{3}$

19. $N = \frac{3}{5}$

20. $N = 7$

21. $N = \frac{1}{3}$

22. **a.** $m = \frac{5}{8}$

b. $m = \frac{5}{8}$

c. $m = \frac{5}{8}$

23. $32\frac{1}{2}$

24. 15

25. **a.** $24 - \frac{1}{2} - 1 - 1 = 21\frac{1}{2}$ buns

b. 64 servings, with $\frac{1}{6}$ of a bun left over (which is $\frac{1}{2}$ of a serving)

26. $\frac{4}{9}$

27. $18\frac{2}{3}$

28. $1\frac{7}{44}$ hours (which is about 1 hour and 10 minutes) for one way and $2\frac{7}{22}$ hours for the round trip.

Connections

29.a. $N = \frac{6}{7}$

  b. $N = \frac{3}{4}$

  c. The original expressions are not equivalent. In part (a), you need to add $\frac{1}{4}$ and $\frac{1}{3}$ before multiplying by N. In part (b), you need to multiply $\frac{1}{3}$ by N before adding $\frac{1}{4}$.

30. $\frac{1}{2}$

31. 2

32. $\frac{1}{3}$

33. 3

34. $\frac{3}{2}$

35. $\frac{4}{3}$

36. $\frac{2}{5}$

37. $\frac{4}{5}$

38. $\frac{12}{7}$

39. $\frac{1}{3}$ and 3. These are reciprocals.

40. $\frac{1}{4}$ and 4. These are reciprocals.

41. $\frac{1}{2}$ and 2. These are reciprocals.

42. $\frac{1}{8} + \frac{5}{6}$ is larger. There are many ways to know this without computing. One way is to reason that you can add 1 small thing and 5 large things or 1 large thing and 5 small things. 5 large things will be larger (assuming the large things are the same size in both instances, and that the small things are also). The two sums are $\frac{23}{24}$ and $\frac{19}{24}$, respectively.

Another way to tell that $\frac{1}{8} + \frac{5}{6}$ is larger is to note that $\frac{1}{6} > \frac{1}{8}$. Thus,
$$\frac{5}{6} + \frac{1}{8} = \left(\frac{1}{6} + \frac{4}{6}\right) + \frac{1}{8} > \left(\frac{1}{6} + \frac{4}{8}\right) + \frac{1}{8} = \frac{1}{6} + \frac{5}{8}.$$
The two sums are $\frac{23}{24}$ and $\frac{19}{24}$, respectively.

43. $\frac{5}{6} - \frac{1}{8}$ is larger. There are many ways to know this without computing. One way is to observe that for a large difference, you want the numbers to be far apart. Because $\frac{5}{6} > \frac{5}{8}$ and $\frac{1}{8} < \frac{1}{6}$, the first difference will be greater than the second. The two differences are $\frac{17}{24}$ and $\frac{11}{24}$ respectively. Another way to tell that $\frac{5}{6} - \frac{1}{8}$ is larger is to note that $\frac{5}{6} > \frac{5}{8}$ and $\frac{1}{6} > \frac{1}{8}$. Thus, $\frac{5}{6} - \frac{1}{8} > \frac{5}{8} - \frac{1}{8} > \frac{5}{8} - \frac{1}{6}$. (Here you use the fact that subtracting a larger number from a given number results in a smaller number.) The two differences are $\frac{17}{24}$ and $\frac{11}{24}$ respectively.

44. $N = \frac{1}{3}$

45. $N = 1$

46. In a simpler form this sentence is $1\frac{13}{24} + m + n = 3$. Using fact families to rewrite it, you have $m + n = 1\frac{11}{24}$. So now you can choose any number for m (less than $1\frac{11}{24}$ if you are working with positive numbers) and calculate n, since $n = 1\frac{11}{24} - m$. Possible solutions are $m = 1$ and $n = \frac{11}{24}$, or $m = \frac{5}{24}$ and $n = 1\frac{6}{24}$, or $m = \frac{15}{24}$ and $n = \frac{20}{24}$, and so forth.

Extensions

47. 0

48. 0

49. 1

50. 1

51. Answers will vary. Identity means the number that leaves the starting value unchanged.

52. $N = -\frac{1}{2}$

53. $N = -\frac{2}{3}$

54. $N = 2$

55. $N = \frac{3}{2}$

56. a. Yes; the additive inverse of a is $-a$. The additive inverse is also called the *opposite* of a number.

b. Nearly all numbers do, but 0 has no multiplicative inverse. The multiplicative inverse is also called the *reciprocal* of a number.

Index

Notes _____

Let's Be Rational **Index**